The Origin and Evolution of Atmospheres and Oceans

Proceedings of a conference held at the
Goddard Institute for Space Studies
National Aeronautics and Space Administration
New York, *April 8–9, 1963*

The Origin and Evolution

of Atmospheres and Oceans

Edited by

PETER J. BRANCAZIO

Goddard Institute for Space Studies and Brooklyn College

A. G. W. CAMERON

Goddard Institute for Space Studies

John Wiley & Sons, Inc., New York · London · Sydney

Preface

On April 8 and 9, 1963, the Goddard Institute for Space Studies, an office of the National Aeronautics and Space Administration, was host to a group of physicists, astronomers, and earth scientists who met to discuss the origin and evolution of planetary atmospheres and oceans. This was the fourth in a continuing series of interdisciplinary meetings held at the Institute on topics that have a special bearing on the main lines of inquiry in the space program. The meeting was organized by H. H. Hess of Princeton University and A. G. W. Cameron of the Goddard Institute.

In general we can expect planetary atmospheres to undergo some changes in composition over long periods of time. These changes may be the net result both of an input of gases into the atmosphere and of a loss of gases from the atmosphere. It is useful to formalize the discussion by listing the general processes that may be important in either of these categories:

1. *Input Processes*
   (*a*) Capture from a primitive solar nebula.
   (*b*) Capture from the solar wind.
   (*c*) Collisions with comets and meteorites.
   (*d*) Outgassing from the interior.
   (*e*) Chemical reactions with surface materials.
2. *Loss Processes*
   (*a*) Thermal evaporation.

v

(b) Sweeping action of the solar wind.

(c) Chemical reactions with surface materials.

(d) Rotational instability of the planet.

In recent years it has become evident that the earth's atmosphere and oceans have been principally produced by the outgassing of volatile materials from the earth's interior. In 1950, W. W. Rubey presented geological evidence indicating that sea water has progressively accumulated in this way. We are very grateful to Dr. Rubey for graciously consenting to reprint his pioneering paper in this book. At about the same time, Harrison Brown noted that oxygen and nitrogen are overabundant in the atmosphere compared to the rare gases, and he therefore drew the conclusion that the oxygen and nitrogen must have been outgassed from the interior, and probably much of the rare gases as well. Hence it appears that process 1(d) has been particularly important for the earth, with subsequent alterations to the atmospheric composition by processes 1(e) and 2(c).

In addition to W. W. Rubey's paper, this book contains discussions of outgassing processes by P. J. Brancazio, K. K. Turekian, and G. J. Wasserburg. The chapter by Brancazio was not presented at the conference but was written for these proceedings to cover an area that was inadequately discussed at the conference. Parts of the papers by G. J. F. MacDonald and R. O. Pepin deal with outgassing of the earth, and MacDonald attempts also to assess the role of process 2(a). The role of chemical reactions in altering the composition of the atmosphere [processes 1(e) and 2(c)] is discussed by H. D. Holland, and the biochemical production of oxygen is analyzed in some detail by L. V. Berkner and L. C. Marshall. Holland extends his discussion of the evolution of the terrestrial atmosphere to give some consideration to possible processes that may have been important in the atmosphere of Venus.

Interest in the gas content of meteorites arises only in small part because of the contribution of meteorites to process 1(c). These meteorites are the only sources of extraterrestrial gas that have yet been subjected to our analysis. There is thus considerable interest in whether the meteorite gas resembles the gas emitted from the interior of the earth, since the earth may have been accumulated from bodies resembling the meteorites. Discussions of meteoritic gas are given by P. Signer and R. O. Pepin, and A. G. W. Cameron presents his interpretation of some of these measurements as evidence in favor of process 1(b) having contributed to the formation of the earth's atmosphere.

The remainder of these proceedings deals with the moon and planets. Gold interprets certain surface features of the moon as indicating the presence of a novel form of outgassing of water from the lunar interior. In addition, he argues for the presence of large amounts of water on Venus by extension of the outgassing processes which have given the earth its oceans. Dollfus describes new measurements he has made giving positive identification of water on both Venus and Mars. These measurements gave rise to spirited discussion at the conference. Field discusses the evidence for an atmosphere on Mercury and some of the associated problems of physics. Sagan reviews the conflicting evidence and views regarding the nature of the atmosphere of Venus. Goody explains some of the difficulties of determining the composition, ground pressure, and structure of the atmosphere of Mars. The compositions of the giant planets of the solar system seem to have a much closer resemblance to the composition of the sun than to that of the terrestrial planets, and therefore it is of interest to compare their atmospheres with their interiors. Peebles discusses the interiors of Jupiter and Saturn, and Wildt reviews our knowledge of the composition of the atmosphere of Jupiter. Sagan and Wildt agreed to review their respective subjects on very short notice at the conference, since the original speakers had become ill and could not attend.

It is evident that the study of the origin and development of planetary atmospheres is in its early stages. This is part of the broader question of the origin and development of the solar system, and its suffers from great paucity of information and reliable data. It is to be expected that significant new insight into planetary atmospheres will be obtained in the next few years by microwave techniques and space probes. Perhaps the general formulation of the problem on a broad interdisciplinary base as represented by these proceedings is a useful step.

The conference was recorded on tape and subsequently a transcript was prepared. First drafts of each of the papers were prepared from the transcript and were sent to the speakers as the basis for preparation of their manuscripts. We wish to thank the speakers for their cooperation in the subsequent preparation of their material. The page proofs were checked by the editors and not by the authors; the editors thereby accept responsibility for any errors that might have resulted.

The chapter by G. J. F. MacDonald has also appeared as a review article, and we wish to express appreciation for having permission to reprint it. We also wish to thank the Geological Society of

America for permission to reprint W. W. Rubey's paper.   Mrs. Enid
Silva was the conference secretary, and we are grateful to her both
for her work in the organization of the conference and in the preparation of these proceedings.   Many other members of the staff of the
Goddard Institute for Space Studies gave valuable assistance with
the conference arrangements, and to them we are greatly indebted.

P. J. BRANCAZIO
A. G. W. CAMERON

New York
August 1964

Contributors

L. V. Berkner, Southwest Center for Advanced Studies, Dallas, Texas
Peter J. Brancazio, Goddard Institute for Space Studies, New York, New York, and Brooklyn College, Brooklyn, New York
A. G. W. Cameron, Goddard Institute for Space Studies, New York, New York
A. Dollfus, Observatoire de Paris, Meudon, France
G. Field, Princeton University, Princeton, New Jersey
Thomas Gold, Cornell University, Ithaca, New York
Richard M. Goody, Harvard University, Cambridge, Massachusetts
Heinrich D. Holland, Princeton University, Princeton, New Jersey
G. J. F. MacDonald, Institute of Geophysics and Planetary Sciences, University of California, Los Angeles, California
L. C. Marshall, Southwest Center for Advanced Studies, Dallas, Texas
P. J. E. Peebles, Princeton University, Princeton, New Jersey
R. O. Pepin, University of California, Berkeley, California
William W. Rubey, University of California, Los Angeles, California
Carl Sagan, Harvard University, Cambridge, Massachusetts
Peter Signer, University of Minnesota, Minneapolis, Minnesota
Karl K. Turekian, Yale University, New Haven, Connecticut
G. J. Wasserburg, California Institute of Technology, Pasadena, California
R. Wildt, Yale University, New Haven, Connecticut

Contents

1

Geologic History of Sea Water

An Attempt to State the Problem

William W. Rubey

ABSTRACT

Paleontology and biochemistry together may yield fairly definite information, eventually, about the paleochemistry of sea water and atmosphere. Several less conclusive lines of evidence now available suggest that the composition of both sea water and atmosphere may have varied somewhat during the past; but the geologic record indicates that these variations have probably been within relatively narrow limits. A primary problem is how conditions could have remained so nearly constant for so long.

It is clear, even from inadequate data on the quantities and compositions of ancient sediments, that the more volatile materials—water, carbon dioxide, chlorine, nitrogen, and sulfur—are much too abundant in the present atmosphere, hydrosphere, biosphere, and in ancient sediments to be explained, like the commoner rock-forming oxides, as the products of rock weathering alone. If the earth were once entirely gaseous or molten, these "excess" volatiles may be residual from a primitive atmosphere. But if so, certain corollaries should follow about the quantity of water dissolved in the molten earth and the expected chemical effects of a highly acid, primitive ocean. These corollaries appear to be contradicted by the geologic record, and doubt is therefore cast on this hypothesis of a dense primitive atmosphere. It seems more probable that only a small fraction of the total "excess" volatiles was ever present at one time in the early atmosphere and ocean.

Reprinted by permission from *Bull. Geol. Soc. Am.* **62**, 1111 (1951).

Carbon plays a significant part in the chemistry of sea water and in the realm of living matter. The amount now buried as carbonates and organic carbon in sedimentary rocks is about 600 times as great as that in today's atmosphere, hydrosphere, and biosphere. If only $\frac{1}{100}$ of this buried carbon were suddenly added to the present atmosphere and ocean, many species of marine organisms would probably be exterminated. Furthermore, unless CO_2 is being added continuously to the atmosphere-ocean system from some source other than rock weathering, the present rate of its subtraction by sedimentation would, in only a few million years, cause brucite to take the place of calcite as a common marine sediment. Apparently, the geologic record shows no evidence of such simultaneous extinctions of many species nor such deposits of brucite. Evidently the amount of CO_2 in the atmosphere and ocean has remained relatively constant throughout much of the geologic past. This calls for some source of gradual and continuous supply, over and above that from rock weathering and from the metamorphism of older sedimentary rocks.

A clue to this source is afforded by the relative amounts of the different "excess" volatiles. These are similar to the relative amounts of the same materials in gases escaping from volcanoes, fumaroles, and hot springs, and in gases occluded in igneous rocks. Conceivably, therefore, the hydrosphere and atmosphere may have come almost entirely from such plutonic gases. During the crystallization of magmas, volatiles such as H_2O and CO_2 accumulate in the remaining melt and are largely expelled as part of the final fractions. Volcanic eruptions and lava flows have brought volatiles to the earth's surface throughout the geologic past; but intrusive rocks are probably a much more adequate source of the constituents of the atmosphere and hydrosphere. Judged by the thermal springs of the United States, hot springs (carrying only 1% or less of juvenile matter) may be the principal channels by which the "excess" volatiles have escaped from cooling magmas below.

This mechanism fails to account for a continuous supply of volatiles unless it also provides for a continuous generation of new, volatile-rich magmas. Possibly such local magmas form by a continuous process of selective fusion of subcrustal rocks, to a depth of several hundred kilometers below the more mobile areas of the crust. This would imply that the volume of the ocean has grown with time. On this point, geologic evidence permits differences of interpretation; the record admittedly does not prove, but it seems consistent with, an increasing growth of the continental masses and a progressive sinking of oceanic basins. Perhaps something like the following mechanism could account for a continuous escape of volatiles to the earth's surface and a relatively uniform composition of sea water through much of geologic time: (1) selective fusion of lower-melting fractions from deep-seated, nearly anhydrous rocks beneath the unstable continental margins and geosynclines; (2) rise of these selected fractions (as granitic and hydrous magmas) and their slow crystallization nearer the surface; (3) essentially continuous isostatic readjustment between the differentiating continental masses and adjacent ocean basins; and (4) renewed erosion and sedimentation, with resulting instability of continental margins and mountainous areas and a new round of selective fusion below.

INTRODUCTION[1]

I trust that all of you recognize that the title of this paper is largely a figure of speech. It would be interesting and even, for some inquiries, useful if we knew the history of the earth's sea water and atmosphere, but this history cannot be told until we have solved nearly all other problems of earth history. This title might much better have been "The Problem of the Source of Sea Water and Its Bearing on Practically Everything Else."

Even with this modification, you still may wonder what qualifications I must think I possess to justify undertaking a subject of such global dimensions. I had originally intended to explain that I am neither an oceanographer, a geochemist, nor a Precambrian geologist, and therefore I have no special qualifications whatever for undertaking this problem. But after discussions with various colleagues—paleontologists, petrologists, geophysicists, structural geologists, and others—I feel somewhat less modest. It seems that the subject I have selected is one in which all geologists, equally, are experts.

My interest in this general problem grew from a paper on which I began working a number of years ago. Trying to test the possibility that the phosphate rock of western Wyoming may have been laid down by direct chemical or biochemical precipitation from sea water, I began searching for some basis on which to estimate the composition of sea water and the carbon dioxide content of the atmosphere in Permian time.

It soon became evident that this question ramifies almost endlessly into nearly every fundamental problem of earth history and far beyond into the foggy borderlands between other scientific disciplines. Eventually I began to realize some of the broader implications of the problem I had tackled. I wish to take this opportunity to review what I think I have learned about the probable history of sea water and to indicate what I think this all means in terms of general earth history.

[1] The principal conclusions of this paper were presented orally, in December 1948 and April 1949, before the Geological Society of Washington under the titles, *The Problem of Changes in Composition of Sea Water and Atmosphere During the Geologic Past,* and *A Possible Mechanism for the Continuous Supply*

COMPOSITION OF SEA WATER AND ATMOSPHERE IN THE PAST

Lines of Possible Evidence

No more than a brief review can be attempted here of the several lines of evidence that afford at least some information about the probable composition of sea water and atmosphere in the past. I cannot refrain, however, from emphasizing the one that seems to me most promising—and most neglected. The intimate dependence of living organisms on the chemical and physical conditions of their environment is so familiar—for example, an adequate supply of oxygen in the air we breathe—that we are inclined to take it all for granted. Were it not for the small amount of ozone in the upper atmosphere, which absorbs most of the deadly ultraviolet radiations, land-living organisms could not survive in direct sunlight (Poole, 1941, p. 346; Giese, 1945, pp. 226, 243–246; Allee and others, 1949, p. 74). Yet, if the amount of ozone were much greater than it is, no anti-rachitic or "sunshine" vitamin, essential to the nutrition of most animals would be produced (Stetson, 1942, pp. 18–19). Similarly, many species of modern invertebrates can tolerate only narrow ranges in the salinity of their environment, largely because of the osmotic pressures involved (Dakin, 1935, pp. 12, 16, 25–27; Rogers, 1938, p. 670; Gunter, 1947). Many organisms have very specific requirements, on the one hand, and tolerances, on the other, for the amounts of dissolved calcium, sodium, potassium, and other elements in the waters in which they live (Rogers, 1938, pp. 430, 680–682). It seems not unlikely that the ancestors of some of these modern forms may have been subject to similarly rigid requirements.

Needless to say, it is hazardous to assume that ancient animals and plants had exactly the same chemical and physical requirements as their modern descendants. Conditions may have changed gradually, and the organisms may have modified their requirements by evolu-

---

of Volatiles at the Earth's Surface. Since then, the main thesis has been given before various groups, in successively revised form and with different points of emphasis.

In preparing this paper I have had the unsuspecting collaboration of nearly every geologist and countless others I have talked with during the past few years. Many of my colleagues of the U. S. Geological Survey and the staff members of the Geophysical Laboratory have been most generous with their criticisms and suggestions. K. J. Murata, James Gilluly, W. T. Pecora, and D. T. Griggs have been especially helpful in leading me across some of my worst gaps of data, logic, and understanding. It is only fair to add, however, that none of these many collaborators is to be held in any way responsible for the pattern of conclusions I have tried to weave from the varied threads of our discussions.

tionary adaptations. Yet precisely this same hazard accompanies any effort whatever to interpret the ecology of ancient plant and animal communities. The considerable measure of success that has been attained in paleoecologic interpretations by paleontologists and ecologists, working together and balancing several lines of evidence, shows that, although the problem is difficult, it is not insuperable (Twenhofel, 1936; Vaughan, 1940, p. 457; Ladd, 1944; Lowenstam, 1948, pp. 104–114, 140–142; Cloud and Barnes, 1948, pp. 31, 58–66).

Paleontologists have given relatively little attention to chemical factors in the environment of ancient organisms. The most noteworthy efforts I know about have been made by a few physiological chemists (Macallum, 1904, p. 561; 1926, pp. 317–322, 341–348; Henderson, 1927, especially pp. 38–190; Conway, 1942, 1943). Macallum believed that the blood serum and body fluids of many animals reflect closely the composition of sea water at the time when their respective ancestral lines became established. From this hypothesis he deduced a history of the composition of sea water. However, many physiologists do not accept Macallum's main premise. Many of you are familiar with L. J. Henderson's fascinating volume, *The Fitness of the Environment*, which presents the thesis that life as we know it today would be impossible if the physical and chemical conditions on the earth were much different from those of the present. All in all, it seems likely that the most definite information about the composition of sea water and atmosphere during the past will come, eventually, from the joint efforts of biochemists, ecologists, and paleontologists.

Another possible line of evidence on the composition of ancient sea water has proved much less dependable than was at first hoped. When A. C. Lane (1908, pp. 63, 125) defined *connate waters*, it was with the thought that they represent samples of the original water in which a sediment was deposited. As information about these brines has grown, however, it has become increasingly evident that many chemical and physical processes have been modifying these waters since deposition of the enclosing sediments: adsorption, base exchange, dolomitization, evaporation, sulfate reduction, hydration and recrystallization of clay minerals, and other processes (Mills and Wells, 1919, pp. 67–68; Newcombe, 1933, pp. 189–196; Piper, 1933, pp. 82, 89; W. L. Russell, 1933; Crawford, 1940, pp. 1221–1222, 1317–1319; Heck, Hare, and Hoskins, 1940; Foster, 1942, pp. 846–851). It now seems likely that most so-called connate waters have been so altered in composition that they do not represent at all accurately the original water of deposition.

Two other lines of evidence that afford some information on the probable composition of sea water and atmosphere in the past may be mentioned briefly: (1) Spectroscopic data on the solar and stellar abundances of chemical elements (Goldschmidt, 1938, pp. 99–101, 120–121; Brown, 1949b, pp. 625–627) and on the composition of the atmospheres of other planets (Wildt, 1942; Kuiper, 1949, pp. 309, 326) set limits to the range of permissible speculation. (2) Sedimentary rocks of certain ages appear to have distinctive chemical or mineral characteristics over wide areas. The iron formations of the Precambrian (Eskola, 1932b, pp. 39–40, 54; Leith, 1934, pp. 161–164), the magnesian limestones of Precambrian and early Paleozoic age (Daly, 1909, pp. 163–167), the coal beds of the Carboniferous, and other examples (Rutherford, 1936, pp. 1212–1214; Landergren, 1945, pp. 26–28; Lane, 1945, pp. 396–398) have been mentioned as possibly indicating changes in chemical conditions on the earth with lapse of time. However, either the existence of these supposed worldwide similarities or, where their existence seems clear, this particular interpretation of their significance has been questioned (Clarke, 1924, p. 579; Leith, 1934, p. 161; Pettijohn, 1943, pp. 957–960; Conway, 1943, pp. 174–179, 200–202; 1945, pp. 593–601, 603–604; Bruce, 1945, pp. 589–590, 601; Miholić, 1947, p. 719). On the whole, it appears likely that there have been some real changes in the composition of sea water and atmosphere with time but that these changes must have been relatively small.

In the interest of brevity, we may summarize by stating that several lines of evidence seem to indicate some actual changes in the composition of sea water and atmosphere with time. Yet, the more closely one examines the evidence, the more these changes appear to be merely second-order differences. Everything considered, the composition of sea water and atmosphere has varied surprisingly little, at least since early in geologic time. This is certainly no startling conclusion to bring to an audience of geologists. It might even be considered as simply one of the underlying facts of geologic history on which the doctrine of uniformitarianism is based. Yet such a relative constancy of the composition of sea water throughout much of the geologic past has far-reaching implications, and these implications are worth a more careful consideration than they have sometimes received.

Method of Geochemical Balances

The most definite information about the paleochemistry of sea water and atmosphere may come eventually from the biologists, but the best evidence now available seems to lie in a comparison of the composition of rocks that have been weathered and of sediments that have been deposited during the geologic past. This general method has been used by Clarke (1924, pp. 31–32), Goldschmidt (1933, pp. 131–133), Kuenen (1946), and others (Leith and Mead, 1915, p. 73; Twenhofel, 1929, pp. 395–399) to estimate the total mass of rocks eroded and sediments deposited. Using a modification of this method, I have attempted to bring these earlier estimates up to date. But we must still rely on much the same data used by others; and attempted refinements of the method still give pretty much the same answers as before. Suffice it to say that when this method is applied to rocks of different ages and to each of the commoner rock-forming elements—silicon, aluminum, iron, calcium, and several others—the results are in surprisingly good agreement with one another. But for another group it is clear, even with present data, that there is no such agreement. All the constituents of this latter group are much too abundant in the present atmosphere and hydrosphere and in ancient sediments to be accounted for as simply the products of rock weathering—the explanation that fits well enough for the commoner elements. Compared with the commoner rock-forming oxides, the members of this group are all relatively volatile.[2] They are the substances which, in the language of the early chemists, we might call the *distillable spirits* of the earth's solid matter.

I had originally intended to present in this paper a detailed statement of the method by which these estimates have been made. The main paper grew out of all bounds in several directions, however, and these estimates and a fuller statement of the method by which they were derived must be reserved for publication in a separate article. The method of geochemical balances, as it might be called, can be outlined only briefly here.

In any given unit of geologic time, the quantity of material weathered and eroded from (a) crystalline rocks and (b) previously formed sedimentary rocks, plus (j) juvenile matter from volcanic gases, hot springs, etc., equals the quantity of material deposited as sediments on (c) continental platforms and (d) the deep-sea floor, plus (s) matter stored in sea water or escaped into interstellar space.

The results of applying this general equation of geochemical balances are the basis for much of the entire discussion that follows. For some elements, such as Si, Al, and Fe, which are relatively non-volatile and sparingly soluble at moderate temperatures, the juvenile and stored-in-sea terms are probably negligible; so that for these

[2] Hence Fenner's convenient term, "volatiles", for the entire group (1926, pp. 696–697).

elements the general equation can be simplified considerably. If we have reasonably good estimates of the chemical composition of crystalline rocks, older sedimentary rocks, new continental deposits, and new deep-sea sediments, we can find for each constituent the relationship between (a) the proportion of crystalline rocks to all rocks eroded, and (c) the proportion of continental sediments to all sediments deposited. From the percentages of two chemical constituents in each kind of rock eroded and sediment deposited, we can find one expression relating (a) to (c). From percentages of more than two constituents in each rock and sediment, we obtain several simultaneous equations that permit a fairly rigorous test of the chemical compositions we have used.

This is all simple enough in theory, but it is difficult in practice because accurate and representative analyses of sediments are not available. It is encouraging that a National Research Council committee is now being organized to improve available information on the chemical composition of sedimentary rocks. But, even from present information, it is possible to learn something by means of this general equation (or rather the series of equations derived from it) and to obtain results that are not grossly in conflict with other types of evidence.

It turns out that, for average crystalline rocks and sediments of Mesozoic and later ages, the average chemical compositions now available agree surprisingly well with one another for most of the permanent rock-forming oxides—SiO_2, Al_2O_3, total Fe, CaO, Na_2O, K_2O, TiO_2, and P_2O_5. If the average composition of igneous rock in earlier times was somewhat nearer that of plateau basalt, this statement is also true for sedimentary rocks of Paleozoic and even Precambrian age.

This general equation gives only ratios between the several kinds of rocks eroded and sediments deposited. Three independent estimates (based on the amount of sodium now dissolved in the ocean, the quantity of continental sediments remaining uneroded today, and the mean rate of deep-sea sedimentation) accord reasonably well in their results and thus afford means for converting these ratios into quantities of rocks eroded and sediments deposited. When all is done, the final estimates have at least this to recommend them: for the greater part they fall well within the range of estimates that Clarke, Goldschmidt, Kuenen, and others have made by simpler and more direct methods.

The foregoing statements apply to the major rock-making constituents, which are the ones that agree rather well with one another in the general equation of geochemical balances. Collectively they make up from 60 to 95% of all the rocks eroded and sediments deposited. But for the remaining constituents it is quite a different story. All but two of these latter form relatively volatile compounds at moderate temperatures and pressures, and it is the source of this group of volatile constituents that seems particularly significant in the geologic history of sea water and atmosphere.

Let us look at the way these "volatile spirits" are now distributed on and near the surface of the earth. In Table 1.1 are summaries of the best estimates I can find or make of the quantities of water, carbon dioxide, chlorine, etc., in today's atmosphere, ocean, fresh water, and organic matter. In the second row are the estimated totals of these constituents that are now buried in sedimentary rocks and that must have been part of the atmosphere and ocean in earlier times. Next we have the sums of the first and second rows, the quantities that must have come from somewhere and whose source should be accounted for. In the fourth row, we have, from the amount of crystalline rocks that must have been eroded to form all the sediments and from the composition of average igneous rocks, the amounts that must have been released by the weathering of crystalline rocks. Finally, in the last row, the differences between the quantities in the third and fourth rows, we have the "excess" volatiles that cannot be accounted for as simply the products of rock weathering.

For the sake of simplicity, carbon is shown as CO_2 in Table 1.1. This arbitrary convention oversimplifies the actual situation, for

TABLE 1.1   Estimated Quantities (in units of 10^{20} grams) of Volatile Materials now at or near the Earth's Surface, Compared with Quantities of These Materials That Have Been Supplied by the Weathering of Crystalline Rocks

	H_2O	Total C as CO_2	Cl	N	S	H, B, Br, A, F, etc.
In present atmosphere, hydrosphere, and biosphere	14,600	1.5	276	39	13	1.7
Buried in ancient sedimentary rocks	2,100	920	30	4.0	15	15
Total	16,700	921	306	43	28	16.7
Supplied by weathering of crystalline rocks	130	11	5	0.6	6	3.5
"Excess" volatiles unaccounted for by rock weathering	16,600	910	300	42	22	13

oxygen does not occur in the right amounts to balance carbon as CO_2 exactly. Estimating directly (in units of 10^{20} g), the amount of oxygen not combined in permanent rock oxides and in water, we find about 12 units in the atmosphere, 26 in the SO_4 of sea water, and small amounts in HCO_3, H_2BO_3, and elsewhere, giving a total of aproximately 39 units of oxygen in the present atmosphere, hydrosphere, and biosphere. In sedimentary rocks, estimates indicate about 490 units in the carbonates, 25 in organic matter, 21 in SO_3, 14 in the oxidation of FeO to Fe_2O_3, and 2 in the interstitial water, giving altogether about 550 units of oxygen in the ancient sedimentary rocks. This, together with that in the atmosphere, etc., makes a total of about 589 units. Approximately 8 units of oxygen have probably been released during the weathering of the small amount of CO_2 in crystalline rocks and 75 units from the sodium, magnesium, calcium, and potassium now dissolved in sea and interstitial water, which comes to a total of 83 units from rock weathering. This leaves $(589 - 83 =)$ 506 units of oxygen "unaccounted for" and is to be compared with $(\frac{12}{44} \times 910 =)$ 248 units of carbon similarly "unaccounted for."

If no other complications were involved, these quantities might be explained by the release of 483 units of CO_2 and 271 units of CO from some other unspecified source. But to find a more meaningful balance between the "excess" carbon and oxygen, we must consider also the probable composition of other gases, besides CO_2 and CO, that may have come from the same unspecified source. Associated with an estimated 68 units of carbon and 25 units of oxygen in the organic matter in sedimentary rocks, there should be about 9.6 units of hydrogen. If this was released originally as H_2O, it would account for 76 of the 506 units of "excess" oxygen in the above calculation. On this assumption, the excess of 248 units of carbon and $(506 - 76 =)$ 430 units of oxygen would be equivalent to 274 units of CO_2 and 404 units of CO.

It is conceivable, however, that the excess Cl, N, S, Br, and F shown in Table 1.1 were originally released as HCl, NH_3, H_2S, HBr, and HF. If so, the 19 units of hydrogen thus required have since lost their identity, presumably by oxidation to H_2O; and this oxidation would have subtracted approximately 150 units of oxygen from the original carbon-oxygen mixture. On this assumption, the original excess of 248 units of carbon and $(430 + 150 =)$ 580 units of oxygen would have been equivalent to 687 units of CO_2 and 141 units of CO.

In these three hypothetical mixtures of CO_2 and CO, the CO_2 ranges between 40 and 83%. If the original gases also contained significant quantities of methane, CH_4 (Poole, 1941, p. 350–351), the percentage of CO_2 would have been correspondingly higher. It is evident that the proportion of "excess" carbon originally released as CO_2 cannot be estimated, even approximately, unless the original composition of all the excess volatiles is known. For this reason, all carbon is shown by arbitrary convention in Table 1.1 as CO_2.

POSSIBLE SOURCES OF THE "EXCESS" VOLATILES

Nomenclature[3]

Only two possible sources of the excess volatiles occur to me: Either (a) they are largely or entirely residual from a primitive atmosphere and ocean; or (b) they have largely or entirely risen to the surface from the earth's interior during the course of geologic time.

A few years ago an eminent geologist, in discussing magmas, divided those who have views on the subject into the *pontiffs* and the *soaks*. The classification is not directly applicable to those who have views on the origin of the ocean. But here, also, we have two opposing schools of thought, and, with apologies to Bowen (1947, p. 264), his classification may readily be modified to fit the occasion. From the very nature of the problem, there can be no anhydrous pontiffs when the origin of the ocean is considered but only soaks of one persuasion or another. Here, we may say, we have the *quick soaks* who prefer to have the wetness of the ocean there at the very beginning, all of it at once; and then there are the *slow soaks* who prefer to increase the liquor gradually by small increments over a much longer period of time. The quantities involved are the same by both courses of action, but the effects are conspicuously different: Taken in small drafts and with a proper regard for timing, an astonishingly large quantity of volatile spirits can be handled by the earth without showing it; but taken hastily, even moderate amounts are almost certain to have noteworthy effects.

Dense Primitive Atmosphere—Solution in the Melt

The two contrasting procedures or viewpoints just mentioned afford a basis for discussing the probable source of these excess volatiles. In the opinion of some who have considered the problem—those who are of the "quick-soak" school of thought—the source of these volatiles can be deduced without too much trouble merely from a consideration of the conditions of the primitive earth. Their argument runs some-

[3] Literally, "name-calling."

thing like this: As the earth was probably once molten throughout, it follows that all or a large part of the water, carbon dioxide, etc., would have been volatilized in a primitive atmosphere. On subsequent cooling, the water vapor would condense into a primitive ocean; and the present hydrosphere and atmosphere are thus residual from this primitive ocean and atmosphere.

Yet, when we examine it more closely, this conclusion is not altogether convincing. To begin with, it is by no means certain that the earth was originally molten (R. T. Chamberlin, 1949, pp. 252–253; Latimer, 1950; Slichter, 1950). The inert gases—neon, argon, krypton, and xenon—are from 10^6 to 10^{10} times less abundant on the earth than in the atmospheres of the stars, the lighter gases showing the greater discrepancies. Compounds and elements of the same molecular weights—water, nitrogen, carbon dioxide, carbon monoxide, and oxygen—would have been lost in the same proportions if they too had existed as gases when the earth was formed. The fact that water is present in considerable quantity on the earth today is evidence that much of it was bound in chemical compounds or occluded in solid (i.e., in relatively cool) matter when the earth accumulated (Aston, 1924; Jeffreys, 1924; Russell and Menzel, 1933, pp. 999–1001; Rayleigh, 1939, p. 463; Brown, 1949a; Gibson, 1949, p. 278; Suess, 1949; Jones, 1950, pp. 420, 423–424, 428–429). This leaves us with two alternatives: either the earth remained solid from the beginning, except for local melting; or it was first cold, then heated by some process until molten throughout (Urry, 1949, pp. 172, 179) and finally solidified again. Whichever one of these two theories may ultimately prevail, the evidence appears distinctly unfavorable to the concept of an atmosphere that ever contained very much of the earth's total volatiles. Instead, this evidence seems to call for some mechanism by which the volatiles were largely retained within the interior of the earth, to the extent of only a few tenths of 1% of the solid matter. This appears entirely possible, whether or not the earth was ever completely molten.

These interpretations are not new, but neither are they as widely accepted as I think they deserve to be. I shall try, therefore, to show why a consideration of the geologic record leads me to these conclusions.

We might start by attempting to follow through, in a semiquantitative way, some of the consequences of a dense primitive atmosphere. If all the water in today's atmosphere and hydrosphere and in ancient sediments were once present in a primitive atmosphere, and if this atmosphere were in contact with molten silicate rock, then some fraction of the water would dissolve in the melt, the amount depending on the vapor pressure, the solubility of water in the melt, and the total quantity of molten material. Using Goranson's data for the solubility of water in a melt of granitic composition, we find that, at this vapor pressure, the melt would dissolve $2\frac{1}{2}\%$ by weight of water.

As the deeper-lying rocks probably now contain considerably less than $2\frac{1}{2}\%$ water, this must be simply a limiting case. If there were then any considerable quantity of molten material and if this were stirred by convection currents, the water that would dissolve in the melt would materially reduce that in the atmosphere until an equilibrium was reached. Making allowance for the water now in deep-lying rocks, calculation shows that a primitive atmosphere in equilibrium with a completely molten earth would contain less than one-tenth the amount of water in the present ocean. As the supposed molten earth cooled and crystallized, the water in the remaining melt and in the atmosphere would be unlikely to remain in equilibrium, for the surface would probably crust over with slag long before the interior had fully crystallized. Thus, when crystallization was completed, the primitive atmosphere, even on this hypothesis, would probably contain at that stage, as it had at the very beginning, much less water than the present ocean.

Goranson's data on the solubility of water in a melt of granitic composition at the temperatures and pressures at which crystallization begins (Goranson, 1932, pp. 229–231) appear to be the most nearly applicable to the conditions here postulated. I find no data on the solubility of other gases in silicate melts of the required composition. We would expect, from the work of Morey and Fleischer (1940, pp. 1051–1057) on the system CO_2-H_2O-K_2O-SiO_2, that the proportion of CO_2 to H_2O dissolved in the melt would be somewhat higher than that in the vapor phase or atmosphere in equilibrium with it, but not enough higher to modify the results of the following calculation significantly.

Under the assumed conditions, the primitive atmosphere would contain 16.6×10^{20} kg of water vapor. Over the 5.1×10^{18} cm² area of the earth's surface, this quantity of water would exert a pressure of 325 kg/cm². Goranson found that a melt of granitic composition at liquidus temperatures dissolved 3% by weight of water at 400 bars[4] and 2% water at 260 bars (Goranson, 1932, p. 234). Interpolating between these values, it appears that, at a vapor pressure of 325 kg/cm², a melt of this composition would dissolve 2.5% water, and the temperature of crystallization would be about 985°C.

[4] One bar = 1.01972 kg/cm² (Birch, Schairer, and Spicer, 1942, p. 319).

If the rock materials of the earth's crust retained after crystallization, and still contained today, an average of about 2.5% water, the results of this calculation would be of greater significance. Actually they now contain much less than this—only 1.15% in Clarke and Washington's average igneous rock (Clarke, 1924, p. 29). On this hypothesis, over half of the calculated 2.5% water in the melt must have escaped to the surface during or after crystallization. This means that some unspecified quantity of the water in today's atmosphere, ocean, and sedimentary rocks was not there earlier and so was not present in the supposed primitive atmosphere. Hence the original vapor pressure would have been less than the 325 kg/cm² calculated from today's total of 16.6×10^{20} kg. The amount of this difference depends largely on the quantity of melt that was involved in the assumed equilibrium.

With present data, the amount of water in the supposed primitive atmosphere can be estimated only within rather broad limits. For purposes of this calculation, the average water content of crystallized rock to a depth of about 40 km may be taken as near 1.15%. This would amount to 6.6×10^{20} kg of water. If this thickness of 40 km of rock were molten, the total water in the primitive atmosphere and melt together would be $(16.6 + 6.6 =) \; 23.2 \times 10^{20}$ kg. From Goranson's data it may be found that, under conditions of equilibrium, 46% of this total water would be dissolved in the melt; the remainder left in the atmosphere would exert a vapor pressure of 244 kg/cm² at the earth's surface. At this pressure the granitic melt would dissolve 1.9% water, and the melting point would be about 1010°C. If it were true that the rocks of the earth's interior now contain 1.15% water to a depth of 300 km, similar reasoning would show that about 85% of the total water would have been dissolved in the melt; the amount remaining in the atmosphere would have had a vapor pressure of 175 kg/cm², and the melt would have contained about 1.3% water.

It is extremely doubtful, however, that rocks lying more than a few tens of kilometers below surface contain as much as 1.15% water. For the rocks of the deep interior, direct determination of the water content is, of course, impossible; and there is little on which to base an estimate other than the composition of stony meteorites (Clarke, 1924, pp. 42–44; Brown, 1949b, pp. 627–629). Meteorites contain few if any hydrous minerals; yet an average of 63 chemical analyses, "of the highest grade obtainable," of stony meteorites gives 0.47% H_2O (Merrill, 1930, pp. 16–17), and a recent digest of all earlier analyses shows an average content of 0.063% H [equivalent to 0.56%

H_2O]. (Brown, 1949b, p. 626.) Some of this water, in even the most carefully collected and analyzed samples, may be the result of weathering after the meteorites reached the earth. At least some, however, is probably present as original impurities or occlusions, as seems indicated by the quantities of H_2, CO_2, and other gases in both stony and iron meteorites (R. T. Chamberlin, 1908, p. 26; Farrington, 1915, pp. 190–196; Nash and Baxter, 1947, pp. 2541–2543). More data on the volatile content of stony meteorites are badly needed; but from present information the best estimate for the siliceous rocks of the earth's interior, from depths of 40 km to 2900 km, is probably about 0.5% H_2O.

If the iron meteorites are similarly taken to represent the materials of the earth's iron core, from 2900 km to the center, we may assume the water content there is negligible.

For rocks of the deep interior, one should logically have data on the solubility of water in melts of basaltic or peridotitic composition. However, in comparison with the uncertainties about present water content of these rocks at depth, the lack of data on the solubility of water in a more basic melt is no actual handicap. Increasing pressure at greater depth would increase very considerably the solubility of water in silicate melts (Goranson, 1931, pp. 492–494). Under the assumed conditions of a molten earth and with the relatively small quantities of water involved, it is probable that nowhere would the amount of water carried down into the interior by convection currents exceed that which could be dissolved in the deeper-lying melt of different composition. The controlling factor therefore would be the solubility of water in the part of the melt that was in contact with the atmosphere.

For the densities of rocks at various depths to the center of the earth, Bullen's values (1940, p. 246; 1942, p. 28), which are calculated from seismic and astronomic data, may be used.

With these various estimates, it may be calculated that, in an earth molten to the base of the silicate mantle at 2900 km, the total water in the primitive atmosphere and silicate melt would have been $(16.6 + 207 =) 224 \times 10^{20}$ kg. Under conditions of equilibrium, approximately 98% of this total would be dissolved in the melt. The remainder left in the atmosphere would have a vapor pressure of 76 kg/cm² at the earth's surface, and the melt would contain about 0.54% by weight of water. In an earth entirely molten to the center of the iron core, approximately 99% of the total water would be dissolved in the melt. The remainder in the atmosphere would have a vapor pressure of 52 kg/cm², and the melt would contain 0.37%

H_2O. This water in the primitive atmosphere, about 2.6×10^{20} kg, would be only 16% of the total in today's atmosphere and ocean and buried in ancient sedimentary rocks. If the estimate used here of 0.5% H_2O in the earth's siliceous mantle is too high, the total quantity of water involved in the equilibria would be less, and the remainder in the primitive atmosphere would be even lower than 16% of that today.

For purposes of presentation, this calculation has proceeded through steps of increasing depth of melting from the earth's surface downward to the center of the earth. Actually the hypothesis of an originally molten earth requires the reverse order, starting with a completely molten condition and solidifying from the bottom or, rather, from the base of the silicate mantle, upward (Adams, 1924, pp. 467–468). If, at any stage of cooling, the surface crusted over with slag, equilibrium between the water content of the atmosphere and melt could no longer be maintained, and the primitive atmosphere would end up with some earlier water content, which would be much less than 16.6×10^{20} kg.

If, on the other hand, the surface did not crust over before the earth solidified throughout, heat from the deep interior would continue to escape rapidly; and solidification would probably have been completed within a few tens of thousands of years (Jeffreys, 1929, pp. 79, 147–148; Slichter, 1941, pp. 567, 582–583). With such rapid freezing, it is improbable that equilibrium could have been maintained between the water content of the atmosphere and that of the immense volume of the melt. Thus, on this alternative also, the primitive atmosphere would probably end up with a water content significantly less than 16.6×10^{20} kg.

Dense Primitive Atmosphere—Chemical Effects

A totally different line of approach also indicates that the fraction of present hydrosphere and atmosphere that might be residual from a primitive ocean and atmosphere is probably very small. Let us assume, for purposes of calculation, that all the excess volatiles were once in a very hot atmosphere; that, on cooling, the water vapor condensed to liquid and dissolved all the chlorine, fluorine, bromine, etc., and that the principal gases—carbon dioxide, nitrogen, and hydrogen sulfide—were dissolved in the water according to their solubilities and partial pressures.

This would mean at first a very acid ocean (pH 0.3). This acid water would attack bare rock with which it came in contact, and the primitive ocean would rapidly take into solution increasing quantities of bases from the rocks, until the solubility product of calcite or dolomite was reached. Thereafter, as more dissolved bases were brought in by streams, carbonate would be deposited, and carbon dioxide subtracted from the atmosphere-ocean system.

Eventually conditions would be reached under which primitive life could exist. Certain mosses have been found to tolerate as much as one atmosphere of carbon dioxide (Ewart, 1896, pp. 404, 406–407), an amount more than 3000 times that in the atmosphere today. If we take this value as a basis for estimating when life and the photosynthetic production of free oxygen began, we find that sea water then would have a pH of about 7.3; a salinity approximately twice that of the present; and, because of buffer effects, considerably more bicarbonate than chlorine in solution. The bases required to balance the acid radicals, added to those previously deposited as carbonates, would call for the weathering by that time of considerably more igneous rock than appears, from other evidence, to have been weathered in all of geologic time. And, even worse, more than half the original carbon dioxide would still remain in the atmosphere and ocean.

This hypothesis also calls for the deposition of tremendous quantities of carbonate rocks before the carbon dioxide of the atmosphere was lowered to the point where life could first exist. No such excessively large quantities of carbonates are known in the earliest Precambrian sediments. Compilations of measured thicknesses of sedimentary rocks suggest that the percentage of limestone in sediments of Precambrian age is about the same as (or perhaps lower than) that in later sedimentary rocks. Sederholm's estimate (1925, p. 4) indicates a very low proportion of limestones and dolomites in the Precambrian rocks of Finland. Schuchert's (1931, pp. 58, 49) figures (25% limestone in the Precambrian, 20% limestone in Cambrian to Pleistocene inclusive) are heavily influenced by estimates, now known to be excessive (Osborne, 1931, pp. 27–28), of the thickness of the Grenville series in southeastern Canada and so should be lowered somewhat. Leith's estimates (1934, pp. 159–162) show from 1 to 48% (average about 19%) limestone in sections of Precambrian rocks in North America, Africa, and Asia and an average of 22% limestone in sedimentary rocks of later age. Thus there is no indication in the geologic record of the tremendous quantities of early Precambrian limestone that would be required under this hypothesis. These and other semiquantitative tests make the hypothesis of a dense primitive atmosphere appear very improbable.

Under the given conditions of temperature, pressure, and composition (essentially no free hydrogen or oxygen), the quantities of the gases, CH_4, NH_3, and SO_2, that would be stable may be taken as negligible, and therefore the excess carbon, nitrogen, and sulfur present as CO_2, N_2, and H_2S. If all the chlorine, bromine, and fluorine were dissolved in 16.6×10^{20} kg water, they would amount to 0.529 acid equivalents per liter. Initially this amount of acid would be balanced almost solely by hydrogen ions, from which a hydrogen-ion concentration of $0.529 = 10^{-0.277}$ or a pH of 0.277 may be calculated.

This acid water would decompose the rocks with which it came in contact, and in so doing it would dissolve some of the bases. As a result, its acidity would decrease, and the chemical effects of dissolved gases would come to play an important part in the overall balance. Better data are available for estimating the required coefficients at moderate temperatures than at those near the boiling point of water; 30°C is here chosen as the basis for calculation. At this temperature and in sea water of normal salinity (35‰ or a "chlorinity" of 19.4‰), the solubility coefficients of CO_2, N_2, and H_2S are estimated at 0.026, 0.0009, and 0.077 moles/liter (Harvey, 1945, p. 66; Sverdrup, Johnson, and Fleming, 1946, p. 191); the first and second apparent dissociation constants of CO_2 at 1.11×10^{-6} and 1.27×10^{-9} (Harvey, 1945, p. 64); the two comparable dissociation constants of H_2S at 3.0×10^{-7} and 2.8×10^{-14} (Latimer, 1938, p. 316); the single dissociation constant of H_3BO_3 at 2.26×10^{-9} (Harvey, 1945, p. 62); and the apparent solubility product of $CaCO_3$ at 1.2×10^{-6} (Revelle and Fleming, 1934, p. 2091; Wattenberg, 1936, p. 176; Smith, 1940, p. 182). Equations that express the relationships between various quantities involved in the CO_2 equilibria of sea water (Harvey, 1945, pp. 61–68) may, with some patience, be solved by the method of successive approximations.

The proportions of the different bases dissolved when igneous rocks are decomposed by weathering may be estimated roughly from the average composition of waters of the type that drain from areas of igneous rock (75 stream waters lowest in salinity and highest in silica; Clarke, 1924, pp. 111, 74–79, 81, 83, 89–91, 95–97, 103–105, 107–108). After correction for "cyclic salts" (Conway, 1942, pp. 135–139, 155), this is found to be, in terms of the four principal bases:

Ca	52%
Mg	11%
Na	27%
K	10%
	100%

Other bases, acid radicals, and colloidal aggregates, including significant amounts of silica and iron, in such waters may be ignored for
purposes of the present estimate.

An independent estimate of the relative abundance of the principal
bases in such stream water may be made by applying Conway's
average percentage losses on weathering of igneous rock (Ca—67%,
Mg—18%, Na—41%, and K—26%; Conway, 1942, p. 153) to Clarke
and Washington's average composition of igneous rocks (Clarke, 1924,
p. 29). This gives, as the expected composition of stream water from
igneous areas (in per cent):

Ca	53
Mg	8
Na	25
K	14
	100

The subsequent calculations depend primarily on the proportion of
dissolved calcium to total bases, and these two estimates therefore
accord closely enough for present purposes.

As decomposition of rocks proceeded, more and more dissolved bases
would be carried to the sea until the solubility product of $CaCO_3$ would
eventually be reached, and carbonates would begin to precipitate.
Using the foregoing data, it may be found that at this stage the concentration of $[Ca^{++}]$ in the sea water would be about 0.15 moles/l, that
of $[CO_3^=]$ about 8×10^{-6} moles/l, and the pH 5.1. Approximately
29% of the total CO_2 would then be dissolved in the sea water, 0.6% of
the N_2, and 52% of the H_2S. The gases remaining in the atmosphere
would have partial pressures of $P_{CO_2} = 12.2$, $P_{N_2} = 1.27$, and $P_{H_2S} =
0.28$. Summing up the quantities of dissolved acids, bases, and
atmospheric gases in the sea water would give a "salinity" of about
46 g/kg. (Table 1.2, column 2.)[5]

With further rock weathering and transportation of dissolved bases
to the sea, carbonates would continue to be deposited and CO_2 subtracted from the atmosphere-ocean system. At the arbitrarily
assumed $P_{CO_2} = 1.00$, at which it is conceivable that living organisms
could survive, it may be found that 980×10^{20} g $CaCO_3$ would have
been precipitated, leaving 53% of the original CO_2 still in the atmosphere and ocean. The concentration of $[Ca^{++}]$ would then have fallen
to about 95×10^{-6} moles/l and that of $[CO_3^=]$ would have risen to
about 13×10^{-6} moles/l. The pH would be 7.3, and the concentration

[5] The full computations would require several pages for adequate presentation;
only the results are given here.

of sodium in the sea water would be about 12.5 g/kg. Approximately 87% of the CO_2 then remaining in the atmosphere-ocean system would be dissolved in the sea water, 0.5% of the total N_2, and 85% of the H_2S. The gases in the atmosphere would have partial pressures of $P_{CO_2} = 1.00$, $P_{N_2} = 1.07$, and $P_{H_2S} = 0.073$. The solids and gases dissolved in the sea water would give a total "salinity" of about 67 g/kg (Table 1.2, column 3).

If we apply Conway's percentage losses of bases when igneous rock is weathered and use igneous rock of average composition, it may be found that approximately $17,000 \times 10^{20}$ g of igneous rock must have been weathered to account for the calcium, magnesium, sodium, and potassium then dissolved in sea water and previously precipitated as carbonates.

It is of interest to compare the results of these calculations with independent estimates of the quantities of some materials that have been weathered, dissolved, or precipitated during the entire course of

TABLE 1.2   Composition of Atmosphere and Sea Water Under Alternative Hypotheses of Origin, Compared with Present-Day Conditions

		All "excess" volatiles in primitive atmosphere and ocean (original P_{CO_2} very high)			Only a fraction of total volatiles in primitive atmosphere and ocean (original $P_{CO_2} \leq 1.0$ life begins early)		
		Initial stage; before rock weathering (1)	Intermediate stage; CaCO$_3$ begins to precipitate (2)	Late stage; life begins at $P_{CO_2} = 1.0$ (3)	Initial stage; before rock weathering (4)	Intermediate stage; CaCO$_3$ begins to precipitate (5)	Present-day conditions (6)
Atmosphere (kg/cm^2)		14.2	13.8	2.1	<1.1	<1.1	1.0
N$_2$		9	9	50	7	7	78
CO$_2$	(% by volume)	89	89	47	90	90	0.03
H$_2$S		2	2	3	3	3	—
O$_2$, others		—	—	—	—	tr	22
Ocean ($\times$ 10^{20} g)		16,600	16,600	16,600	<990	<990	14,250
Cl, F, Br		18.3	18.3	18.3	18.3	18.3	19.4
ΣS, ΣB, others		0.8	0.8	1.3	0.1	0.1	2.8
ΣCO$_2$		14.3	15.8	25.2	<1.1	<1.7	0.1
Ca		—	5.9	tr	—	<5.5	0.4
Mg	(g/kg)	—	1.3	5.2	—	<1.2	1.3
Na		—	3.1	12.5	—	<2.9	10.8
K		—	1.2	4.7	—	<1.1	0.4
H		0.5	tr	—	0.5	tr	—
"Salinity"‰		33.9	46.4	67.2	<20.0	<30.8	35.2
pH		0.3	5.1	7.3	0.3	5.7	8.2
CaCO$_3$ pptd. ($\times$ 10^{20} g)		None	None	980	None	None	1500 $\pm$
Igneous rock eroded ($\times$ 10^{20} g)		None	4200 $\pm$	17,000 $\pm$	None	<240	11,000 $\pm$

geologic history. By methods mentioned briefly in an earlier part of this paper, I have estimated the total amount of carbonate rocks of all ages now remaining uneroded at 1500×10^{20} g and the total amount of igneous rock that has been weathered at $11,000 \times 10^{20}$ g (Table 1.2, columns 3 and 6).

These figures do not accord at all well with those required by the hypothesis of a dense primitive atmosphere. Even after precipitation of 980×10^{20} g $CaCO_3$, 53% of the original CO_2 would still remain in the atmosphere and ocean. To reduce this to its present small amount would mean the weathering of even more than the $17,000 \times 10^{20}$ g of igneous rock required at this stage and the deposition of additional carbon as $CaCO_3$ and organic carbon. It is thus seen that this assumption of a dense primitive atmosphere requires the weathering of more igneous rock and the deposition of more carbonates than seems likely to have been weathered and deposited in all of geologic time.

The same conclusion may be reached more directly, without using the estimated quantities of igneous rocks eroded and carbonates deposited. The amount of sodium now dissolved in sea water is known within relatively narrow limits of uncertainty. Adding any reasonable estimates that we may prefer for the sodium in ancient salt deposits and the sodium dissolved in the interstitial water of sediments, it still comes out that this hypothesis of a dense primitive atmosphere requires the solution of much more sodium in sea water, even before life began, than appears, from other evidence, to have been dissolved in all of geologic time.

Results not significantly different from these are obtained if we assume that the first rocks that were decomposed by the supposed highly acid sea water had a composition quite different from that of average igneous rock. Applying Conway's percentage losses to the weathering of average plateau basalt (Daly, 1933, p. 17) gives as the probable relative abundance of the principal bases in stream water:

Ca	73%
Mg	12%
Na	13%
K	2%
	100%

Plateau basalt makes up only a small fraction of all the various rocks now exposed and undergoing erosion on the continents of the earth. Yet it just happens that present-day streams (Clarke, 1924, p. 119), after correction for "cyclic salts," are carrying these four bases to the ocean in proportions (per cent) similar to those that would be expected in streams from outcrops of plateau basalt:

$$
\begin{array}{ll}
\text{Ca} & 73 \\
\text{Mg} & 11 \\
\text{Na} & 9 \\
\text{K} & 7 \\
\hline
& 100
\end{array}
$$

If stream water of this composition, instead of that from areas of average igneous rock, is used in these calculations, it may be found that, at the stage when $P_{CO_2} = 1.0$, not quite so much igneous rock needs to have been weathered ($13,000 \times 10^{20}$ instead of $17,000 \times 10^{20}$ g) but that even more $CaCO_3$ must have been deposited (1500×10^{20} instead of 980×10^{20} g). With these quantities, as with those calculated from the weathering of average igneous rock, the conclusion remains that this hypothesis of a dense original atmosphere seems to require entirely improbable amounts of rock weathering and of carbonate deposition in the early stages of earth history.

Moderate Primitive Atmosphere and Gradual Accumulation of Ocean

Let us contrast this hypothesis with an alternative one that seems much more probable. The difficulties just mentioned—with what might be called the "quick-soak" hypothesis—could be avoided if, instead of all the excess volatiles, only a small fraction was ever present at any one time in the primitive atmosphere, and if the partial pressure of carbon dioxide never exceeded, let us say, one atmosphere. Following the same reasoning as before about the accumulation of bases in sea water, we find that—with the alternative "slow-soak" hypothesis—carbonates would begin to precipitate when the atmosphere and ocean contained less than 10% of the total excess volatiles. At that stage, the atmosphere would have a total pressure only one-tenth greater than at present; the salinity of the sea water would be nearly the same as that of today; and its pH would be about 5.7. The fourth and fifth columns of Table 1.2 show some of the conditions for two stages of this alternative hypothesis. With gradual addition of more volatiles, and as free oxygen accumulated after the advent of plant life (Van Hise, 1904, p. 956), conditions would approach closer and closer to those of today (Table 1.2, last column). Something of this sort seems a much more likely picture of the earth's early atmosphere and ocean.

The preceding calculation started with all the excess volatiles in the primitive atmosphere and ocean and followed through the consequences to be expected if the high initial pressure of CO_2 were reduced by deposition of carbonate sediments to some point where primitive forms of life could survive. This alternative hypothesis starts with the assumption that at no time did the excess volatiles in the atmosphere and ocean exceed such an amount that the partial pressure of CO_2 was greater than 1.0. This would permit, as seems to be required by geologic and chemical evidence (Rankama, 1948, pp. 390–392, 409–414), the existence of primitive forms of life as early as, or earlier than, the deposition of the first carbonate sediments. From this alternative hypothesis (assuming that not enough free oxygen had yet accumulated to oxidize the H_2S to SO_4) and from the previous values for the composition of incoming stream water, it is possible to estimate the conditions that would have prevailed when carbonates first began to precipitate from the sea. It may thus be found that, if P_{CO_2} never exceeded 1.0, then not more than 6% of the total excess volatiles could have been present in the early atmosphere and ocean; and the volume of the primitive ocean would therefore have been much smaller than at present.

At this stage the concentration of $[Ca^{++}]$ would be about 0.14 moles/l, that of $[CO_3^=]$ about 8.8×10^{-6} moles/l, and the pH 5.7. Approximately 3.2% of the CO_2 in the system at that time would be dissolved in the small ocean, 0.04% of the N_2, and 6.7% of the H_2S. The gases in the atmosphere would have partial pressures of $P_{CO_2} = 1.0$, $P_{N_2} = 0.077$, and $P_{H_2S} = 0.033$. The solids and gases dissolved in the sea water at this stage would give a "salinity" of about 31 g/kg (Table 1.2, column 5).

Poole (1941, pp. 346–347, 359) has suggested that an initial supply of free oxygen, sufficient to support life and permit photosynthesis by green plants, may have been produced by photochemical dissociation of water vapor in the upper ionized layers of the atmosphere and by subsequent escape of hydrogen. In this connection, it is of interest to note that purple sulfur bacteria and certain other present-day forms can synthesize organic matter from CO_2 in an anaerobic environment that contains some H_2S. It is possible that primitive organisms of this type may have helped prepare the way for the advent of green plants on the earth (Rabinowitch, 1945, pp. 4, 82–83, 99–106, 124–125). If, as here assumed, the partial pressure of CO_2 was once as high as 1.0 atmosphere, even the rain water would have been so highly carbonated that it would leach much iron and silicon from exposed rocks, and the streams would transport significant amounts of these elements in solution (Gruner, 1922, pp. 433–436; Moore and Maynard, 1929, pp. 276, 293–298, 522–527; Cooper, 1937, p. 307), much as seems to have happened in parts of Precambrian time (Leith, 1934, pp. 161–164).

The conditions calculated for stream water from average igneous rocks would remain essentially unchanged if we used stream water from plateau basalt instead. If, however, the partial pressure of CO_2 were less than 1.0, the fraction of total excess volatiles in the atmosphere-ocean system would be proportionately less than 6%; and several of the other quantities (Table 1.2, column 5) would likewise be decreased.

I am sure I need not warn you that the results of these calculations, of course, are not to be taken too seriously. They are based on inadequate data and laden with many "ifs" and "ands." Nevertheless I believe they point rather clearly to the right answer. If so, not more than a small part of the total excess volatiles could be residual from a primitive atmosphere and ocean. The only alternative I can think of is that these volatiles have risen to the surface from the earth's interior.

SIGNIFICANCE OF CARBON DIOXIDE IN THE ATMOSPHERE-OCEAN SYSTEM

Inventory of Carbon Dioxide

Moreover, these volatiles must have risen to the surface gradually and not in a few great bursts. Table 1.3 is an attempt to bring together an inventory or summary of separate estimates and thus arrive at a figure for the total carbon dioxide and carbon on and near the surface of the earth today. The present atmosphere and ocean contain approximately $1\frac{1}{2} \times 10^{20}$ g CO_2—a small part of it in

TABLE 1.3   Inventory of Total Carbon (as CO_2) in Atmosphere, Hydrosphere, Biosphere, and Sedimentary Rocks

	$\times 10^{18} g$	
Atmosphere	2.33	
Ocean and fresh water	130	
Living organisms and undecayed organic matter	14.5	147
Sedimentary rocks (including interstitial water)		
Carbonates	67,000	
Organic C	25,000	92,000
Coal, oil, etc.	27	

the atmosphere, somewhat more in organic matter, and most of it dissolved in water. It is significant to note that, altogether, this is less than 1 part in 600 of the total CO_2 and organic carbon that has at one time or another been in circulation in the atmosphere and ocean and is now buried in ancient sedimentary rocks.

The amount of CO_2 in the atmosphere is taken directly from Humphreys (1940, p. 81); that in sea water has been calculated as 129×10^{18} g from data on the solubility and dissociation constants in sea water of 35‰ salinity, at an average temperature of 8°C, and in equilibrium with a partial pressure of 0.0003 atmospheres of CO_2 (Harvey, 1945, pp. 59, 62, 64–66). The total quantity of fresh water is here estimated at 335×10^{20} g and, from Clarke's data on average composition of stream and lake waters (1924, pp. 119, 138), the amount of dissolved CO_2 is calculated to be 0.9×10^{18} g.

The quantity of CO_2 equivalent to the carbon in living organisms is estimated at 0.036×10^{18} g in the oceans, using data from Krogh (1934b, pp. 433, 436); and at 0.029×10^{18} g on the lands, using data from Krogh (1934a, pp. 421, 422), Riley (1944, p. 133), and Rabinowitch (1945, p. 6), assuming a rough proportionality between the amount of living organic matter and the rate of carbon fixation. Undecayed particulate organic debris is estimated as equivalent to 11.8×10^{18} g CO_2 in the oceans (Krogh, 1934a, p. 422; 1934b, pp. 435–436) and, very roughly, as equivalent to 2.6×10^{18} g CO_2 on the land areas, using data from Rabinowitch (1945, p. 6) on the areas of soil types and from Twenhofel (1926, p. 17) on the humus content of soils.

The estimates of carbonates and organic carbon in ancient sediments are those derived from the equations of geochemical balance mentioned above; space does not permit a more complete statement of them here. The estimates for coal, oil, etc., have been taken directly or calculated from the following sources and are here summarized in units of 10^{18} g carbon: Coal—7.2 (Assoc. for Planning and Regional Reconstruction, Broadsheet No. 10, 1942, p. 4); oil—0.1 (Weeks, 1950, p. 1952); oil shale—0.1; tar sands—0.025; natural gas—0.025 (Hubbert, 1950, pp. 174–175; graphite—1.0×10^{-5} (U.S. reserves—Currier and others, 1947, p. 249—multiplied by 10). These total to an amount equivalent to 27.3×10^{18} g CO_2.

Carbon Dioxide Equilibria in Sea Water

If only a small part of this total buried carbon dioxide were suddenly added to today's atmosphere and ocean, it would have profound effects on the chemistry of sea water and on the organisms in the sea. These effects become more evident when we consider the important part played by carbon dioxide in the chemistry of sea water. Table 1.4 is presented as a reminder of the composition of sea water and to illustrate several essential points. Sea water varies widely in its total salinity, but scarcely at all in the proportions of its dissolved constituents. The most significant exceptions are the quantities of bicarbonate and carbonate ions, which depend only in part on salinity but are affected much more by hydrogen-ion concentration and by the amount of carbon dioxide in the atmosphere with which the water is in contact.

Note, in the column to the right of Table 1.4, that the positive ions would exceed the negative ions by 2.38 milli-equivalents were it not that the difference between them, the so-called excess base, is balanced by dissociated ions of carbonic and boric acid. The process of balancing the excess base is one of the results of the buffer action of

TABLE 1.4 Composition of Normal Sea Water (Salinity 35‰, 8°C, $\rho = 1.025$, pH 8.17)

	Dissolved matter (g/kg)	Millimol liter	Milli-equivalents liter	
Cl^-	19.360	560.70	560.70	
SO_4^{2-}	2.701	28.88	57.76	
Br^-	0.066	0.85	0.85	
F^-	0.001	0.07	0.07	
CO_2 H_2CO_3	0.001	0.01	—	
HCO_3^-	0.116	1.90	1.90	"Carbonate
CO_3^{2-}	0.012	0.20	0.40	alkalinity"
H_3BO_3	0.022	0.35	—	
$H_2BO_3^-$	0.005	0.08	0.08	
			619.38 2.38	
Na^+	10.770	480.80	480.80	
Mg^{2+}	1.298	54.78	109.56	
Ca^{2+}	0.408	10.46	20.92	
K^+	0.387	10.18	10.18	
Sr^{2+}	0.014	0.15	0.30	
	35.161		621.76 − 619.38 = 2.38 = Excess base	

Recalculated for Cl = 19.37‰, $\rho = 1.025$, and pH = 8.17 from Sverdrup, Johnson, and Fleming (1946, p. 173).

sea water. Note also that, if the amount of sodium in sea water has been increasing continuously through geologic time, as commonly assumed, then some of the acid radicals, such as chlorine, must also have been increasing by the same amounts. Otherwise sea water would have been acid rather than alkaline throughout much the greater part of the past.

The exceedingly delicate balance that prevails between the positive and negative ions in sea water may be appreciated more fully if we consider the consequences of a decrease of only 1 part in 100 of the dissolved sodium. For the salinity and temperature shown in Table 1.4, this would mean reducing the dissolved sodium from 480.80 to 475.99 milli-equivs/l and the total of dissolved bases from 621.76 to 616.95. If the acid radicals, other than the carbonic and boric acid ions, remain unchanged, then they will exceed the bases; and the excess base becomes a negative quantity of $619.38 - 616.95 = 2.43$ milli-equivs/l. It may readily be shown, using the appropriate constants (Harvey, 1945, pp. 59, 61–68), that under these conditions the total concentration of carbonic and boric acid ions, $C_{HCO_3^-} + 2C_{CO_3^=} + C_{H_2BO_3^-}$, would be only 5.6×10^{-6} milli-equivs/l, an entirely negligible quantity by comparison. Chemical balance would therefore be maintained by a concentration of $2.43 \times 10^{-3} = 10^{-2.61}$ moles or gram-ions of hydrogen per liter. That is to say, the pH of the sea water would fall from its present average value of 8.17 to 2.61.

The carbon dioxide equilibria of sea water are numerous and complex, but related to one another in such a way that, for a given temperature, salinity, and partial pressure of carbon dioxide, all the other variables are fixed. Published tables (Harvey, 1945, pp. 59, 62, 64–66) make it possible to work out, for any given salinity and temperature, the amounts of dissolved carbon dioxide, carbonic acid, bicarbonate, and carbonate ions in equilibrium with different amounts of carbon dioxide in the atmosphere, and also to find the resulting hydrogen-ion concentration in the sea water. In the left-hand diagram of Figure 1.1, the amounts of carbonate range from high values, which would cause precipitation of calcium carbonate, at low pressures of CO_2, to low concentrations of carbonate, which would cause solution of calcium carbonate, at high pressures of CO_2. The vertical line through the middle of both graphs represents the amount of CO_2 in the present atmosphere.

These values at low and high pressures of CO_2 would not represent stable conditions in nature. If the solubility product of $CaCO_3$ was greatly exceeded, carbonate would be precipitated from the sea water, either directly or by organic agencies, and it would continue to precipi-

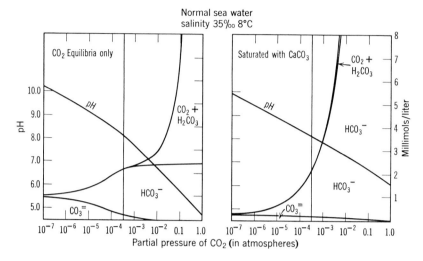

Figure 1.1   Carbon dioxide components and hydrogen-ion concentration of sea water at different partial pressures of carbon dioxide.

tate until equilibrium was re-established. If, on the other hand, much of the water was significantly unsaturated with $CaCO_3$, carbonate sediments lying on the sea floor would be dissolved, or calcium would simply accumulate from incoming stream water until the point of saturation was reached. From Smith's values of the solubility product for 20 and 30°C and 36‰ salinity (Smith, 1940, p. 182) and from Wattenberg's temperature and salinity coefficients (1936, p. 176), the solubility product for 8°C and 35‰ salinity may be estimated at 2.1×10^{-6}.

The right-hand diagram of Figure 1.1 shows, for comparison, the conditions when sea water is saturated with $CaCO_3$. Note that the total CO_2 dissolved in sea water increases much more with increase in the partial pressure than on the other diagram. Also the proportion of bicarbonate is much greater, and the pH varies much less.

These quantities of dissolved CO_2 in sea water and of partial pressure in the atmosphere may, if we wish, be converted into total CO_2 of the atmosphere and ocean combined. This can be done simply by multiplying through by the quantities of sea water and of atmosphere on the earth today and then adding these together. We then may see more readily the effects of changes in the total amount of CO_2 in the atmosphere-ocean system.

Figure 1.2 shows the effects that changes in the total CO_2 in the atmosphere-ocean system would have on the hydrogen-ion concentration. Note that the dashed line gives the pH values based merely on the carbon dioxide equilibria and that these are the values that would follow relatively soon, geologically speaking, after sudden changes of total CO_2. The rate at which sea water could re-establish equilibrium after a change in atmospheric CO_2 depends mainly on the rate at which the deeper water is brought into contact with the air. From what is known about oceanic circulation, it has been estimated that the entire volume of sea water is exposed to the atmosphere in a period of from 2000 to 5000 years (Callendar, 1938, p. 224). The solid line in Figure 1.2 gives the pH values that would follow, perhaps more slowly, as $CaCO_3$ was precipitated or dissolved. Figure 1.3 shows the effects that changes in the total CO_2 would have on the partial pressure of CO_2 in the atmosphere. The values of total CO_2 shown in Figures 1.2 and 1.3 are the original ones before the adjustment that would be caused by solution or precipitation of $CaCO_3$.

The relationships shown in Figures 1.2 and 1.3 are for the present-day volume of sea water, a salinity of 35‰, and a temperature of 8°C. The effects of reducing the volume of sea water, of decreasing the salinity, or of raising the temperature are to shift the lines for pH in Figure 1.2 and for P_{CO_2} in Figure 1.3 somewhat to the left; but the essential relationships are unchanged.

Effects on Organisms

What would be the effects of such changes in total CO_2 on organisms living in the sea? We have already considered the narrow tolerance ranges of some animals for total salinity and for composition of the waters in which they live. For many forms of life, the concentration of bicarbonate and hydrogen ions and the CO_2 tension are among the most critical factors in their chemical environment. A number of higher marine animals (the herring, e.g.) are extremely sensitive to small changes in the pH of their environment. A large proportion of the eggs of some marine animals remains unfertilized if the acidity of sea water departs more than about 0.5 pH from normal. Lower organisms are commonly less sensitive; but many species of mollusks, sea urchins, Medusa, diatoms, bacteria, algae, and others seem unable to tolerate a range of more than about 1 unit of pH. Recent workers attribute a larger part of these observed biologic effects to the carbon dioxide tension or to the concentration of bicarbonate ions than to hydrogen-ion concentration directly (McClendon, 1916, p. 148; Shelford, 1918, pp. 101–102; Gail, 1919, pp. 288,

295, 297; Powers, 1920, pp. 381–382; 1939, p. 73; Atkins, 1922, pp. 734–735; Legendre, 1925, p. 213; Singh Pruthi, 1927, p. 743; Valley, 1928, pp. 215–216, 218–220; Davidson, 1933; Rogers, 1938, pp. 97, 285, 286, 294, 430, 653–656, 679, 680; Edmondson, 1944, pp. 43–45, 63, 64; Allee and others, 1949, pp. 175, 197).

Having thus reviewed in outline the part played by carbon dioxide in the chemistry of sea water and in the environment of marine organisms, let us now return to the inventory of carbon dioxide and to the significance of the fact that more than 600 times as much of it is buried in ancient sedimentary rocks as there is now in circulation in all the atmosphere, hydrosphere, and biosphere.

If only one-one hundredth of all this buried CO_2 were suddenly added to today's atmosphere and ocean [i.e., if the amount in the present atmosphere and ocean were suddenly increased $(600/100 + 1 =)$ sevenfold, from 1.3×10^{20} to 9.1×10^{20} g], it would have profound effects on the chemistry of sea water and on the organisms living in the sea. The first effect would be to change the average pH of sea water from about 8.2 to 5.9 (Fig. 1.2a). This acid water

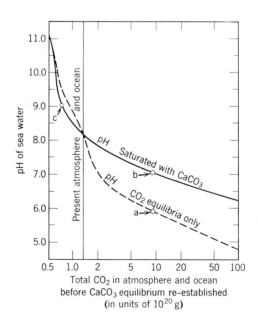

Figure 1.2   Effects of changes in the total carbon dioxide in the atmosphere-ocean system on the hydrogen-ion concentration of sea water (at 35%₀ salinity and 8°C).

would be much less than saturated with $CaCO_3$, and thus further changes would follow. Eventually, when equilibrium was re-established, the partial pressure of CO_2 in the atmosphere would be about 110 times its present value, and the pH of the sea water would end up at an average of about 7.0 (Fig. 1.2b).

The two values of pH, 5.9 and 7.0, are those for present volume and salinity of sea water and a mean water temperature of 8°C. For three-fourths of the present volume of sea water but with present salinity and temperature, these values are 5.8 and 6.9, respectively. For a salinity of 27‰ instead of 35‰, but with present volume and temperature of water, the corresponding values are 5.8 and 7.1. For a mean water temperature of 30°C, but with present volume and salinity of sea water, these values are 5.9 and 6.8.

The effects of these changes on living organisms would be drastic. If the supposed increase of CO_2 happened suddenly, it would probably mean wholesale extinction of many of the marine species of today. If, however, the increase were gradual, so that organisms could adapt themselves by generations of evolutionary changes, the effects would be much less disastrous—but perhaps no less clearly recorded in the physiological adaptations of the surviving forms. From the paleontologic record it appears improbable that any change so drastic as an abrupt sevenfold increase of CO_2 has happened, at least since the beginning of the Cambrian.

Effects on Composition of Sediments

The conclusion that the amount of carbon dioxide in the atmosphere and ocean cannot have varied widely through much of the geologic past does not rest solely on the narrow bicarbonate and pH tolerances of many organisms. The mineralogical and chemical compositions of sedimentary rocks tell much the same story.

Carbon dioxide is constantly being added to the present atmosphere and ocean by the weathering of limestones and other rocks, by artificial combustion (Callendar, 1940, p. 399), and from volcanoes, geysers, and hot springs. At the same time, it is also being subtracted by the deposition and burial of $CaCO_3$ and of organic carbon in sediments.

Let us, for the moment, ignore the contributions of CO_2 from artificial combustion and from volcanoes and hot springs, and compare only the rates of addition by rock weathering and of subtraction by sedimentation. These rates are not known accurately, of course, but from several lines of evidence it appears that the loss by sedimentation must exceed the gain from weathering by something like 10^{14} g CO_2

each year. At this rate of net loss, the total carbon dioxide in the atmosphere and ocean would be reduced to about one-fourth its present value in one million years, and the concentration of hydroxyl ions in sea water would be so high that $Mg(OH)_2$—the mineral brucite—would be precipitated and almost completely take the place of calcite as a common marine sediment. Even if liberal allowance is made for a probable slowing down of weathering and of the synthesis of organic matter as CO_2 is subtracted from the atmosphere-ocean system, it would still be only about 2 million years until brucite would largely take the place of calcite deposition. Apparently no such occurrences of sedimentary brucite are known in rocks of any age, and it seems unlikely that this condition was ever reached in the geologic past. It seems much more likely that the net losses by sedimentation have been roughly balanced by a source neglected in the foregoing calculation—that is, by continuous additions of CO_2 from volcanoes and hot springs.

It seems clear that the loss of CO_2 from the atmosphere-ocean system by sedimentation must, in the long run, somewhat exceed the gain from rock weathering, but the amount of the difference is uncertain. Sedimentary rocks contain, on the average, roughly equivalent amounts of CaO and CO_2 (Clarke, 1907a, p. 169; 1907b, p. 269; 1924, p. 30). Their decomposition by weathering or precipitation by sedimentation does not disturb this equivalent ratio significantly. But igneous rocks contain many times more CaO than CO_2 (Clarke, 1924, p. 29). Thus the proportion of igneous rocks to all rocks undergoing erosion at any time is a rough measure of the amount of CO_2 that must be supplied from some other source in order to maintain the observed ratio in newly formed sediments. Several different methods of estimation (based on the probable quantities of CO_2, organic carbon, and calcium in rocks undergoing erosion, in material being transported by streams, and in sediments being deposited, both now and in the geologic past) yield values for the net loss of CO_2 from the atmosphere-ocean system of from 0.3×10^{14} to 4.0×10^{14} g/yr. The estimates of 1×10^{14} to 2×10^{14} g appear somewhat more reliable, and, for purposes of the following calculations, a value of 1×10^{14} g CO_2/yr has been adopted.

At this rate of net loss, the total CO_2 would be reduced from 131×10^{18} to 31×10^{18} g in

$$\frac{(131 - 31) \times 10^{18} \text{ g}}{1 \times 10^{14} \text{ g/yr}} = 1,000,000 \text{ years.}$$

and the pH of sea water would then be about 9.0. Wattenberg and Timmermann (1938, pp. 87–88) found the solubility product of

$Mg(OH)_2$ to be 5×10^{-11} in sea water; and Harvey remarks that "when the hydrogen-ion concentration of sea water falls and the pH rises above circa pH 9, magnesium hydroxide separates as a precipitate with calcium carbonate" (1945, p. 25). If CO_2 subtraction continues after the precipitation of $Mg(OH)_2$ has begun, the relative amounts of magnesium and calcium in sea water and the various CO_2 equilibria cause $Mg(OH)_2$ to accumulate in far greater amounts than $CaCO_3$.

This estimate of the time required to reduce the total CO_2 in the atmosphere and ocean to the point when brucite would be deposited neglects several factors—one that would operate to decrease the time and two that would operate to increase it. The several chemical relations involved require that, as the pH of sea water is raised from 8.2 to 9.0, 70 mg/l of $CaCO_3$ must, on the average, be subtracted by precipitation to maintain the various equilibria. With the present volume of sea water, this would mean the deposition as carbonate of about 43×10^{18} g of CO_2 in addition to the average net subtraction of 10^{14} g/yr based on present conditions. The total subtraction of $(131 - 31 =)$ 100 units of CO_2 is thus made up in part of 57 units lost because of normal sedimentation. If this is not replaced by CO_2 from other sources, this primary loss causes the precipitation, as carbonate, of 43 additional units of CO_2 in order to maintain the various equilibria. Figure 1.2 shows the effects of primary rather than secondary changes of total CO_2 in the system; and point c (pH 9.0) is therefore plotted at $(131 - 57 =)$ 74 units instead of at 31 units. For purposes of the present calculation, we are interested in the time required for the primary loss of 57 units of CO_2. That is, if there were no other corrections to be considered, the time required to reduce the pH to 9.0 would be only

$$\frac{(131 - 31 - 43) \times 10^{18} \text{ g}}{1 \times 10^{14} \text{ g/yr}} = 570,000 \text{ years.}$$

The total rate of loss of CO_2 by sedimentation is the rate of deposition of carbonates and that of organic carbon. Over the years, the mean rate of carbonate deposition depends on the rate at which streams bring new calcium to the sea, and this in turn depends on the rate of rock weathering on the lands. It seems reasonable to assume that the rate of chemical weathering is controlled in large measure by the partial pressure of CO_2 in the atmosphere (Van Hise, 1904, pp. 465, 476; Clarke, 1924, pp. 110–111) and by the quantity of decomposing organic matter (Jensen, 1917, pp. 255–258, 267–268), which similarly depends on atmospheric CO_2, subsequently discussed somewhat more fully. As the atmospheric CO_2 would decrease under the assumed conditions of this calculation, the rate of rock weathering and hence the rate of carbonate deposition would also decrease. Similarly the rate of accumulation and burial of organic carbon is probably roughly proportional to the rate at which new organic matter is produced, both on the lands and in the sea. This in turn depends largely if not entirely on the rate of carbon fixation by photosynthesis, which at optimum light intensities varies almost directly with the partial pressure of CO_2, up to a P_{CO_2} of about 3, 4, or 5 times that of the present (Brown and Escombe, 1905, pp. 40–41; Hoover, Johnston, and Brackett, 1933, pp. 10–17; Rabinowitch, 1945, pp. 330–331). Thus, as the partial pressure of CO_2 decreased under the assumed conditions, the rates of deposition of both carbonate sediments and organic carbon would probably decrease in roughly the same proportion.

From the relationship between CO_2 and P_{CO_2}, it may be found that, when the total CO_2 is reduced to 31×10^{18} g (Fig. 1.3d, plotted at 74×10^{18} g to show the effects of primary loss), the P_{CO_2} would be reduced to only one-forty-fourth its present value. Numerical integration indicates that over this range the P_{CO_2} would average about 28% of its present value. Thus the mean rate of CO_2 deposition would be only about 0.28×10^{14} g/yr. Combining the effects of these several corrections, a revised estimate of the time required to reduce the total CO_2 to the point where $Mg(OH)_2$ would begin to precipitate would be

$$\frac{(131 - 31 - 43) \times 10^{18} \text{ g}}{0.28 \times 10^{14} \text{ g/yr}} = 2{,}000{,}000 \text{ years.}$$

This is a relatively brief interval in geologic time, and it seems necessary to conclude that CO_2 must have been supplied to the atmosphere-ocean system more or less continuously from some extraneous source in order to account for the absence of brucite as a common marine sediment. The foregoing calculations are based on the constants for sea water of normal salinity at a mean temperature of 8°C. The calculated values are somewhat different if other salinities and temperatures are assumed but not enough so to modify this conclusion significantly.

Possible variation in the account of CO_2 in the atmospheres of the past might be estimated, if sufficiently reliable data were available on the rate at which organic carbon has been deposited during different geologic periods. As stated before, the amount of organic carbon that becomes buried along with sediments and thus removed from circulation at any time is probably roughly proportional to the amount of it then in existence as organic matter. This in turn depends, through a narrow but significant range, on the partial pressure of atmospheric CO_2. The rate of deposition of organic carbon is thus a rough measure of the partial pressure of CO_2 in the atmosphere. For this reason, it is tempting to suppose that the CO_2 content of the atmosphere may have been much greater than at present during those parts of the Carboniferous, Cretaceous, and Tertiary periods when great quantities of coal and other organic deposits accumulated.

Available data do not support this possibility, however. To begin with, the total amount of carbon in all coal, petroleum, oil shale, etc., is negligible in comparison with the carbon present (to the extent of only a few tenths of 1%) in the far more abundant ordinary sedimentary rocks (Table 1.3). Furthermore, local deposits of highly organic sediments do not necessarily mean unusually large accumulations at that same time over the entire earth. Finally, even widespread deposits of highly organic sediments are not in themselves sufficient evidence; the time elapsed during accumulation of the sediments is an essential factor in determining whether or not the rate of carbon deposition was abnormally rapid.

Merely to list the data needed for this calculation is sufficient to demonstrate how far we now are from being able to appraise at all accurately, from this type of evidence, the rates of burial of organic carbon through the geologic past. We need (a) reliable information on the organic carbon content of different types of sediment of different ages, (b) reasonably good estimates of the relative amounts of different sediment types deposited during a given interval of time, and (c) data on the number of years required for deposition. Of these several categories of essential data, the third is probably now known better than the other two.

Nevertheless, something of interest may still be obtained, even from such data as now exist. The average composition of the principal types of sedimentary rocks (Clarke, 1924, pp. 30, 547, 552) affords one of the bases for estimation; the relative abundance of sandstone, shale, and limestone in rocks of different ages may be taken from such compilations as Schuchert's (1931, p. 49); and the estimated durations, in millions of years, of the different periods are available from several sources (e.g., Holmes, 1947b, p. 144). When these various estimates are combined, along with estimates of the amounts of contemporaneous deep-sea sediments, we find no indication whatever that the rate of carbon burial has ever exceeded that of today. In fact this evidence, taken at face value, appears to show that the rate of carbon accumulation has been increasing gradually and rather uniformly ever since the beginning of geologic time.

This apparent evidence of an increasing rate of carbon deposition needs to be viewed with considerable skepticism, however. It may readily be recognized as simply one other aspect of the widely observed relationship that the maximum thicknesses of sedimentary rocks deposited during a unit of time appear to increase progressively as we ascend through the geologic column. This general relationship has been noted and variously interpreted by a number of geologists. Gilluly (1949, pp. 574–582) has clearly pointed out that it does not necessarily mean any real increase in the rate of sedimentation with time but may be explained equally well as the result of the accidents of preservation and exposure of ancient sediments. Whatever may be the correct explanation of this commonly observed relationship, we find no indication from this type of evidence that the average rate of deposition of organic carbon was greater at any time in the past than it is today.

Possible Limits of Variation in the Past

Even if the rate of carbon deposition, averaged over fairly long intervals of time, has remained approximately constant through much of the past, it still seems likely that the rate would have varied somewhat from this average, as the result of irregularities of volcanic eruptions and other possible sources of supply. The observed fact that many plants are capable of a higher rate of carbon dioxide assimilation and photosynthesis, if the carbon dioxide content of the atmosphere is several times greater than normal, is perhaps most simply explained as the result of the adaptation of ancestral forms to an atmosphere that was at times somewhat richer in CO_2 than at present. If we adopt this interpretation and take a P_{CO_2} of about 0.0015 (or five times that of the present) as an optimum condition for photosynthesis (Brown and Escombe, 1905, pp. 40–41; Hoover, Johnston, and Brackett, 1933, pp. 15–16), we have a basis for estimating what may have been the total amount of CO_2 in the atmosphere-ocean system at such times.

With the present volume and salinity of sea water, a mean water temperature of about 8°C, and a prevailing P_{CO_2} of 0.00030, the quantity of CO_2 in the atmosphere and ocean is calculated to be 2.33×10^{18} and 129×10^{18} g, respectively. If, with the other conditions remaining constant, the total quantity of CO_2 in the atmosphere and ocean were increased from 131×10^{18} to 157×10^{18} g, the various CO_2 equilibria would distribute the CO_2 between atmosphere and water so that the P_{CO_2} would rise to the assigned value of 0.00150 (Fig. 1.3e) and the pH would fall to 7.5. This sea water would then be much less than

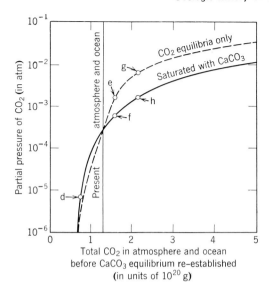

Figure 1.3   Effects of changes in the total carbon dioxide in the atmosphere-ocean system upon the partial pressure of carbon dioxide in the atmosphere (at 35‰ salinity and 8°C).

saturated with $CaCO_3$, and, as a result, $CaCO_3$ would, on the average, be dissolved from the ocean floor until equilibrium was re-established. At that stage, the total quantity of CO_2 in the atmosphere and ocean would be about 177×10^{18} g; the pH would rise to 8.0 (nearly its original value), and the P_{CO_2} would fall back to about 0.00059 (Fig. 1.3f).

It would probably give a more reasonable estimate of the limiting conditions to assume that the arbitrary P_{CO_2} of 0.00150 prevailed *after* rather than *before* adjustment to $CaCO_3$ equilibrium, which would mean that the P_{CO_2} was at times well above that limit.   On this alternative assumption, the total quantity of CO_2 would have increased from 131×10^{18} to 212×10^{18} g, the addition having come from some unspecified source.   The CO_2 equilibria alone would distribute this total between the atmosphere (49×10^{18} g) and sea water (163×10^{18} g), so that the P_{CO_2} would rise to 0.00630 (Fig. 1.3g) and the pH would fall to 6.9.   Sea water of this acidity would dissolve $CaCO_3$ from the ocean floor until about 62×10^{18} g of CO_2 had been added to the system, thereby bringing the total to $(212 + 62 =) 274 \times 10^{18}$ g.   At that stage, when equilibrium was re-established, the quantity of CO_2 in the atmosphere and ocean would be about 11.6×10^{18} and $262 \times$

10^{18} g, respectively; the P_{CO_2} would fall back to the assigned value of 0.00150 (Fig. 1.3h); and the pH would end up at 7.8. It is worth noting that, although the quantity of CO_2 in the atmosphere would have increased by a factor of $11.6/2.33 = 5$, the quantity in the ocean would have increased by only $262/129 = 2$.

The volume and salinity of sea water and the temperature of the water have been held constant in the foregoing calculation. The probable effects of their variation may be estimated by similar calculations. If the volume of the ocean were only three-fourths as great as at present, the quantity of CO_2 dissolved in sea water would be only 194×10^{18} instead of 262×10^{18} g when the P_{CO_2} was 0.00150. For salinity ranges of as much as 20% above and below those of present average sea water, the net effects on the distribution of CO_2 between atmosphere and sea water are almost negligible. If the mean water temperature were 30°C instead of 8°C, the quantity of CO_2 dissolved in sea water would be about 138×10^{18} instead of 262×10^{18} g when the P_{CO_2} was 0.00150. Thus the effects of each of these other controlling variables is such that, if the P_{CO_2} were 5 times that of today, the total CO_2 in the atmosphere-ocean system would probably not have been much more than about twice the present total of 131×10^{18} g.

All these calculations have considered only the amounts of CO_2 in the atmosphere and ocean and have ignored any changes in the total quantity of living organisms and undecayed organic matter in the biosphere, as the P_{CO_2} increased from 0.00030 to 0.00150. By an extension of the reasoning followed above (Effects on Composition of Sediments), it might be estimated that the quantity of organic matter in the biosphere at any time would be roughly proportional to the rate of photosynthesis, which in turn is proportional to the P_{CO_2} through this range. This would mean that, as the P_{CO_2} increased by a factor of 5, the quantity of CO_2 equivalent to organic carbon in the biosphere would also have increased from the estimated 14.5×10^{18} g of today (Table 1.3) to about 72.5×10^{18} g. This would bring the total quantity of carbon in circulation in the atmosphere, hydrosphere, and biosphere under these limiting conditions to about $(274 + 72 =)$ 346×10^{18} g CO_2. A similar "correction" might be made for organic carbon in the biosphere in each of the other calculations. None of the conclusions would be modified, however, and the basis for the "correction" itself seems too uncertain to warrant this refinement.

The possible effect of variation in the CO_2 content of the atmosphere on world climate has been discussed by meteorologists and others for many years. The hypothesis, developed in some detail by Arrhenius (1896) and T. C. Chamberlin (1897, pp. 680; 1899), was that an increase of atmospheric CO_2 would act as a trigger mechanism, retarding radiation of heat from the earth, and thereby starting a train of events that would cause general warming. Physical measurements subsequently indicated that the heat absorption by water vapor far outweighs that by CO_2, and the hypothesis fell into general disfavor (reviews in Clarke, 1924, pp. 52–53, 147–149; Humphreys, 1940, pp. 584–586, 621–622). Recent work, however, seems to have reopened the question to some extent (Callendar, 1938, pp. 231–232; 1941; Dobson, 1942; Elsasser, 1942, p. 64). Callendar's later estimates (1938, p. 231; 1941, p. 32) call for an increase of twenty- to thirtyfold over the present atmospheric CO_2 in order to account for the warmest climates indicated by Tertiary floras, and they call for a decrease to about one-tenth the present content (corresponding to a decrease to about 0.4 of the present total CO_2 in atmosphere and ocean) to account for the coldest epochs of continental glaciation. Other lines of evidence, discussed elsewhere in this paper, make it seem unlikely that the P_{CO_2} has been 20 to 30 times greater than at present, at least in later parts of geologic time. But it appears possible, if CO_2 has the climatic effects some have claimed for it, that decreases in the amount of atmospheric CO_2 may have been a contributory cause of some of the epochs of glaciation.

From several lines of evidence, it seems difficult to escape the conclusion that, for a large part of geologic time, CO_2 has been supplied to the atmosphere and ocean gradually and at about the same rate that it has been subtracted by sedimentation.

Sources of Supply

If the bulk of carbon dioxide in the atmosphere, hydrosphere, biosphere, and sedimentary rocks cannot have been residual from a primitive atmosphere, we must look for other sources of this gradual and continuous supply. At first glance, the possibility seems tempting that this unidentified source may have been the great reserve of carbonates and organic carbon in the ancient sediments. Crustal movements bring these older sedimentary rocks to the surface, where they undergo weathering and gradually release their contained carbon to the streams and atmosphere. If sedimentary deposits accumulated only on the continents and continental shelves and if no igneous rocks were eroded, this problem of the supply of carbon would not concern us, for the quantities of older sedimentary rocks eroded from and new sediments deposited on the continents have probably maintained a reasonably close balance through much of geologic time. But igneous rocks have also been eroded, and sediments have accumulated not only on the continents but also in large quantity in the deep-sea basins (Twenhofel, 1929, pp. 394, 400; Kuenen, 1937, 1941, 1946). It is evident, therefore, that the weathering of sedimentary rocks alone could not suffice to maintain the supply of carbon dioxide to the atmosphere-ocean system.

If weathering of sedimentary rocks is not sufficient, what about the carbon released by metamorphism or by actual melting of the older sediments? Many of the successive steps in metamorphism of siliceous carbonate rocks involve progressive decarbonation of the mineral species (Bowen, 1940, pp. 245, 256–257, 266); and actual melting of sediments would drive off all carbon dioxide or carbon monoxide that could not be dissolved in the resulting melt. In many areas, volcanic rocks and associated schists of Precambrian age have largely been converted into carbonates (Van Hise, 1904, p. 972; Collins and Quirke, 1926, pp. 31–32; Macgregor, 1927, pp. 159–162), possibly as the result of high concentrations of carbon dioxide driven off from nearby sources.

The extent to which ancient sediments have undergone decarbonation by metamorphism or melting is not known. It seems very improbable, however, that such processes are adequate to account for the continuous supply of carbon dioxide to the atmosphere and ocean. As an outside estimate, we may assume that *all* Precambrian and *half* of all Paleozoic sedimentary rocks now remaining uneroded on the continents have undergone complete (not merely partial) decarbonation and that *all* the resulting CO_2 escaped into the atmosphere-ocean system. This would reduce the estimated amount of CO_2 now buried in sedimentary rocks from 920×10^{20} (Table 1.1) to about 780×10^{20} g and would mean that the amount now buried is about 530 (instead of 600) times as great as that in circulation in the present atmosphere, hydrosphere, and biosphere. In other words, even if decarbonation of sedimentary rocks has been far more extensive than seems likely, the essential problem of accounting for this huge discrepancy still remains.

It may be worth noting also that, judged by the estimated relative abundances shown in Table 1.1, the volatile constituents that could be released on complete decarbonation, dehydration, etc., of average sedimentary rock would be very different in overall composition from the excess volatiles.

One other possible source of carbon dioxide may be worth mentioning. Stony and iron meteorites contain an average of 0.04% and 0.11% carbon, respectively (Brown, 1949b, p. 626). Conceivably the supply of carbon dioxide to the earth's surface might have been replenished continuously by showers of meteoritic dust from interplanetary or interstellar space (Van Hise, 1904, pp. 970, 973, 974). A brief consideration, however, of the exceedingly slow rate at which meteoritic debris is reaching the earth today (less than 1 mm/billion years—Jeffreys, 1933—to about 10 cm/billion years—Nininger, 1940, p. 461) and the apparent absence of geologic evidence that the rate has been significantly higher any time since sedimentary rocks began to accumulate makes it seem highly improbable that extraterrestrial sources have made important contributions to the earth's supply of CO_2 since very early in the history of the planet.

The conclusion, arrived at so laboriously here—that CO_2 has been supplied to the atmosphere and ocean gradually and at about the same rate that it has been subtracted by sedimentation—is not particularly new. The Swedish geologist, A. G. Högbom, clearly recognized in 1894 (summarized in Arrhenius, 1896, pp. 269–273) that CO_2 has been supplied continuously to the earth's surface since early in geologic history and that the chief source of this supply must have been volcanic or juvenile. Essentially this same conclusion has been restated many times (T. C. Chamberlin, 1897, pp. 654–656; Fairchild, 1904, pp. 97, 109–110; Clarke, 1924, pp. 58–59; Macgregor, 1927, pp. 156–157; Jeffreys, 1929, p. 312; Goldschmidt, 1934, p. 415; 1938, p. 101; Eskola, 1939; Conway, 1943, pp., 170–174; Cotton, 1944; Hutchinson, 1944, pp. 180, 192; 1947, pp. 300–301); but it is a significant fact about the history of the earth that has sometimes been ignored, and as such it deserves frequent repetition.

SIMILARITY OF EXCESS VOLATILES AND MAGMATIC GASES

The evidence bearing on the probable source and rate of supply of carbon dioxide has been emphasized in the preceding discussion because the chemical and physiological effects of carbon dioxide are relatively well known. Perhaps for this reason, carbon dioxide appears to be of particular significance in our understanding of the history of the atmosphere and ocean. Comparable data on the effects of other volatiles are apparently not available, but from scattered information approximately the same conclusions are suggested for the source and rate of supply of chlorine, oxygen, and several other constituents of the atmosphere and hydrosphere.

In summarizing the evidence on the source of carbon dioxide, Hutchinson put it succinctly when he stated that "it seems unreasonable to accept juvenile addition in the case of one constituent, and,

TABLE 1.5 Volume Percentages of Gases from Volcanoes, Rocks, and Hot Springs

| | Volcano gases from Kilauea and Mauna Loa* (26 samples) | | | Gases from rocks | | | | | | | Gases from fumaroles of the Katmai region† and from steam wells and geysers of California and Wyoming‡ (23 samples) | | |
| | | | | Basaltic lava and diabase* (13 samples) | | | Obsidian, andesitic lava, and granite* (17 samples) | | | | | | |
	Minimum	Maximum	Median	Minimum	Maximum	Median	Minimum	Maximum	Median		Minimum	Maximum	Median
CO_2	0.87	47.68	11.8	0.89	15.30	8.1	0.08	20.26	2.0	CO_2	0.03	1.24	0.02
CO	0.00	3.92	0.5	0.02	8.28	0.2	0.01	2.22	0.5	CO	—	0.01	tr
H_2	0.00	4.22	0.4	0.38	6.18	1.2	0.08	11.60	0.4	O_2	0.00	0.08	tr
N_2	0.68	37.84	4.7	0.27	7.21	2.0	0.03	3.90	1.2	CH_4	0.00	0.30	0.11
A	0.00	0.66	0.2	0.00	0.04	tr	0.00	0.02	tr	H_2	0.00	0.29	0.15
SO_2	0.00	29.83	6.4	—	—	—	—	—	—	$N_2 + A$	0.00	0.31	0.02
S_2	0.00	8.61	0.2	0.08	1.96	1.1	0.00	2.89	0.2	NH_3	—	0.02	0.01
SO_3	0.00	8.12	2.3	—	—	—	—	—	—	H_2S	0.00	0.10	0.02
Cl_2	0.00	4.08	0.05	0.06	1.33	0.5	0.01	10.59	0.5	HCl	0.01	0.57	0.06
F_2	—	—	—	0.00	14.12	3.8	0.25	7.80	2.3	HF	0.00	0.10	0.03
H_2O	17.97	97.09	73.5	71.32	92.40	83.1	69.44	98.55	92.9	H_2O	98.04	99.99	99.58
			100.0			100.0			100.0				100.00

* Analyses by E. S. Shepherd (1938, pp. 321, 326).
† Allen and Zies (1923, pp. 126, 142).
‡ Allen and Day (1927, p. 76; 1935, p. 87).

in the absence of very strong reasons, to deny it in the case of the others" (1944, p. 180). A number of other writers have reached much the same conclusion (Fairchild, 1904, pp. 98, 103; Evans, 1919; Jeffreys, 1929, pp. 147, 312; Eskola, 1932b, pp. 66–67, 69–70; Lane, 1932, p. 318; Gilluly, 1937, pp. 440–441; Goldschmidt, 1938, pp. 17, 24, 101; Wildt, 1939, p. 143; R. T. Chamberlin, 1949, pp. 253, 255–256). (*See also* references regarding the earth's loss of inert gases in section on Dense Primitive Atmosphere-Solution in the Melt.)

Let us now return to the excess volatiles we started with and see how they compare in composition with gases that are escaping from volcanoes, fumaroles, and hot springs, and with gases that are occluded in igneous rocks. Considering that these gases have come in contact and presumably reacted with diverse rock types and ground waters and that they probably contain at least some recirculated or *resurgent* volatiles that have been absorbed from earlier sedimentary rocks (Shepherd, 1938, pp. 312–313), it is to be expected that they will be variable in composition. The extreme ranges of composition of these gases are in fact wide; but median compositions by groups indicate consistent differences in the gases in rocks and lavas of different types (Tables 1.5 and 1.6). If we compare these median gas compositions

TABLE 1.6 Composition of Gases from Volcanoes, Igneous Rocks, and Hot Springs, and of Excess Volatiles in Atmosphere, Hydrosphere, and Sedimentary Rocks

(Median analyses, recalculated from volume to weight percentages)

	Kilauea and Mauna Loa	Basalt and Diabase	Obsidian, Ande-site, and Granite	Fuma-roles, Steam Wells, and Geysers	Excess Volatiles
H_2O	57.8	69.1	85.6	99.4	92.8
Total C as CO_2	23.5	16.8	5.7	0.33	5.1
S_2	12.6	3.3	0.7	0.03	0.13
N_2	5.7	2.6	1.7	0.05	0.24
A	0.3	tr	tr	tr	tr
Cl_2	0.1	1.5	1.9	0.12	1.7
F_2	—	6.6	4.4	0.03	tr
H_2	0.04	0.1	0.04	0.05	0.07
Others	—	—	—	—	tr
	100.04	100.0	100.04	100.01	100.04

Composition of Gases and of Excess Volatiles

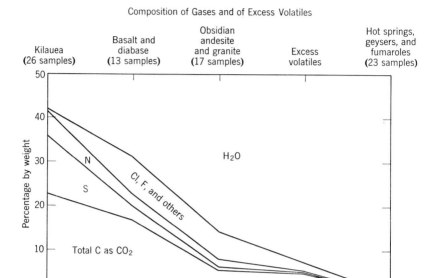

Figure 1.4   Composition of gases from volcanoes, igneous rocks, and hot springs compared with excess volatiles.

with the relative abundance of the constituents of the excess volatiles, we see that an average of the gases in granitic rocks and those from hot springs and fumaroles approximates closely the overall composition of the excess volatiles (Fig. 1.4). Judged solely by compositions then, it is conceivable that all the hydrosphere and atmosphere may have come from such gases (Allen, 1922, pp. 39–42, 52). Several questions must be answered, however, before we may consider such a conclusion.

ESCAPE OF VOLATILES DURING CRYSTALLIZATION OF MAGMAS

Is there some reasonable mechanism by which these gases from the interior could be the source of the excess volatiles? In the cooling and gradual crystallization of complex silicate melts, certain minerals crystallize out first and thus enrich the remaining melt in other constituents, such as silica, alumina, and the alkalies (Bowen, 1928, pp. 293, 297–298) and water, carbon dioxide, and other volatiles (Allen, 1922, p. 57). As crystallization proceeds, the concentration of the remaining volatiles rises and therefore their vapor pressures also rise. As Morey (1922, 1924) and others (Goranson, 1931, p. 499;

Ingerson, 1940, p. 784) have pointed out, when these vapor pressures become greater than the weight of overlying rocks, escape to the surface may be violent, as in volcanic eruptions; or where the crystallizing melt lies at greater depths, the volatiles may escape more gradually along fractures in the overlying rocks.

How adequate is such a mechanism to explain the quantity of volatiles that must have risen to the earth's surface in the course of geologic time? Probably the total quantity of extrusive rocks that has risen to the earth's surface in all of geologic time, although large, is still insufficient to furnish more than a few per cent of the water of the ocean, unless extrusive rocks bulk larger than the total of all sedimentary rocks and unless they originally contained more than 10% water (*see also* Verhoogen, 1946, p. 746). Intrusive rocks, on the other hand, appear to be a more adequate source. Goranson's experimental work has shown that a melt of granitic composition can dissolve as much as 9.3% water at 900°C and at pressure equivalent to a depth of 15 km (Goranson, 1931, p. 493). The amount of water in natural magmas, however, is a subject about which petrologists are not agreed. Gilluly's estimates, which are fairly representative of others,[6] are that the water content of many magmas has been "fully 4% for basalts and perhaps as much as 8% for deep granites" (1937, p. 441).

Let us estimate 4% water in an average magma. Then, as igneous rocks now contain an average of about 1% water, this would mean that magmas have commonly given off about 3% of water during crystallization. On these assumptions, the crystallization of a shell of igneous rock 40 km thick would account for the entire volume of water in the ocean. In a similar calculation, Gilluly (1937, pp. 440–441) estimated that the ocean could have been derived from the escape of 5.8% of water from the sialic rocks of the crust.

HOT SPRINGS AS POSSIBLE CHANNELS OF ESCAPE

How might this quantity of volatiles have escaped to the earth's surface? Hot springs are much less spectacular than volcanoes, but they are more numerous and more widely distributed, and they may be the principal channels by which volatiles escaping from crystallizing magmas have reached the surface. For example, Allen and Day (1935, pp. 40, 87; Allen, 1935, pp. 6, 12; Day, 1939, pp. 328–329) have

---

[6] In a paper that appeared after this was written, Ingerson (1950, pp. 813–814) has reviewed the estimates made by a number of geologists. Gilluly's estimates lie near the middle of the entire range.

estimated, from the temperature of escaping steam in Yellowstone Park, that the hot springs of that area are discharging ground water that has been heated by mixing with about 10 to 15% of magmatic steam.[7]

Hot springs are much more abundant in the area of the Idaho batholith than in that of the much younger lava flows of the adjacent Snake River Plains (Meinzer, 1924, pp. 296–297; Stearns, Stearns, and Waring, 1937, fig. 11, p. 82). More than 100 hot springs and groups of hot springs are known within the limits of the Idaho batholith, and the discharge and temperature of a number of them have been measured (Stearns, Stearns, and Waring, 1937, pp. 136–151). If these springs are heated by the same process of mixing of ground water and magmatic steam that is believed to operate in the Yellowstone, then we may estimate roughly that the average percentage of magmatic water is about $2\frac{1}{2}\%$. The Idaho batholith is thought to be of Cretaceous age (Ross, 1936, pp. 382–383), yet it is still discharging hot waters. Can it be that batholiths cool much more slowly than is generally supposed? If so, this may be one explanation for the long-continued and relatively uniform supply of volatiles that seems to be indicated by the geologic record.

The average temperature of the hot springs of Idaho that have been measured is about 39°C, and the mean annual temperature there is near 8°C. Making the same assumptions about original temperature and mixing as those used in the similar calculation that follows, we find that 1 g of magmatic steam would be sufficient to heat 35.5 g of ground water to 39°C. This would mean 2.7% magmatic water in the final hot-spring mixture.

A crude estimate of the total quantity of water being discharged today from all the hot springs of the earth may be made from available data on the springs of a smaller area. Stearns, Stearns, and Waring (1937, pp. 115–191) list more than 1000 thermal springs or groups of springs within the limits of the continental United States. Undoubtedly some of these are heated by deep artesian circulation, but probably only a small proportion, for many are located in areas of igneous rock. To allow roughly for such artesian heating, the hot springs of the eastern two-thirds of the United States are here omitted

[7] Rubey and Murata (1941) have investigated a small but apparently typical group of hot springs farther south along the Wyoming-Idaho border. From relations between the compositions of water and of contained gases and the temperatures at different outlets, it appears that approximately 5% of the water of these springs is of magmatic origin. For estimates of the amount of magmatic water in other areas, see Zies (1929, pp. 73–74) and White and Brannock (1950, p. 573).

from calculation. If the total area of the States, as thus "corrected," is a fair sample of the continents and if the oceans contribute about half as much per unit area, then the annual discharge of all hot springs, multiplied by 3 billion years, gives a total volume somewhat more than 100 times that of the present ocean. That is to say, if hot springs are delivering to the surface an average of only 0.8% of juvenile water, they could, in the course of geologic time, account for the entire volume of the ocean. This is not counting any contribution of water directly from volcanic eruptions.

Stearns, Stearns, and Waring consider only springs with water more than about 8°C above local mean annual temperature. Of the 1059 hot springs they list for the entire United States, 721 show estimated discharges, and 616 show water temperatures. The total discharge of the 721 measured or estimated springs is 511,600 gal/min. The 338 springs for which no discharge is recorded include the 96 hot springs and geysers of Yellowstone National Park, for which an estimate of 49,400 gal/min is available from another source (Allen, 1935, p. 5). Estimating separately by states for the unmeasured springs, it appears that a total of approximately 800,000 gal/min is a fair approximation for the discharge of all 1059 springs. Comparing the water temperatures with estimated mean annual temperatures and weighing the differences in proportion to the quantities discharged, we arrive at the estimate that the springs are heated, on the average, about 20°C above mean annual temperature.

By the same methods, the hot springs of the western one-third of the country (Ariz., Calif., Colo., Idaho, Mont., Nev., N. Mex., Ore., Utah, Wash., and Wyo.) yield a total of approximately 700,000 gal/min or 1.4×10^{15} g/yr of water. Taking the area of the continental United States as one-thirtieth that of all the continents and using the discharge from only these 11 western states would give a total from all continents of 42×10^{15} g H_2O/yr. The rate of hot-spring discharge on the ocean floor is unknown. Presumably it is lower than that on the continents, but to judge by the evidence of extensive lava flows there (Pettersson, 1949, p. 186), it is probably considerable. If the mean rate per unit area from the oceans is taken as half that from the continents, then the hot-spring discharge from the continents and oceans combined is about 66×10^{15} g H_2O/yr. This rate, continued over a period of 3 billion years, the assumed age of the earth (Holmes, 1947a; Bullard and Stanley, 1949; Ahrens, 1949, pp. 254, 257–258; H. N. Russell, 1949, pp. 11, 12, 15, 20, 24), would yield a total of 2.0×10^{26} g H_2O. The $16,600 \times 10^{20}$ g of "excess" water (Table 1.1) would be 0.0083 of this amount.

It is of some interest to compare this rough estimate of 0.8% juvenile water with another estimate arrived at in quite a different way. Judged by those measured, the hot springs in the 11 western states have an average temperature of about 29°C, which is roughly 20° above the local mean annual temperatures. For purposes of calculation, let us assume that these springs are heated by deep-seated magmatic steam at an original mean temperature of, let us say, 600°C, and that this steam is cooled to 29° by mixing with ground water at the mean annual temperature of 9°C. In cooling from 600° to 29°, steam and water would release about 1100 gram-calories for each gram of magmatic water (estimated from data in Keenan and Keyes, 1936, pp. 79–81). This would be sufficient to heat (1100/20 =) 55 grams of ground water from 9° to 29°. On these assumptions, the hot springs of the United States are being heated by mixing with an average of (1/56 =) 1.8% of magmatic water.

It would, of course, be rash to attach any great significance to the numerical results of these calculations, for the difference between the two estimates is subject to several possible explanations. Nevertheless, it may be worth reminding ourselves that the estimate of 0.8% is for new *juvenile* water and the 1.8% estimate is for total *magmatic* water of whatever source. It is conceivable that the difference of 1.0% between the two estimates may be a rough measure of the *resurgent* water, not newly risen from the earth's interior for the first time but recirculated water that magmas have resorbed from earlier sedimentary rocks—"second-hand" water that is now being returned to the surface.

GENERATION OF LOCAL MAGMAS

Even if we should grant all that has gone before about the probable juvenile origin of the "excess" volatiles, there still remains the question of why the magmas that released the volatiles have not long since cooled off and crystallized completely. In spite of seismic evidence that indicates the possibility, at least in some areas, of a layer of molten rock at a depth of about 80 km (Gutenberg and Richter, 1939*b*; Gutenberg, 1945, pp. 302–307), serious difficulties restrain us from assuming a world-encircling layer (Daly, 1946, pp. 712, 721–722) of slowly crystallizing magma from which volatiles have been escaping continuously ever since the world began. However, the abundant field evidence of local intrusive masses, some of them very large, that have been generated repeatedly throughout the past suggests a possible answer.

If we are willing to adopt the eclectic method of borrowing from various theories those parts of each that we like best, then a possible mechanism suggests itself—a mechanism by which local masses of hydrous magma might be generated more or less continuously throughout geologic time. The geothermal gradient varies from place to place (Van Orstrand, 1939, pp. 132–141; Landsberg, 1946); but probably below a depth of 50 to 100 km, rocks are heated to significantly higher temperatures (Holmes, 1915, p. 111; Adams, 1924, pp. 468–472; Jeffreys, 1929, p. 154; Gutenberg, 1939, p. 162; Urry, 1949, p. 176; or one may calculate his own thermal gradient from revised data on the radioactive generation of heat in different rock types—Keevil, 1943, p. 299; Birch, 1950a, pp. 612–613, 616, 619), temperatures at which they would melt, if the confining pressures were not so great (Holmes, 1916, p. 269; Adams, 1924, pp. 462, 468–472; Anderson, 1938, pp. 50–51, 56–57, 72–73; Benfield, 1940, pp. 157–158; Buddington, 1943, p. 139).

Under these conditions, several processes may operate to cause local melting. As sediments accumulate in a region, their low thermal conductivity makes them act as a blanket to impede the upward flow of heat (Jeffreys, 1930, p. 328). And in geosynclinal troughs, where sediments accumulate to great thicknesses, the entire column of underlying rocks is depressed into zones where the temperature is significantly higher (Eskola, 1932a, pp. 456–457, 468–469). Temperatures may thus be reached at which some of the minerals in the deeper rocks are melted. Moreover, as strains accumulate in the earth's crust and the rocks eventually fail by fracture, sudden localized relief of pressure and shearing stresses may, without increasing the temperature, bring some of the minerals above their melting points (Johnston and Adams, 1913, pp. 210–223, 248–253; Johnston and Niggli, 1913; pp. 602–603, 613–615; Bowen, 1928, p. 314; Holmes, 1932, p. 556; Wahl, 1949, p. 148). As has been shown by Bowen (1928, pp. 311–320), Eskola (1932a, p. 474), and others (Holmes, 1926, pp. 315–316; 1932, pp. 545, 556; Kennedy, 1938, pp. 38–39; Buddington, 1943, pp. 132–133, 137–139; Wahl, 1949, pp. 161–163), such selective fusion of the lower-melting minerals would form magmas more granitic and at the same time richer in volatiles than the original rock.

Fusion would cause increase of volume, and the resulting hydrous, granitic magmas would tend to rise, partially recrystallizing as they moved into higher, cooler zones. This process would "pump" nearly all the volatile materials from the original rock; in recrystallizing, these magmas could form suites of intermediate and granitic rocks, and the volatiles would largely escape to the earth's surface. By this mechanism, the volume of granitic rocks would increase near areas of sedimentation and where the crust was for any other reason unstable. As these unstable areas migrated with the continental margins and with the sites of mountain making, the granitic rocks would thus increase progressively in volume (Eskola, 1932a, pp. 468–469, 480; Lawson, 1932, pp. 358–361; Wilson, 1950, pp. 101, 108, 111; Bucher, 1950, pp. 500–504; Hurley, 1950).

COROLLARIES AND TESTS OF THE SUGGESTED MECHANISM

Isostatic Considerations

This leads to an important corollary of the suggested mechanism. If granitic rocks have grown progressively in volume through geologic time, then isostatic equilibrium would require more or less continuous readjustments, by which the thickening blocks of lighter, granitic or continental types of rocks would rise higher and higher above adjacent blocks of undifferentiated material. In another terminology, this would mean that the ocean basins must sink deeper as the continental blocks thicken. If the ocean basins have sunk as approximately the same rate as the volumes of granitic rocks and of sea water have grown, then it is no coincidence, but the effects of one single process, that the surface of the sea has oscillated back and forth near the same level on the continental shelves throughout the geologic past.

Isostatic balance between the oceanic and continental blocks affords a basis for estimating the relative quantities of water and granitic rocks and of the original subcrustal matter from which they may have been derived by selective fusion. The area of the earth's surface that rises above sea level is roughly 1.49×10^{18} cm²; but the actual margins of the continental blocks lie much farther oceanward, beyond the continental shelves and near the base of the steep continental slopes. If 3000 meters below sea level is taken as approximately the base of the continental slopes, then the total area of the continental blocks is about 2.32×10^{18} cm² (Sverdrup, Johnson, and Fleming, 1946, pp. 15, 19, 21). The mean elevation of the continental blocks, as thus defined, is about 0.12 km above sea level, and the mean depth of the ocean basins (below the −3000 meters contour) is about 4.6 km below sea level. The average density of sea water *in situ* is approximately 1.04 (Sverdrup, Johnson, and Fleming, 1946, p. 219). From independent estimates, mentioned briefly elsewhere in this paper, it appears that the mean thickness of deep-sea sediments may be about 1.3 km and their mean density, when filled with interstitial

water, about 2.3. For purpose of this calculation, the average density of rocks to several tens of kilometers below the continents (the sedimentary, "granitic," and "intermediate" shells) may be taken as 2.9, and that of undifferentiated ultrabasic rocks to similar depths below the deep-sea sediments as 3.2.

From these several estimates, the average depth of compensation below the continents may be found to be

$$0.12 + \frac{(0.12 \times 2.9) + 4.6\ (3.2 - 1.04) + 1.3\ (3.2 - 2.3)}{3.2 - 2.9} = 38.3 \text{ km}$$

This value accords reasonably well with the average depth to the Mohorovičić discontinuity, which is found widely distributed beneath the continents but is not recognized with certainty over extensive areas beneath the oceans (Macelwane, 1939, pp. 237–239; Gutenberg and Richter, 1939a, pp. 321–322). This major discontinuity is often interpreted as representing the approximate base of the crustal materials that make up the continents.

It seems permissible to assume that these densities of continental and oceanic materials have remained approximately the same throughout the past. It follows then that, if there was a time when the mean depth of the ocean basins and the mean thickness of deep-sea sediments were half their present values, isostatic equilibrium would require that the mean elevation of the continents and the mean depth of compensation below the surface of the continental blocks would, at that time, also be just half their present values. If the total areas of the continental blocks and of the oceanic basins have remained approximately the same (peripheral growth of the continents having approximately balanced subtraction by continental foundering), this strictly proportionate deepening of the oceanic basins and thickening of the continental crust, which is required by isostatic balance, would accord with the suggested mechanism of selective fusion which likewise would require that the volumes of sea water and of continental rocks have grown in strict proportionality.

The total mass of the continental blocks today may be estimated from the results of the previous calculation at $(2.32 \times 10^{18} \text{ cm}^2)$ $(38.3 \times 10^5 \text{ cm}) \times 2.9 \text{ g/cm}^3 = 258 \times 10^{23} \text{ g}$. Allowing for the probable quantity of crystalline rocks that has been eroded from the continents in the past and is now represented as deep-sea sediment on the ocean floor, we obtain an estimate of $2.65 \times 10^{25} \text{ g}$ for the total mass of crustal rocks that have been formed on and in the continental blocks. It is to be noted that this estimate makes no allowance for any similarly differentiated crustal rocks that may now be lying foundered beneath the sea.

According to the eclectic hypothesis here suggested, this 2.65×10^{25} g of crustal rock has been formed, largely by selective fusion and subsequent recrystallization of the resulting magma, from an unknown quantity of subcrustal rock materials. The total mass of the earth's silicate mantle that lies directly below the continents, to a depth of 2900 km and above the earth's "iron core," may be estimated at about 185×10^{25} g. Much of this subcrustal matter may still be in very nearly its original condition (Birch, 1950b). But that part of it lying above the maximum depth (of about 700 km) to which deep-focus earthquakes are recorded (Gutenberg and Richter, 1941, pp. 4–11; Benioff, 1949, pp. 1844–1854) may have been worked over and subjected, at one time or another during the course of geologic history, to at least some selective fusion. The total mass of this subcrustal matter below the continental areas and between depths of 38 and 700 km is about 50×10^{25} g.

On the assumption that this is roughly the quantity of subcrustal matter that may have yielded both the "granitic" magmas that became the continental rocks and the volatile substances that have formed the atmosphere and ocean, it is of interest to compare the relative amounts of each. With an average water content of 1.15% (Clarke, 1924, p. 29), the 2.65×10^{25} g of present crustal rocks would contain 3050×10^{20} g H_2O. This, added to the $16,600 \times 10^{20}$ g of "excess" H_2O in the present atmosphere, ocean, and sedimentary rocks, gives a total of $19,650 \times 10^{20}$ g H_2O that has escaped, along with the 2.65×10^{25} g of "granitic" magmas from the subcrustal matter. Thus the original $(50 + 2.65) \times 10^{25}$ g of subcrustal matter would have yielded, by selective fusion, $2.65/52.65 = 5.0\%$, or 1 part in 20, of magmas that have risen to form the crustal rocks and $0.1965/52.65 = 0.37\%$ H_2O. If the "granitic" magmas originally held all this water in solution, they would have contained at that time an average of $0.1965/2.65 = 7.4\%$ H_2O, of which $0.166/2.65 = 6.3\%$ subsequently escaped to the surface during recrystallization of the magmas.

These estimates are, of course, only crude ones based on very uncertain foundations. They make no allowance for possible "granitic" rocks now foundered beneath the oceanic depths; to whatever extent any continental rocks now lie beneath the ocean floor, the calculated percentages of water in the "granitic" magmas and of water lost from the subcrustal matter must be reduced proportionately.

A rough but independent check on the reasonableness—or otherwise—of this estimate of the amount of subcrustal matter that has been selectively fused can be made by considering certain substances that may have been concentrated in the crustal rocks or at the surface as the result of the supposed differentiation. In the absence of better information, the average composition of the original undifferentiated peridotitic material may be taken as similar to that of stony meteorites (Bowen, 1928, pp. 315–316; 1950; *see also* references in section on Dense Primitive Atmosphere—Solution in the Melt). The silicate phase of stony meteorites contains an average of 0.063% hydrogen [equivalent to 0.56% H_2O] and 0.199% potassium [equivalent to 0.24% K_2O] (Brown, 1949b, p. 626). Thus the calculation that 0.37% H_2O has escaped from the subcrustal matter to a depth of 700 km would mean that, on the average, $0.37/0.56 = 66\%$ of this mass of material has undergone selective fusion.

If the residual unmelted fraction remaining after selective fusion has an average composition similar to that of dunite, it would contain about 0.04% K_2O (Daly, 1933, p. 20). The average igneous rocks now exposed on the continents contain 3.13% K_2O (Clarke, 1924, p. 29). From these average compositions, we may calculate that the original subcrustal matter has yielded about $(0.24 - 0.04)/(3.13 - 0.04) = 6.5\%$, or 1 part in 15, of magmas that have crystallized to form the present crustal rocks. This ratio of 1 part of magma to 15 parts of subcrustal matter, when compared with the previous estimate of 1 part in 20 (based on total material to 700 km), would mean that on the average about 75% of the mass of subcrustal matter to a depth of 700 km has undergone selective fusion.

It is only fair to add that ratios of much more and much less than 1 part in 15 may be obtained by using for comparison other elements than potassium and other rock types (peridotite instead of dunite and diorite instead of the average igneous rock now exposed at the upper surface of the continental blocks). Yet when we consider that the process of selective fusion would act unequally on different constituents of the subcrustal matter and would probably remove much larger proportions of the readily volatile substances, such as water, than of the more refractory rock-forming minerals, it is surprising to find even such rough agreements as those just mentioned. About all that may safely be concluded is that the general order of magnitude of the ratio of "granitic" magmas to subcrustal matter appears not unreasonable.

Other Geologic Tests

The least we can ask of any hypothesis is that it be consistent with the known facts. But it is not always as easy as it sounds to apply this test, because much information and hard work are sometimes required to formulate corollaries of a hypothesis so that they can be tested by the known facts. We shall mention just a few geologic tests of this suggested mechanism.

At first thought, the widespread epicontinental seas of the past seem to contradict the suggestion flatly. But areas are not to be confused with volumes. If the ocean basins have been sinking relative to the continental blocks, then we must look largely to the ocean floor, rather than to the continents, for evidence of a growing volume of sea water. Unfortunately, our information about the ocean floor is still very sketchy. The flat-topped sea mounts, or guyots, discovered by Hess (1946) indicate a considerable sinking of the ocean floor, some part of which may mean a general rise of sea level and not merely local deformation. Other lines of evidence, such as submerged terraces and great thicknesses of shallow-water limestones on some oceanic islands (Carsey, 1950, p. 376), suggest, although likewise they do not prove, the same conclusion. It has long been recognized that very few areas that once were part of the deep sea have later risen to become part of the continents (Walther, 1911, p. 60–61). Furthermore, the truncation of structural trends at some continental margins and the geographic distribution of certain animals and plants seem to require that parts of some land masses have broken off and foundered to oceanic depths (Barrell, 1927, pp. 303–305; Moore, 1936, p. 1786). These are all rather obvious, general tests that yield results consistent with, but certainly not proving, an increasing volume of ocean basins through geologic time.

Undoubtedly other and more rigorous tests should be looked for in the stratigraphic and structural record on the continents where many more facts are available than we yet know about the ocean basins. A gradually increasing volume of sea water and of marine sediments would mean a gradual rise of sea level and relatively slow marine transgressions, modified of course by the effects of local deformation, and interrupted by relatively rapid withdrawals of the sea, when the ocean floor sank to new positions of equilibrium. Such sudden withdrawals of the sea would affect parts of all continents at the same time (Moore, 1936, pp. 1803–1805, 1808). On the other hand, if hydrous granitic magmas have formed by the mechanism indicated, then mountain-making movements, as contrasted with emergences of the continental shelves, need not have been even approximately contemporaneous from one continent to another (Gilluly, 1949).

How well or how poorly do the geologic facts bear out such corollaries as these? Or if these are not valid tests of the suggested mechanism, I trust that others will think up much better ones.

As I warned at the beginning, this subject ramifies almost endlessly into many problems of earth history. A satisfactory solution of the problem of the source and history of the earth's air and water depends on the solution of a great many other questions. Because it is so closely related to many others, this problem is likely long to remain one of those hardy perennials that need a new look and reappraisal every few years, as new observations accumulate. Perhaps what has been presented here is simply another case of putting 2 and 2 together and getting 22, instead of 4. But this review and these tentative conclusions will have served their purpose if they help stimulate—or if they provoke—critical observations and critical thinking about the history and significance of sea water.

REFERENCES

Adams, L. H., 1924. Temperatures at moderate depths within the earth, *Acad. Sci. J.*, **14**, 459–472.

Ahrens, Louis, 1949. Measuring geologic time by the strontium method, *Bull. Geol. Soc. Am.*, **60**, 217–266.

Allee, W. C., A. E. Emerson, Orlando Park, Thomas Park, and K. P. Schmidt, 1949. *Principles of Animal Ecology,* W. B. Saunders Co., Philadelphia, 837 pp.

Allen, E. T., 1922. Chemical aspects of volcanism, with a collection of analyses of volcanic gases, *J. Franklin Inst.*, **193**, 29–80.

———————— 1935. Geyser basins and igneous emanations, *Econ. Geol.*, **30**, 1–13.

———————— and A. L. Day, 1927. *Steam Wells and Other Thermal Activity at "The Geysers,"* California Carnegie Inst., Washington, Pub. no. 378, 106 pp.

———————— 1935. *Hot springs of the Yellowstone National Park* (Microscopic examinations by E. H. Merwin), Carnegie Inst. Washington, Pub. no. 466, 525 pp.

———————— and E. G. Zies, 1923. A chemical study of the fumaroles of the Katmai region, *Nat. Geog. Soc., Contrib. Tech. Papers, Katmai Ser.,* no. 2, 75–155.

Anderson, E. M., 1938. Crustal layers and the origin of magmas. Part II, Geophysical data applied to the magma problem, *Bull. Volcanologique,* ser. 2, **3**, 42–82.

Arrhenius, Svante, 1896. On the influence of carbonic acid in the air upon the temperature of the ground, *Philos. Mag.,* 5th ser, **41**, 237–276.

Association for Planning and Regional Reconstruction, 1942. *Coal in Relation to World Energy Supplies,* Broadsheet No. 10, 32 Gordon Square, London, W. C. 1, 4 pp.

Aston, F. W., 1924. The rarity of the inert gases on the earth, *Nature,* **114**, 786.

Atkins, W. R. G., 1922. The hydrogen ion concentration of sea water in its biological relations, Part I, *Marine Biol. Assoc. Jour.,* **12**, 717–771.

Barrell, Joseph, 1927. On continental fragmentation and the geologic bearing of the moon's surficial features, *Am. Jour. Sci.,* 5th ser., **13**, 283–314.

Benfield, A. E., 1940. Thermal measurements and their bearing on crustal problems, *Am. Geophys. Union Tr.,* pt. II, 155–159.

Benioff, Hugo, 1949. Seismic evidence for the fault origin of oceanic deeps, *Geol. Soc. Am. Bull.,* **60**, 1837–1856.

Birch, Francis, 1950*a*. Flow of heat in the Front Range, *Bull. Geol. Soc. Am.,* **61**, 567–630.

——————— 1950*b*. Elasticity and composition of the earth's interior (Abstract), *Science,* **112**, 453.

——————— J. F. Schairer, and H. C. Spicer, editors, 1942. Handbook of physical constants, *Geol. Soc. Am., Spec. Papers,* no. 36, 325 pp.

Bowen, N. L., 1928. *The Evolution of the Igneous Rocks,* Princeton University Press, 334 pp.

——————— 1940. Progressive metamorphism of siliceous limestone and dolomite, *J. Geol.,* **48**, 225–274.

——————— 1947. Magmas, *Geol. Soc. Am. Bull.,* **58**, 263–280.

——————— 1950. Petrologic-cosmogonic dilemma (Abstract), *Science,* **112**, 453–454.

Brown, Harrison, 1949*a*. Rare gases and the formation of the earth's atmosphere, in G. P. Kuiper, editor, *The Atmospheres of the Earth and Planets.* University of Chicago Press.

——————— 1949*b*. A table of relative abundances of nuclear species, *Rev. Mod. Phys.,* **21**, 625–634.

Brown, Horace T. and F. Escombe, 1905. Researches on some of the physiological processes of green leaves, with special reference to the interchange of energy between the leaf and its surroundings, *Royal Soc. London, Pr.,* ser. B, **76**, 29–111.

Bruce, E. L., 1945. Pre-Cambrian iron formations, *Bull. Geol. Soc. Am.,* **56**, 589–602.

Buchner, W. H., 1950. Megatectonics and geophysics, *Am. Geophys. Union,* **31**, 495–507.

Buddington, A. F., 1943. Some petrological concepts and the interior of the earth, *Am. Mineral,* **28**, 119–140.

Bullard, E. C. and J. P. Stanley, 1949. The age of the earth, Helsinki, *Veroff. Finn. Geod. Inst.,* **36**, 33–40.

Bullen, K. E., 1940. The problem of the earth's density variation, *Bull. Seismol. Soc. Am.,* **30**, 235–250.

——————— 1942. The density variation of the earth's central core, *Bull. Seismol. Soc. Am.,* **32**, 19–29.

Callendar, G. S., 1938. The artificial production of carbon dioxide and its influence on temperature, *Roy. Meteor. Soc., Quart. J.,* **64**, 223–240.

——————— 1940. Variations of the amount of carbon dioxide in different air currents, *Roy. Meteor. Soc., Quart. J.,* **66**, 395–400.

——————— 1941. Atmospheric radiation, *Roy. Meteor. Soc., Quart. J.,* **67**, 31–32.

Carsey, J. B., 1950. Geology of Gulf Coastal area and continental shelf, *Bull. Am. Assoc. Petrol. Geol.,* **34**, 361–385.

Chamberlin, R. T., 1908. *The Gases in Rocks,* Carnegie Inst. Washington, Pub. no. 106, 80 pp.

———————— 1949. Geological evidence on the evolution of the earth's atmosphere, in G. P. Kuiper, editor, *The Atmospheres of the Earth and Planets,* University of Chicago Press.

Chamberlin, T. C., 1897. A group of hypotheses bearing on climatic changes, *J. Geol.,* **5,** 653–683.

———————— 1899. An attempt to frame a working hypothesis of the cause of glacial periods on an atmospheric basis, *Jour. Geol.,* **7,** 545–584, 667–685, 751–787.

Clarke, F. W., 1907a. The composition of red clay, *Roy. Soc. Edinburgh, Pr.,* **27,** 167–171.

———————— 1907b. The composition of terrigenous deposits, *Roy. Soc. Edinburgh, Pr.,* **27,** 269–270.

———————— 1924. The data of geochemistry, *U. S. Geol. Survey Bull.,* **770,** 841 pp.

Cloud, P. E. and V. E. Barnes, 1948. Paleoecology of early Ordovician sea in central Texas, *Nat. Research Council, Rept. of Comm. on Treatise on Marine Ecology and Paleoecology, 1947–1948,* no. 8, 29–83.

Collins, W. H. and T. T. Quirke, 1926. Michipicoten iron changes, *Geol. Survey Canada Mem.,* **147,** 141 pp.

Conway, E. J., 1942. Mean geochemical data in relation to oceanic evolution, *Roy. Irish Acad., Pr.,* **XLVIII,** Sect. B, no. 8, 119–159.

———————— 1943. The chemical evolution of the ocean, *Roy. Irish Acad., Pr.,* **XLVIII,** Sect. B, no. 9, 161–212.

———————— 1945. Mean losses of Na, Ca, etc. in one weathering cycle and potassium removal from the ocean, *Am. Jour. Sci.,* **243,** 583–605.

Cooper, L. H. N., 1937. Some conditions governing the solubility of iron, *Roy. Soc. London, Pr.,* ser. B., **124,** 299–307.

Cotton, C. A., 1944. Volcanic contributions to the atmosphere and ocean, *Nature,* **154,** 399–400.

Crawford, J. G., 1940. Oil-field waters of Wyoming and their relation to geologic formations, *Bull. Am. Assoc. Petrol. Geol.,* **24,** 1214–1329.

Currier, L. W., G. R. Gwinn, and W. H. Waggaman, 1947. Graphite, 247–249, In *Mineral Position of the United States,* Hearings before a Subcommittee of the Com. on Public Lands, U. S. Senate, 80th Cong., 1st session.

Dakin, W. J., 1935. The aquatic animal and its environment, *Linnean Soc. New South Wales, Pr.,* **60,** 7–32.

Daly, R. A., 1909. First calcareous fossils and the evolution of the limestones, *Bull. Geol. Soc. Am.,* **20,** 153–170.

———————— 1933. *Igneous Rocks and the Depths of the Earth,* McGraw-Hill Book Co., 598 pp.

———————— 1946. Nature of the asthenosphere, *Bull. Geol. Soc. Am.,* **57,** 707–726.

Davidson, F. A., 1933. Temporary high carbon dioxide content in an Alaskan stream at sunset, *Ecology,* **14,** 238–240.

Day, A. L., 1939. The hot spring problem, *Geol. Soc. Am. Bull.,* **50,** 317–336.

Dobson, G. M. B., 1942. Atmospheric radiation and the temperature of the lower stratosphere, *Roy. Meteor. Soc., Quart. Jour.,* **68,** 202–204.

Edmondson, W. T., 1944. Ecological studies of sessile Rotatori, Part I, Factors affecting distribution, *Ecol. Monog.,* **14,** 31–66.

Elsasser, W. M., 1942. *Heat Transfer by Infra-red Radiation in the Atmosphere,* Harvard Meteor. Studies, Blue Hill Meteor. Observ., **6**, 107 pp.

Eskola, Pentti, 1932*a*. On the origin of granitic magmas, *Mineralog. Petrog. Mitt.,* **42**, 455–481.

——————————— 1932*b*. Conditions during the earliest geological times, as indicated by the Archaean rocks, Suomalaisen Tiedeakatemian Toimituksia, *Sarja A., Nid.,* **36**, no. 4, 1–70.

——————————— 1939. Maapallon hiili, happi ja elama, *Suomalaisen Tiedeakat. Esitelmat Poytakirjat,* **70**. (Cited by Rankama and Sahama, 1950, pp. 394, 401, 407, 535, 539, 540, 614.)

Evans, J. W., 1919. A modern theory of the earth, *Observatory,* **42**, 165–167.

Ewart, A. J., 1896. On assimilatory inhibition in plants, *Linnean Soc. Botany Jour.,* **31**, 364–461.

Fairchild, H. L., 1904. Geology under the new hypothesis of earth origin, *Am. Geol.,* **33**, 94–116.

Farrington, O. C., 1915. *Meteorites,* University of Chicago Press, 233 pp.

Fenner, C. N., 1926. The Katmai magmatic province, *Jour. Geol.,* **34**, 673–772.

Foster, M. D., 1942. Base-exchange and sulphate reduction in salty ground waters along Atlantic and Gulf Coasts, *Bull. Am. Assoc. Petrol. Geol.,* **26**, 838–851.

Gail, F. W., 1919. Hydrogen ion concentration and other factors affecting the distribution of Fucus, *Puget Sound Biol. Sta.,* **2**, 287–306.

Gibson, D. T., 1949. The terrestrial distribution of the elements, *Chem. Soc. London, Quart. Rev.,* **3**, 263–291.

Giese, A. C., 1945. Ultraviolet radiations and life, *Physiol. Zool.,* **18**, 223–250.

Gilluly, James, 1937. The water content of magmas, *Am. Jour. Sci.,* **33**, 430–441.

——————————— 1949. Distribution of mountain building in geologic time, *Bull. Geol. Soc. Am.,* **60**, 561–590.

Goldschmidt, V. M., 1933. Grundlagen der quantitativen Geochemie, *Fortsch. Mineral. Krist. Petrog.,* **17**, 112–156.

——————————— 1934. Drei Vortrage uber Geochemie, *Geol. Foren. Stockholm Forh.,* **56**, 385–427.

——————————— 1938. Geochemische Verteilungsgesetze der Elemente. IX. Die Mengenverhaltnisse der Elemente und der Atom-Arten, Skrifter Norske Videnskaps-Akad. Oslo, I. *Mat. Natur. Klasse* **1937**, no. 4, 1–148.

Goranson, R. W., 1931. The solubility of water in granitic magmas, *Am. Jour. Sci.,* 5th ser., **22**, 481–502.

——————————— 1932. Some notes on the melting of granite, *Am. Jour. Sci.,* 5th ser., **23**, 227–236.

Gruner, J. W., 1922. The origin of sedimentary iron ore formations, The Biwabik formation of the Mesabi Range, *Econ. Geol.,* **17**, 407–460.

Gunter, Gordon, 1947. Paleo-ecological import of certain relationships of marine animals to salinity, *Jour. Paleon.,* **21**, 77–79.

Gutenberg, Beno, 1939. The cooling of the earth and the temperature of its interior, pp. 153–164, in B. Gutenberg, editor, *Internal Constitution of the Earth, Physics of the Earth,* VII, McGraw-Hill Book Co., New York.

——————————— 1945. Variations in the physical properties within the earth's crustal layers, *Am. Jour. Sci.,* **243–A** (Daly vol.), 285–312.

——————————— and C. F. Richter, 1939*a*. Structure of the crust. Continents and oceans, in B. Gutenberg, editor, *Internal Constitution of the Earth, Physics of the Earth,* VII, McGraw-Hill Book Co., New York.

—————————— 1939b. New evidence for a change in physical conditions at depths near 100 kilometers, *Seismol. Soc. Am. Bull.*, **29**, 531–537.

—————————— 1941. Seismicity of the earth, *Geol. Soc. Am., Spec. Papers*, no. 34, 131 pp.

Harvey, H. W., 1945. *Recent Advances in the Chemistry and Biology of Sea Water*, Cambridge University Press, 164 pp.

Heck, E. T., C. E. Hare, and H. A. Hoskins, 1940. Origin and geochemistry of connate waters in West Virginia (Abstract), *Geol. Soc. Am. Bull.*, **51**, 1995.

Henderson, L. J., 1927. *The Fitness of the Environment; an Inquiry into the Biological Significance of the Properties of Matter*, Macmillan, 317 pp.

Hess, H. H., 1946. Drowned ancient islands of the Pacific Basin, *Am. Jour. Sci.*, **244**, 772–791.

Hogbom, A. G., 1894. Om sannolikheton for sekulara forandringar i atmosfarens kolsyrehalt, *Svensk. Kem. Tid.*, **6**, 169 (Summarized in Arrhenius, 1896, pp. 269–273).

Holmes, Arthur, 1915. Radioactivity and the earth's thermal history. II. Radioactivity and the earth as a cooling body, *Geol. Mag.*, n. ser., Decade 6, **2**, 102–112.

—————————— 1916. Radioactivity and the earth's thermal history. III. Radioactivity and isostasy, *Geol. Mag.*, n. ser., Decade 6, **3**, 265–274.

—————————— 1926. Contributions to the theory of magmatic cycles, *Geol. Mag.*, **63**, 306–329.

—————————— 1932. The origin of igneous rocks, *Geol. Mag.*, **69**, 543–558.

—————————— 1947a. A revised estimate of the age of the earth, *Nature*, **159**, 127–128.

—————————— 1947b. The construction of a geological time-scale, *Geol. Soc. Glasgow*, **21**, pt. 1, 117–152.

Hoover, W. H., E. S. Johnston, and F. S. Brackett, 1933. Carbon dioxide assimilation in a higher plant, *Smithson. Misc. Coll.*, **87**, no. 16, 19 pp.

Hubbert, M. K., 1950. Energy from fossil fuels, *Am. Assoc. Adv. Sci.*, Centennial 171–177.

Humphreys, W. J., 1940. *Physics of the Air*, 3rd ed., McGraw-Hill Book Co., 676 pp.

Hurley, P. M., 1950. Progress report on geologic time measurement (Abstract), *Science*, **112**, 453.

Hutchinson, G. E., 1944. Nitrogen in the biogeochemistry of the atmosphere, *Am. Scientist*, **32**, 178–195.

—————————— 1947. The problems of oceanic geochemistry, *Ecol. Mon.*, **17**, 299–307.

Ingerson, Earl, 1940. Nature of the ore-forming fluid; a discussion, *Econ. Geol.*, **35**, 772–785.

—————————— 1950. The water content of primitive granitic magma, *Am. Mineral.*, **35** (Larsen vol.), 806–815.

Jeffreys, Harold, 1924. The rare gases of the atmosphere, *Nature*, **114**, 934.

—————————— 1929. *The Earth; Its Origin, History and Physical Constitution*, second edition, Cambridge University Press, 346 pp.

—————————— 1930. The thermal effects of blanketing by sediments, *Roy. Astron. Soc., Monthly Notices, Geophys. Suppl.*, **2**, 323–329.

—————————— 1933. Quantity of meteoric accretion, *Nature*, **132**, 934.

Jensen, C. A., 1917. Effect of decomposing organic matter on the solubility of certain inorganic constituents of the soil, *Agric. Research Jour.*, **9**, 253–268.

Johnston, John and L. H. Adams, 1913. On the effect of high pressures on the physical and chemical behavior of solids, *Am. Jour. Sci.*, 4th ser., **35**, 205–253.

———— and Paul Niggli, 1913. The general principles underlying metamorphic processes, *Jour. Geol.*, **21**, 481–516, 588–624.

Jones, Sir H. S., 1950. The evolution of the earth's atmosphere, *Sci. Prog.*, **38**, 417–429.

Keenan, J. H. and F. G. Keyes, 1936. *Thermodynamic Properties of Steam*, John Wiley and Sons, 89 pp.

Keevil, N. B., 1943. Radiogenic heat in rocks, *Jour. Geol.*, **51**, 287–300.

Kennedy, W. Q., 1938. Crustal layers and the origin of magmas; Part I, Petrological aspects of the problem, *Bull. Volcanologique*, ser. 2, **3**, 24–41.

Krogh, August, 1934a. Conditions of life in the ocean, *Ecol. Mon.*, **4**, 421–429.

———— 1934b. Conditions of life at great depths in the ocean, *Ecol. Mon.*, **4**, 430–439.

Kuenen, P. H., 1937. On the total amount of sedimentation in the deep sea, *Am. Jour. Sci.*, **34**, 457–468.

———— 1941. Geochemical calculations concerning the total mass of sediments in the earth, *Am. Jour. Sci.*, **239**, 161–190.

———— 1946. Rate and mass of deep-sea sedimentation, *Am. Jour. Sci.*, **244**, 563–572.

Kuiper, G. P., 1949. Survey of planetary atmospheres, in G. P. Kuiper, editor, *The Atmospheres of the Earth and Planets,* University of Chicago Press, 304–345.

Ladd, H. S., 1944. Reefs and other bioherms, *Nat. Research Council, Rept. of Comm. on Marine Ecology as related to Paleontology, 1943–1944,* no. 4, 26–29.

Landergren, Sture, 1945. Contributions to the geochemistry of boron. II. The distribution of boron in some Swedish sediments, rocks and iron ores. The boron cycle in the upper lithosphere, *Arkiv. Kemi. Mineral. Geol.*, **19A**, no. 26, 1–31.

Landsberg, H. E., 1946. Note on the frequency distribution of geothermal gradients, *Am. Geophys. Union,* **27**, 549–551.

Lane, A. C., 1908. Mine waters, *Lake Superior Min. Inst.*, **13**, 63–152.

———— 1932. Eutopotropism, *Geol. Soc. Am. Bull.*, **43**, 313–330.

———— 1945. The evolution of the hydrosphere, *Am. Jour. Sci.*, **243-A** (Daly vol.), 393–398.

Latimer, W. M., 1938. *The Oxidation States of the Elements and Their Potentials in Aqueous Solutions,* Prentice-Hall, New York, 352 pp.

———— 1950. Astrochemical problems in the formation of the earth, *Science,* **112**, 101–104.

Lawson, A. C., 1932. Insular arcs, foredeeps, and geosynclinal seas of the Asiatic coast, *Geol. Soc. Am. Bull.*, **43**, 353–381.

Legendre, Rene, 1925. *La concentration en ions hydrogene de l'eau de mer,* Paris, 291 pp.

Leith, C. K., 1934. The pre-Cambrian, *Geol. Soc. Am.*, **1933**, 151–180.

———— and W. J. Mead, 1915. *Metamorphic Geology,* Henry Holt and Co., 337 pp.

Lowenstam, H. A., 1948. Biostratigraphic study of the Niagaran inter-reef formations in northeastern Illinois, *State Mus. Sci. Papers,* **4**, 1–146.

Macallum, A. B., 1904. The paleochemistry of the ocean in relation to animal and vegetable protoplasm, *Royal Canad. Inst.,* **7,** 535–562.

——————— 1926. Paleochemistry of body fluids and tissues, *Physiol. Rev.,* **6,** 316–357.

Macelwane, J. B., 1939. Evidence on the interior of the earth derived from seismic sources, 219–290, in B. Gutenberg, editor, *Internal Constitution of the Earth, Physics of the Earth,* VII, McGraw-Hill Book Co., New York.

Macgregor, A. M., 1927. The problem of the pre-Cambrian atmosphere, *S. African Jour. Sci.,* **24,** 155–172.

McClendon, J. F., 1916. The composition, especially the hydrogen-ion concentration, of sea-water in relation to marine organisms, *Jour. Biol. Chem.,* **28,** 135–152.

Meinzer, O. E., 1924. Origin of the thermal springs of Nevada, Utah, and southern Idaho, *Jour. Geol.,* **32,** 295–303.

Merrill, G. P., 1930. Composition and structure of meteorites, *Smithson. Inst. Bull.,* **149,** 62 pp.

Miholic, Stanko, 1947. Ore deposits and geologic age, *Econ. Geol.,* **42,** 713–720.

Mills, R. van A., and R. C. Wells, 1919. The evaporation and concentration of waters associated with petroleum and natural gas, *U. S. Geol. Survey Bull.,* **693,** 104 pp.

Moore, E. S., and J. E. Maynard, 1929. Solution, transportation and precipitation of iron and silica, *Econ. Geol.,* **24,** 272–303, 365–402, 506–527.

Moore, R. C., 1936. Stratigraphic evidence bearing on problems of continental tectonics, *Geol. Soc. Am. Bull.,* **47,** 1785–1808.

Morey, G. W., 1922. Development of pressure in magmas as a result of crystallization, *Wash. Acad. Sci. Jour.,* **12,** 219–230.

——————— 1924. Relation of crystallization to the water content and vapor pressure of water in a cooling magma, *Jour. Geol.,* **32,** 291–295.

——————— and Michael Fleischer, 1940. Equilibrium between vapor and liquid phases in the system CO_2-H_2O-K_2O-SiO_2, *Geol. Soc. Am. Bull.,* **51,** 1035–1058.

Nash, L. K. and G. P. Baxter, 1947. The determination of the gases in meteoritic and terrestrial irons and steels, *Am. Chem. Soc. Jour.,* **69,** 2534–2544.

Newcombe, R. B., 1933. Oil and gas fields of Michigan, *Mich. Geol. Survey,* **38,** 293 pp.

Nininger, H. H., 1940. Collecting meteoritic dust, *Sci. Mo.,* **50,** 460–461.

Osborne, F. F., 1931. Non-metallic mineral resources of Hastings County, *Ontario Dept. Mines, 39th Ann. Rept.,* **39,** pt. 6, 22–59.

Pettersson, Hans, 1949. The floor of the ocean, *Endeavor,* **8,** 182–187.

Pettijohn, F. J., 1943. Archean sedimentation, *Geol. Soc. Am. Bull.,* **54,** 925–972.

Piper, A. M., 1933. Ground water in southwestern Pennsylvania, *Penna. Geol. Surv. Bull.,* **W1,** 4th ser., 406 pp.

Poole, J. H. J., 1941. The evolution of the atmosphere, *Royal Dublin Soc., Sci. Pr.,* **22** (n.s.), 345–365.

Powers, E. B., 1920. The variation of the condition of sea-water, especially hydrogen-ion concentration, and its relation to marine organisms, *Wash. State Univ., Puget Sound Biol. Sta.,* **2,** 369–385.

—————————— 1939. Chemical factors affecting the migratory movements of the Pacific salmon, in *The migration and conservation of salmon, Am. Assoc. Adv. Sci.,* **8,** 72–85.

Rabinowitch, E. I., 1945. *Photosynthesis and Related Processes.* Vol. I: *Chemistry of Photosynthesis, Chemosynthesis and Related Processes in Vitro and in Vivo,* Interscience, New York, 599 pp.

Rankama, Kalervo, 1948. New evidence of the origin of pre-Cambrian carbon, *Geol. Soc. Am. Bull.,* **59,** 389–416.

—————————— and T. G. Sahama, 1950. *Geochemistry,* Univ. Chicago Press, 912 pp.

Rayleigh, Lord (R. J. Strutt), 1939. Nitrogen, argon, and neon in the earth's crust with applications to cosmology, *Roy. Soc. London,* ser. A., **170,** 451–464.

Revelle, Roger and R. H. Fleming, 1934. The solubility product constant of calcium carbonate in sea water, *Fifth Pacific Sci. Cong., Canada, 1933,* **3,** 2089–2092.

Riley, G. A., 1944. The carbon metabolism and photosynthetic efficiency of the earth as a whole, *Am. Scientist,* **32,** 132–134.

Rogers, C. G., 1938. *Textbook of Comparative Physiology,* 2nd ed., McGraw-Hill Book Co., 715 pp.

Ross, C. P., 1936. Some features of the Idaho batholith, *Intern. Geol. Cong., Rept. XVI Session, United States,* **1,** 369–385.

Rubey, W. W. and K. J. Murata, 1941. Chemical evidence bearing on origin of a group of hot springs (Abstract), *Wash. Acad. Sci. Jour.,* **31,** 4, 169–170.

Russell, H. N., 1949. The time scale of the universe, in *Time and Its Mysteries,* series III, New York University Press.

—————————— and D. H. Menzel, 1933. The terrestrial abundance of the permanent gases, *Nat. Acad. Sci.,* **19,** 997–1001.

Russell, W. L., 1933. Subsurface concentration of chloride brines, *Am. Assoc. Petrol. Geol. Bull.,* **17,** 1213–1228.

Rutherford, R. L., 1936. Geologic age of potash deposits, *Geol. Soc. Am. Bull.,* **47,** 1207–1216.

Schuchert, Charles, 1931. Geochronology or the age of the earth on the basis of sediments and life, in A. Knops, editor, *The Age of the Earth; Physics of the Earth,* IV, National Academy of Sciences, National Research Council.

Sederholm, J. J., 1925. The average composition of the earth's crust in Finland, *Commiss. Geol. Finlande Bull.,* **12,** 70, 3–20.

Shelford, V. E., 1918. The relation of marine fishes to acids with particular reference to the Miles acid process of sewage treatment, *Puget Sound Biol. Sta.,* **2,** 97–111.

Shepherd, E. S., 1938. The gases in rocks and some related problems, *Am. Jour. Sci., 5th ser.,* **35A,** 311–351.

Singh Pruthi, H., 1927. The ability of fishes to extract oxygen at different hydrogen ion concentrations of the medium, *Marine Biol. Assoc. Jour.,* **14,** 741–747.

Slichter, L. B., 1941. Cooling of the earth, *Geol. Soc. Am. Bull.,* **52,** 561–600.

—————————— 1950. The Rancho Santa Fe conference concerning the evolution of the earth, *Nat. Acad. Sci.,* **36,** 511–514.

Smith, C. L., 1940. The Great Bahama Bank, II. Calcium carbonate precipitation, *J. Marine Res.,* **3,** 171–189.

Stearns, N. D., H. T. Stearns, and G. A. Waring, 1937. Thermal springs in the United States, *U. S. Geol. Survey, W. S. Paper*, **679-B**, 59–206.

Stetson, H. T., 1942. The sun and the atmosphere, *Sigma Xi Quart.*, **30**, 16–35.

Suess, H. E., 1949. Die Haufigkeit der Edelgase auf der Erde und im Kosmos, *Jour. Geol.*, **57**, 600–607.

Sverdrup, H. U., M. W. Johnson, and R. H. Fleming, 1946. *The Oceans, Their Physics, Chemistry and General Biology*, Prentice-Hall, 1087 pp.

Twenhofel, W. H., 1926. *Treatise on Sedimentation*, 1st ed., Baltimore, 661 pp.

————————— 1929. Magnitude of the sediments beneath the deep sea, *Geol. Soc. Am. Bull.*, **40**, 385–402.

————————— 1936. Organisms and their environment, *Nat. Res. Council, Rept. of Committee on Paleoecology, 1935–36*, 1–9.

Urry, W. D., 1949. Significance of radioactivity in geophysics—Thermal history of the earth, *Am. Geophys. Union*, **30**, 171–180.

Valley, George, 1928. The effect of carbon dioxide on bacteria, *Quart. Rev. Biol.*, **3**, 209–224.

Van Hise, C. R., 1904. A treatise on metamorphism, *U. S. Geol. Survey Mon.*, **47**, 1286 pp.

Van Orstrand, C. E., 1939. Observed temperatures in the earth's crust, 125–151, in B. Gutenberg, editor, *Internal Constitution of the Earth, Physics of the Earth*, VII, McGraw-Hill Book Co., New York.

Vaughan, T. W., 1940. Ecology of modern marine organisms with reference to paleogeography, *Geol. Soc. Am. Bull.*, **51**, 433–468.

Verhoogen, Jean, 1946. Volcanic heat, *Am. Jour. Sci.*, **244**, 745–771.

Wahl, Walter, 1949. Isostasy and the origin of sial and sima and of parental rock magmas, *Am. Jour. Sci.*, **247**, 145–167.

Walther, Johannes, 1911. Origin and peopling of the deep sea (Translation by C. M. Le Vene), *Am. Jour. Sci.*, **31**, 55–64.

Wattenberg, Hermann, 1936. Kohlensaure und Kalziumkarbonat im Meere, *Fortsch. Mineral.*, **21**, 168–195.

————————— and E. Timmermann, 1938. Die loslichkeit von Magnesium-karbonat und Strontiumkarbonat im Seewasser, *Kiel. Meeresforsch.*, **2**, 81–94.

Weeks, L. G., 1950. Concerning estimates of potential oil reserves, *Am. Assoc. Petrol. Geol. Bull.*, **34**, 1947–1953.

White, D. E. and W. W. Brannock, 1950. The sources of heat and water supply of thermal springs, with particular reference to Steamboat Springs, Nevada, *Am. Geophys. Union*, **31**, 4, 566–574.

Wildt, Rupert, 1939. Constitution of the planets, *Am. Philos. Soc.*, **81**, 135–152.

————————— 1942. The geochemistry of the atmosphere and the constitution of the terrestrial planets, *Rev. Mod. Phys.*, **14**, 151–159.

Wilson, J. Tuzo, 1950. Recent applications of geophysical methods to the study of the Canadian Shield, *Am. Geophys. Union*, **31**, 101–114.

Zies, E. G., 1929. The Valley of Ten Thousand Smokes. II. The acid gases contributed to the sea during volcanic activity, *Nat. Geog. Soc., Contrib. Tech. Papers, Katmai Series*, **1**, 4, 61–79.

2

Convection in the Earth's Mantle

Peter J. Brancazio

The question of the existence of convection currents in the mantle of the earth has been the cause of a considerable amount of controversy. In recent years, a rather extensive body of observations has been built up purporting to give evidence in favor of the convection hypothesis. The bulk of this evidence is impressive although not really conclusive; there are at the same time some rather nagging discrepancies. However, the major barrier against the general acceptance of the convection hypothesis seems to be the lack of an adequate theoretical description of the currents themselves. A good part of the difficulty here is tied up with our lack of knowledge of the properties of the mantle material.

The significance of convection in the mantle with respect to the origins of the oceans and the atmosphere is that convection currents, if they exist, would undoubtedly represent very important mechanisms for bringing water and gases from the interior to the surface. In this article, we will review the present situation with regard to the convection hypothesis by summarizing the present state of the theory and discussing some of the evidence for and against the existence of convection currents. We will then consider the role of convection with regard to degassing processes.

THEORY OF CONVECTION CURRENTS

The general picture of convection currents in the mantle suggests that convective overturn of the mantle material occurs intermittently.

That is, a sufficient temperature gradient ΔT must be built up before convection can occur; once this ΔT is reached, there is a half-turn of the mantle material so that the hot material rises to the surface and the cold material sinks. At this point, convection stops until radioactive heating in the interior and cooling at the surface have established a ΔT sufficient to trigger a new overturn. The usual value taken for the velocity of the current is on the order of 1–10 cm/yr near the surface, with a value of perhaps 100 cm/yr in the interior (Runcorn, 1962). Griggs (1939) has estimated that is should take 60 million years to complete one overturn, and about 500 million years to set up a ΔT sufficient to trigger a new overturn.

Chandrasekhar (1953) has solved the idealized problem of convection in a fluid confined to a spherical shell under the influence of a radial gravitational field. The results show that the convection cells are roughly as wide as they are deep, and thus as the ratio of the inner radius to the outer radius of the shell increases, the cells will become smaller in size and will increase in number.

However, when we attempt a solution on the basis of a more realistic picture of conditions in the mantle, formidable difficulties are encountered. First of all, we should not picture the mantle as an homogeneous fluid. In actuality, the mantle material has a finite strength, and the physical properties vary with depth. Another difficulty is that the heat sources are themselves in motion. Finally, one of the more critical parameters is the viscosity, and there is considerable debate as to what value to use in calculations. Suggested values range from 10^{22} gm/cm-sec, based on the postglacial uplift of Fennoscandia (Gutenberg, 1959), to 10^{26} gm/cm-sec, based on the time response of the nonequilibrium bulge of Earth that results from deceleration due to tidal friction (MacDonald, 1963). As an example of how one's choice of a viscosity value can crucially affect the discussion, let us look at the calculation usually given to establish whether convection is possible. By equating the viscous and buoyant forces, we obtain as a condition for convection (Runcorn, 1962):

$$g\rho\alpha \, \Delta T = \frac{\mu v}{r^2}$$

where g = acceleration of gravity
  ρ = density
  α = thermal coefficient of volume expansion
  ΔT = temperature difference between rising and falling columns
  μ = viscosity
  v = velocity of convection current
  r = depth of mantle, taken from surface of the earth.

Taking $g = 10^3$ cm/sec^2, $\rho = 5$ gm/cm^3, $\alpha = 2 \times 10^{-5}/\text{C}°$, $v = 10$ cm/yr, and $r = 1.5 \times 10^8$ cm, we obtain

$$\Delta T = 1.5 \times 10^{-22} \, \mu$$

The next step in this argument is to obtain the heat flow rate to the surface based on the calculated ΔT. If 10^{22} gm/cm-sec is used for μ, the calculated heat flow is not very different from the observed value, whereas if 10^{26} gm/cm-sec is used, the calculated heat flow is much too large. This argument can be (and has been) used by both sides in the dispute. Its validity, however, depends entirely on the validity of the viscosity determinations.

A major shortcoming of the lack of a realistic theoretical picture is that we are unable to decide with any certainty the number, size, and location of the convection cells. This severely limits the testability of the hypothesis. It is not certain whether the cells would extend from the core to the crust. The region of the earth's interior from 200 to 900 km depth is marked by a very rapid increase in density. If this is due to a change in composition, then the existence of this region indicates the absence of full-scale convection. On the other hand, if there is a phase change in this region, the currents will not be greatly affected.

In addition, it was shown by Elsasser (1963) that convection currents may necessarily be confined to the upper few hundred kilometers of the mantle. Assuming a certain temperature distribution, he showed that the viscosity of the mantle material should increase with depth, and that the viscosity should vary by a factor of 10^2 to 10^3 from the top of the mantle to the bottom. On this basis, the flow would be expected to be concentrated near the top of the mantle.

We will now go on to look at some of the evidence that has been presented with regard to the convection hypothesis. We will begin with some of the more indirect lines of evidence.

MISCELLANEOUS GEOLOGICAL EVIDENCE

The theory predicts that overturn should occur intermittently. We might expect that there would be some indication of this in the geological record. In fact, there is considerable evidence for the episodic nature of geological activity. Gastil (1960) has conducted a survey of the radioactive ages of rocks from all continents and found several peaks in the graph of the number of rocks vs. age. These age peaks are indicative of periodic upsurges in geologic activity.

Birch (1951) has shown that the density of the mantle, when reduced to surface temperature and pressure conditions, is essentially constant from 900 km depth down to the core. Thus the mantle appears to be homogeneous in composition and phase in this region, as would be expected if convection systems were in operation.

It is a common view that the secular variations of the geomagnetic field result from convection currents in the earth's core (Gutenberg, 1959). Bullard (1949) has shown that if these currents do in fact exist in the core, the heat transferred out of the core is more than can be transferred through the mantle by conduction. On this basis, if there is convection in the core, there must also be convection in the mantle.

It is now generally accepted that the crust of the earth is in isostatic equilibrium. Thus we have a picture of the crust "floating" on the mantle, which indicates that at least a part of the mantle is plastic and capable of flow. In fact, the existence of the so-called low-velocity layer has been well established (Gutenberg, 1959); this is a region from about 60 km depth down to 250 km in which the material is of relatively low rigidity. The existence of the low-velocity layer is not in itself evidence for convection, but it is significant in that it demonstrates that mantle material can have a low enough rigidity to permit flow.

Related to the existence of isostatic equilibrium is the problem of explaining gravity anomalies found at various points on the earth. Vening Meinesz has pointed out that many negative gravity anomalies are associated with the trenches near island arcs (Heisnaken and Vening Meinesz, 1958). He suggests that such trenches are places where currents descend into the mantle. We would expect crustal thickening here; however, Worzel and Shurbet (1955), on the basis of seismic measurements, found no such thickening. In addition, Ewing and Heezen (1955) found low-density sediments in the bottom of the Puerto Rico trough and showed that these sediments could account for the gravity anomaly.

A most intriguing line of thought is that which relates the surface topography of the earth to convection currents in the mantle. Following an analysis by Prey, Vening Meinesz (1962) analyzed the surface features of the earth in terms of spherical harmonics and found that several terms, notably the 3rd, 4th, and 5th order terms, are particularly strong. However, Chandrasekhar (1953), in his solution of the problem of convection in a spherical shell, found that for a shell with the dimensions of the earth's mantle, the 3rd, 4th and 5th harmonics of convective flow would be dominant. It is thus suggested that the surface features of the earth are a function of the convection currents in the mantle. Vening Meinesz has extended the topography analysis to the 31st order and accounted for the stronger orders by a refinement of the picture of convection in the mantle to include six or seven layers of rotating cells stacked in the mantle.

One criticism of this picture is offered by MacDonald (1963), who feels that the gravitational potential of the earth should also show the same harmonics if topography is indeed a result of convection. Kaula (1963) has shown that there is a negligible correlation between topographic and geodesic harmonics.

CONTINENTAL DRIFT

The hypothesis of continental drift, which has also become a center of controversy of late, is closely related to the convection hypothesis. For if it can be shown that continental drift has in fact taken place, then convection currents would be the most likely mechanism for supplying the force to move the continents. It should be noted, however, that theories for continental drift without convection currents have been proposed (Heezen, 1962); these generally speculate that the earth is expanding through one process or another. Nevertheless, we will proceed to consider some of the evidence for continental drift.

Historically, the first piece of evidence suggesting continental drift was the observation of the remarkable correspondence between the coastlines of Africa and South America. There have been several discoveries of correspondence between geological or geographic features on opposite sides of oceans; for example, Wilson (1962) has noted the strong similarities in structure and age of the Great Glen Fault in Scotland and the Cabot Fault on the northeastern coast of North America.

In addition, considerable climatological evidence has been gathered indicating that there has been relative motion between the continents and the geographic poles. For example, such climatological anomalies as glaciation at the Equator in Africa and coal deposits, coral reefs, and petrified trees in polar regions have been observed (Durham, 1962; Opdyke, 1962). On the other hand, Axelrod (1963) has studied the distribution of flora during the eras when the continents were supposedly at different latitudes, and he states that the climates suggested by the fossil flora are inconsistent with the proposed latitudes of the continents. Perhaps the paleotemperature measurements now being made on the basis of the O^{18}/O^{16} ratios for various fossils will provide a better approach to this problem.

Perhaps the strongest line of evidence for continental drift results from the paleomagnetic data of Runcorn et al. (1962). The basic assumptions made are that (1) rocks acquire an essentially permanent magnetization upon formation, so that the direction of the magnetization in the rock gives the direction of the magnetic field at the time of formation; and (2) that the earth's magnetic field has always been essentially a dipole. On this latter point, MacDonald (1963) has pointed out that there have apparently been reversals in the field, and there may well have been intervals during which the field was not dipolar. At any rate, Runcorn and his co-workers have looked at rocks of the same age and from the same continents and have found that the directions of magnetization point to a specific location for the magnetic pole, without a great deal of error. From this information, they have plotted polar wandering curves; on comparing the curves for different continents, a divergence is exhibited which indicates that the continents have moved relative to one another. Runcorn suggests that there has been no substantial motion of the continents since the Middle Tertiary.

As can be seen, there is some attractive evidence in favor of continental drift; yet continental drift has many geological implications which have yet to be accounted for (Heezen, 1962). Verification of the continental drift hypothesis would constitute a strong argument for the existence of convection currents in the mantle.

EVIDENCE FROM THE OCEAN FLOOR

During recent years, the ocean floors have been the subject of rather intense study. This research has produced evidence for convection which is considerably more direct than what has been presented thus far.

One of the undersea features which has been the subject of recent study is the Mid-Atlantic Ridge, which lies along the length of the Atlantic Ocean, midway between the continents; it is, in fact, part of a worldwide system of midoceanic ridges. The most interesting feature of the ridge is the deep rift running along the center of the ridge. Furthermore, the vast majority of earthquake epicenters in the Atlantic Ocean lie within a narrow belt that coincides with the rift. Also, the rate of heat flow from the interior of the earth is five to six times higher than average along the ridge (Heezen, 1962).

Another anomalous structure to be found on the ocean floor is the

East Pacific Rise. This is a bulge in the ocean floor which runs roughly parallel to the Coast of South America, meeting the North American continent at lower California. This structure has been found to have on its crest a heat flow rate eight times greater than normal; shallow earthquakes seem to be common along the crest, and the crust has been shown to be thinner than usual along the rise.

All of this information can be fitted into a relatively consistent picture, assuming the existence of convection currents, as follows: both the Mid-Atlantic Ridge and the East Pacific Rise lie over regions where rising convection currents come to the surface. The rising hot material would be a source of earthquake activity, and would account for the anomalously high heat-flow rates. As the rising currents reach the surface of the mantle, they turn and flow horizontally under the crust; this action would tend to produce tension in the crust in the vicinity of the rising currents. This tension is exhibited in the thinning of the crust over the East Pacific Rise and in the development of the central rift along the Mid-Atlantic Ridge. This mechanism also accounts for the numerous fracture zones that are found lying perpendicular to the axes of both the Ridge and the Rise.

This description is not without its inadequacies. For example, the lack of a rift valley in the vicinity of the East Pacific Rise needs to be explained. A possible explanation for this is that the Mid-Atlantic Ridge is a product of an older, well-developed convection system, while the East Pacific Rise is a result of the early stages of development of a new convection cell. In fact, Hess (1962) estimates that the East Pacific Rise is less than 100 million years old. He also points out that there is evidence for the existence of an ancient trans-Pacific ridge; this ridge apparently began to subside about 100 million years ago, and has almost completely disappeared except for a belt of atolls and guyots stretching across the Pacific.

Another problem is to find the areas where the convection currents turn and sink into the mantle. We would expect to find in such locations low heat flow and compression in the crust, coupled with extensive earthquake activity. Oceanic trenches generally have such properties, but there does not seem to be a consistent worldwide picture linking the regions of rising currents to the regions of sinking currents.

On the other hand, the observations of heat flow rates constitute a thorny problem for the anticonvectionists. In view of the differences between the continental and oceanic crust, it came as quite a surprise when it was noted that the heat-flow rates for continents and oceans were essentially the same (Gutenberg, 1959). The picture was even more confused by the discovery of localized regions of abnormally high or low heat flow such as we have just described. This situation is much more easily accounted for if convection, rather than conduction, is the major heat transfer mechanism for the earth.

An additional argument for convection is the relatively thin layer of sediments found in ocean basins. Based on calculations on the rate of deposition of sediments and the indication that this rate may not have varied since the Miocene, Hess (1962) calculates that the present layer of sediments was built up in 200 to 300 million years. This seems to indicate that the ocean floor has been swept clean periodically by overturns of the mantle. As further evidence for the periodic regeneration of the ocean floor, Hess points to the relatively small number of volcanoes found in the oceans.

CONVECTION, DEGASSING, AND THE ORIGIN OF THE OCEANS

There has apparently been little discussion of the effect of convection currents on the degassing of the interior. Clearly convection would be important, for through this mechanism a great deal more of the mantle would be in a position to provide gases for the exterior. For a solid earth, only the upper layers of the mantle are likely to be degassed. Quantitative studies are difficult to make for several reasons, however. Without knowing the dimensions of the convection cells, we cannot tell how much mantle material will be available for degassing. In addition, the mechanisms by which gases escape from the mantle, enter the crust, and then escape to the atmosphere are difficult to specify. Finally, we must know the distribution of the gas-producing elements (uranium, thorium, potassium, etc.) in the mantle.

In this vein, an interesting calculation has been made by Hess (1962) in which he shows that the oceans may have resulted from the transfer of water from the mantle to the crust via convection. Hess gives evidence that the oceanic crust contains a layer of serpentinized peridotite directly beneath the sediments. He assumes that this layer has been serpentinized by water carried up by rising convection currents. At the point where the convection currents bend downward, the crust is also bent downward and into a region of higher temperature. Here the serpentine layer is dehydrated and the water enters the ocean. Hess assumes that the transfer of water to the crust occurs all along the 25,000-km length of the oceanic ridge system. He also assumes a current velocity of 1 cm/yr and takes this to mean that a layer 1 cm thick is formed on each side of the ridge each year. Based on seismic velocity measurements, he estimates the water content of the uprising materials, and from this determines that approximately 0.4 km^3 of water leave the mantle in this manner per year. Assuming that this rate has been the same for 4×10^9 yr, and subtracting the water still remaining in the serpentine layer, he obtains a value of 1.3×10^9 km^3 of water released from the mantle over geologic time. This is approximately the volume of water now present in the oceans. We might argue that the evidence as to the level of the sea over geologic history indicates that the volume of the ocean has not changed appreciably, but this is not a valid argument because we would expect the oceanic crust to adjust isostatically to the additional weight of new water; thus changes in sea level are not necessarily good indicators of changes in the volume of the ocean.

CONCLUSIONS

The situation with regard to convection is somewhat confused at present. The weight of the evidence (most of which is indirect) tends to be in favor of the convection hypothesis, but acceptance is hampered by the lack of a good theoretical description, or at least a consistent worldwide picture of where the currents rise and fall. The evidence against convection is not particularly formidable; perhaps the best argument against convection is that the viscosity of the mantle may be too high. A clear-cut determination of the viscosity of the mantle would certainly tip the balance one way or another. Perhaps the Mohole experiment will provide us with some useful information in this respect.

It is realized that convection currents would play a significant role in the formation of the oceans and atmosphere. However, because of the many uncertainties involved, a clear understanding of the effect of convection on degassing has not yet been attained.

REFERENCES

Axelrod, D., 1963. Fossil floras suggest stable, not drifting continents. *Jour. Geophys. Res.*, **68**, 3257.

Birch, F., 1951. Remarks on the structure of the mantle, and its bearing upon the possibility of convection currents, *Trans. Am. Geophys. U.*, **32**, 533.

Bullard, E. C., 1949. The magnetic field within the earth, *Proc. Roy. Soc. A* **197**, 433.

Chandrasekhar, S., 1953. The onset of convection by thermal instability in spherical shells, *Phil. Mag.*, **44**, 233, 1129.

Durham, J. W., 1962. The drifting continents, *Natural History*, **71**, No. 4, 30.

Elsasser, W. M., 1963. Early history of the earth, in *Earth Science and Meteoritics* (compiled by J. Geiss and E. D. Goldberg), John Wiley & Sons, New York.

Ewing, M. and B. C. Heezen, 1955. Puerto Rico trench topography and geophysical data, *Geol. Soc. Am. Spec. Papers*, **62**, 255.

Gastil, G., 1960. The distribution of mineral dates in time and space, *Am. Jour. Sci.*, **258**, 1.

Griggs, D. T., 1939. A theory of mountain-building. *Am. Jour. Sci.*, **237**, 611.

Gutenberg, B., 1959. *Physics of the Earth's Interior*, Academic Press, New York.

Heezen, B. C., 1962. The deep-sea floor, in S. K. Runcorn, editor, *Continental Drift*, Academic Press, New York.

Heisnaken, W. A., and F. A. Vening Meinesz, 1958. *The Earth and Its Gravity Field*; McGraw-Hill Book Co., New York.

Hess, H. H., 1962. History of ocean basins, in A. E. J. Engle, H. L. James, and B. L. Leonard, editors, *Petrologic Studies: A Volume to Honor A. F. Buddington, Geol. Soc. Am.*, 599.

Kaula, W. M., 1963. Elastic models of the mantle corresponding to variations in the external gravity field, *Jour. Geophys. Res.*, **68**, 4967.

MacDonald, G. J. F., 1963. The internal constitution of the inner planets and the moon, *Space Science Reviews*, **2**, 473.

Menard, H. W., 1960. The East Pacific Rise, *Science*, **132**, 1737.

Opdyke, N. D., 1962. Palaeoclimatology and continental drift, in S. K. Runcorn, editor, *Continental Drift*, Academic Press, New York.

Runcorn, S. K., 1962. Palaeomagnetic evidence for continental drift and its geophysical cause, *Continental Drift*, Academic Press, New York.

Vening Meinesz, F. A., 1962. Thermal convection in the earth's mantle, in S. K. Runcorn, editor, *Continental Drift*, Academic Press, New York.

Wilson, T., 1962. Cabot fault, an Appalachian equivalent of the San Andreas and Great Glen faults and some implications for continental displacement, *Nature*, **195**, 135.

Worzel, J. L., and G. L. Shurbet, 1955. Gravity anomalies at continental margins, *Geol. Soc. Am. Spec. Papers*, **62**, 87.

3

Degassing of Argon and Helium from the Earth

Karl K. Turekian

INTRODUCTION

That the A^{40} in the atmosphere is of radiogenic origin and results primarily from the degassing of the earth is now generally accepted. The difficulties in constructing a degassing model for argon, however, are formidable. We must know (1) the abundance of potassium in the earth, (2) the distribution of potassium in the earth as a function of time, and (3) the mechanisms for degassing in the crust and the mantle. All we can do at present is to use reasonable estimates of these parameters and check for internal consistency.

Within the last ten years there have been several attempts at quantifying the argon degassing problem. Rankama (1954) assumed that the whole crust of the earth has been available for continuous weathering and that the argon in the atmosphere was a consequence of release during this process. The model is not attractive in that we know that some of the oldest continental rocks (containing the most argon) have not been weathered, and that even with weathering there is a persistent retention of the argon in the clay minerals (Hurley et al., 1963).

Shillibeer and Russell (1955) designate a protocrust which has been accumulating argon since the beginning of the earth. As various parts of the protocrust are transformed into crust at later times, the accumulated argon is released, after which the newly formed crust becomes highly retentive. This basically assumes that the transformation involves only the release of argon, with no change in the potassium content.

Nicolet (1956) assumes a fairly low potassium content of the earth, divided equally between the crust and the mantle. After about 600 million years of argon growth, the complete degassing of the earth provides (for his potassium concentration) all the argon for the atmosphere; subsequent to this event, argon degassing is assumed minor.

Damon and Kulp (1958) arrive at the present degassing rate of A^{40} from a treatment of the He^3 and He^4 budget in the atmosphere. Finding the calculated value of the degassing rate too low to supply the atmospheric argon over 4.5×10^9 years, they postulate a major degassing of the crust about 3.5×10^9 years ago, using Jacobs and Allen's (1956) model of a primordially segregated crust. The choice of this early data requires some addition of argon from the mantle.

Turekian (1959) developed the argon degassing from a solid chondritic earth without any specification of the location of the potassium, but with the condition that degassing was a continuous function of the argon present in the solid earth.

LIMITATIONS ON ARGON DEGASSING MODELS

One of the common features of several of the above models is a crust or protocrust which behaves as a closed system. The concept of a primordially differentiated earth is generally the basis for such models, although their utility lies in their computational simplicity. Lest greater significance be ascribed to the results of closed-crust model calculations than may be warranted, it is of value to explore other consequences of such a rigid model.

Two options remain if we reject a closed-crust model: (1) using as evidence contemporary and ancient volcanism, there appears to be addition of material to the crust from the mantle; (2) there may be continuous exchange between the crust and the mantle, the gross chemical composition of each remaining the same on the long time scale. If either or both of these options are applicable, then the most general model, in which the total earth is being degassed, may be preferred over specific processes involving one part or another of the earth.

Strontium Isotopes in the Crust

If we assume that the crust has been a closed system in existence for 4.55×10^9 million years, the observed Sr^{87}/Sr^{86} ratios in crustal rocks will give us certain limiting conditions for argon supply from the crust.

We can write for a closed-crust system

$$\left(\frac{Sr^{87}}{Sr^{86}}\right)_{present} = \left(\frac{Sr^{87}}{Sr^{86}}\right)_{primordial} + (e^{\lambda t} - 1) \left(\frac{Rb^{87}}{Sr^{86}}\right)_{present} \tag{1}$$

The primordial Sr^{87}/Sr^{86} value for the earth is assumed to be 0.701, which is the time-corrected ratio in high-calcium achondrites (Gast, 1962).

Using some common assumptions about the nature of the deep crust, Gast (1960) and Hurley et al. (1962) arrive at values between 0.720 to 0.730 for the present-day crust, obtained from weighted averages of the Sr^{87}/Sr^{86} ratio and from strontium concentrations of various parts of the crust. With these ratios, sufficient amounts of potassium (by association with rubidium) would be expected to supply the atmospheric A^{40} on complete degassing of the crust.

On closer examination, however, we see that we cannot apply this ratio to the model of a closed crust periodically generating magma, for most dated rocks (which have not been subject to later metamorphism) and basalts indicate a Sr^{87}/Sr^{86} ratio of less than 0.710 at the time of emplacement (Hurley et al., 1962).

Logically, this is a strong argument for addition of material to the crust from the mantle, as both Gast (1960) and Hurley et al. (1962) have stated, and in itself suggests a supply of A^{40} from the mantle as well.

Pursuing the closed-crust model we can avoid this contradiction by invoking the obvious limitation to which crustal estimates are subject, namely, that we really do not have any absolute knowledge of the strontium content and isotopic ratio of the deeper crust.

If we then choose a closed crust of constant mass and composition, in existence from the origin of the earth and periodically reworked in processes commencing 2500 to 3500 million years ago, the strontium isotopic composition of the emplaced products of these events requires a sufficiently high Sr/Rb ratio to result in only a slow growth of the Sr^{87}/Sr^{86} ratio with time. We choose the value of 0.708 for the present crustal ratio from the data on Cenozoic granitic stocks and recent basalts (Hurley et al., 1962).

Substituting[1] 0.708 for the present crustal Sr^{87}/Sr^{86} ratio, the presumed primordial ratio of 0.701, and using $\lambda = 1.47 \times 10^{-11}$ yr^{-1},

---

[1] Although the ratios used are subject to revision (Hedge and Walthall, 1963), the difference will remain at about 0.007 or less.

and $t = 4.55 \times 10^9$ yr, we get:

$$\left(\frac{Rb}{Sr}\right)_{\text{closed crust (present)}} = 0.0354$$

Limits on the crustal value of strontium are then determined from the data of Turekian and Kulp (1956). The highest strontium concentrations are for their "high-calcium" granitic rocks (440 ppm) and basaltic rocks (465 ppm). "Low-calcium" granitic rocks and ultramafic rocks are both lower than this. Consequently, the Sr concentration in the crust is ≤ 450 ppm; thus from the above ratio Rb (crust) ≤ 16 ppm. The potassium-rubidium ratio for a large number of rock types and meteorites is about 300 (Gast, 1960), hence the potassium concentration of the crust ≤ 4800 ppm, which is one quarter of the value used by Shillibeer and Russell (1955), and Damon and Kulp (1958).

If the crust suddenly degassed about 3 billion years ago, with this closed-crust model, the supply of A^{40} would be 1.8×10^{41} atoms, or about 18% of the observed abundance of A^{40} in the atmosphere.

Radioactive Age Preservation

Various authors have noted the zoned nature of ages in the continents, indicating some form of continental growth starting about 3 billion years ago. In many of these rocks most of the argon has been retained after the end of initial severe thermal pulses.

If we assume that 20% of all the argon produced in a crust with a 2% potassium concentration (a value commonly used for the crust) from 3 billion years ago to the present is released to the atmosphere, this will yield about 0.92×10^{41} atoms of A^{40}, as compared to 9.85×10^{41} atoms in the present atmosphere. If we are consistent about maintaining the potassium content of the closed-crust model (0.48%) from the strontium isotope evidence in the previous section, and also retain the 3 billion years date, the value becomes 0.23×10^{41} atoms.

In summary, if we choose a crust having constant mass and composition since the beginning of the earth (4.55×10^9 years ago) with argon production consistent with the strontium isotope data, and require a major degassing of the crust 3×10^9 years ago, 18% of the atmospheric A^{40} will be supplied at the time of degassing. In addition, if the same closed crust retains 80% of the argon produced subsequent to the 3×10^9 year ago major outgassing, the supply of A^{40} by this continuous low-temperature gas loss will be 2.5% of the present atmospheric abundance. This leaves 80% of the present-day atmospheric argon to be derived from the mantle.

TABLE 2.1   Constants Used in This Paper for the A^{40} Argument

Abundance of potassium in chondrites (ppm)	880
Abundance of K^{40} in chondrites (ppm)	0.10472
Abundance of K^{40} in chondrites 4.55×10^9 years ago (ppm)	1.280
Mass of earth (g)	5.976×10^{27}
Total primordial K^{40} in earth assuming chondritic composition at 4.55×10^9 years ago (K_0')(g)	7.65×10^{21}
Branching ratio $\lambda_{E.C.}/\lambda_{\beta^-} = R$	0.124
Number of A^{40} atoms in present-day atmosphere (a_2)	9.85×10^{41}
$K_0 = \dfrac{R}{1+R} K_0'$(g)	8.44×10^{20}

GENERALIZED DEGASSING MODEL FOR ARGON

We can, of course, adjust these models in a variety of ways, but it is not a particularly fruitful occupation because the mechanisms of crustal growth and the degassing processes from both crust and mantle are inadequately known.   For these reasons a perfectly general model which considers only the solid earth and the combined atmosphere and hydrosphere as the significant features may be useful (Turekian, 1959).   The following assumptions are used:

1. Two phases are considered only, namely the solid earth and the combined hydrosphere and atmosphere.   The model does not concern itself with the internal constitution of the earth.
2. The constants chosen are those given in Table 2.1.
3. The earth is 4.55×10^9 years old.
4. There was little or no primordial A^{40} when the earth was formed.
5. The loss of argon from the solid earth obeys a first-order law.

We can now set up the differential equation describing how the argon content of the solid earth varies with time:

$$\frac{dA}{dt} = \lambda K_0 e^{-\lambda t} - \alpha A \qquad (2)$$

where A is the amount of argon in the solid earth at any time, t
    t is measured from the beginning of the earth $(t_0 = 0)$
    λ is the decay constant for K^{40}

$$K_0 \text{ is equal to } \frac{R}{1+R} K_0'$$

where K_0 is the primordial abundance of K^{40} in the earth, R is the branching ratio of K^{40} ($\lambda_{E.C.}/\lambda_{\beta-}$), and α is the "degassing" constant.

Solving equation (1),

$$A e^{\alpha t} = \frac{K_0}{\alpha - \lambda} e^{\alpha t} e^{-\lambda t} + C \tag{3}$$

The constant C can be evaluated on the assumption that at $t = 0$, $A = 0$. Hence:

$$A = \frac{\lambda K_0}{\alpha - \lambda} (e^{-\lambda t} - e^{-\alpha t}) \tag{4}$$

As the present value of A/K_0 is known to be 0.8411 (from our assumption and the abundance of A^{40} in the atmosphere), the value of α/λ is determined graphically to be 0.051, resulting in a value of $\alpha = 2.81 \times 10^{-11}$ yr^{-1}.

It is now possible to determine for any desired time the argon content produced in the whole earth (a_1), the argon content of the solid earth (A), and the argon content of the atmosphere (a_2). The results of these calculations are given in Table 2.2.

TABLE 2.2   The Abundance and Distribution of A^{40} in the Earth with Time, Degassing Constant $\alpha = 2.81 \times 10^{-11}$ yr^{-1}

Time after beginning (in 10^9 yr)	a_1 (total A^{40} produced in earth $\times 10^{42}$ atoms)	A (amount of A^{40} in solid earth $\times 10^{42}$ atoms)	$a_2 = (a_1 - A)$ (amount of A^{40} in atmosphere $\times 10^{42}$ atoms)
0.5	3.078	3.059	0.019
1.0	5 418	5.338	0.078
1.5	7 192	7.028	0.164
2.0	8.540	8 270	0.270
2.5	9.564	9 172	0.392
3.0	10.342	9 817	0.525
3.5	10.932	10 267	0.665
4.0	11.382	10 569	0.813
4.5	11.722	10.761	0.961
4.55	11.752	10.773	0.985
5.0	11.982	10.869	1.113

The rate of supply of argon to the atmosphere at the present time may now be calculated. The rate of entry of A^{40} into the atmosphere at any time t is given by:

$$\frac{da_2}{dt} = K_0\lambda \frac{\alpha/\lambda}{\alpha/\lambda - 1} [e^{-\lambda t} - e^{-(\alpha/\lambda)\lambda t}] \qquad (5)$$

For $t = 4.55 \times 10^9$ yr,

$$\frac{da_2}{dt}_{\text{present}} = 3.02 \times 10^{32} \text{ atoms/year,} \qquad \text{or } 1.88 \times 10^6 \text{ atoms/cm}^2\text{-sec}$$

APPLICATION TO HELIUM

The use of the argon degassing constant for other gases is, of course, dependent on their similarity of behavior. For the deep interior, it seems reasonable that the rates of release for all the rare gases must be related to the amount present, rather than to mass-dependent diffusion. This may be even more justifiable if a convective model of the earth's interior is valid.

Assuming a chondritic composition for the earth, crustal abundance estimates (Gast, 1960) require that 67% of the uranium and thorium are in the crust. On this premise the mantle degassing constant applies then to 33% of the helium produced in a chondritic earth. Using an equation analogous to that for argon with $\alpha = 2.8 \times 10^{-11}$ yr^{-1}, the present-day supply rate of helium to the atmosphere from the mantle is 0.263×10^{32} atoms/yr.

The crust is obviously more easily degassed of helium than the mantle, considering the observed high leakage rate from crustal materials. We do not need to consider whether the uranium and thorium have always been concentrated in the outer parts of the earth, because the residence time (10^7 yr) of helium is short compared to the length of geologic eras (10^8 yr). If, with Mayne (1956), Nicolet (1957), Bates and McDowell (1957), and others, we assume for the sake of simplicity that the rate of production of He^4 in the crust is equal to the rate of loss from the crust to the atmosphere, we arrive at a present-day crustal degassing rate of 1.83×10^{32} atoms/yr. The total supply at the present time from both the crust and mantle is then 2.1×10^{32} atoms/yr or 1.3×10^6 atoms/cm^2-sec.

A comparison of various estimates of the He^4 flux is presented in Table 2.3. The difference between the range of values obtained by MacDonald and by Turekian is directly due to the model of distribution of uranium and thorium in the earth and the degassing model

TABLE 2.3   Estimates of He^4 Supply Rate from the Solid Earth to the
Atmosphere

Model	Rate He^4 atom/cm^2-sec
A. MacDonald (1963): Assume 10% of present production is lost from the whole earth. (1.1 × 10^{-8} g/g uranium and 4.4 × 10^{-8} g/g thorium the whole earth)	2.6 × 10^5
B. MacDonald (1963) calculated from Wasserburg et al. (1963): Assume most common He/A ratio in natural gases and all argon from interior	3.5 × 10^6
C. Turekian (1959): Assume first order degassing law with degassing constant calculated from argon (1.1 × 10^{-8} g/g uranium, 4.3 × 10^{-8} g/g thorium, 880 × 10^{-6} g/g potassium) corrected	5.0 × 10^5
D. Present model: See text	1.3 × 10^6

for argon used. The choice is between argon loss from the solid earth
as a function of total argon in the earth (Model *C*) and a loss rate
at any time equal to the production rate of argon (Models *A* and *B*).
Model *D*, described in this paper, considers the fact that uranium
and thorium are preferentially concentrated in the crust, and uses
the assumption that the helium produced is available for immediate
release to the surface. The ratio of the two extreme calculations
of MacDonald is 13.5 while the ratio for the two models is 2.6.

CONCLUSIONS

1. An earth of chondritic composition, 4.5 billion years old, will by
now have generated about ten times the amount of A^{40} present in the
atmosphere.

2. It follows that if 10% of the potassium of a chondritic earth were
in the crust from the beginning, then the amount of A^{40} generated in
the crust until now would equal the amount in the atmosphere.

3. If we assume a closed crust having constant mass and composition
since the origin of the earth, with periodic magma formation, the
Sr^{87}/Sr^{86} ratio at the time of emplacement implies a low rubidium
and potassium content of the crust (namely, 0.48% potassium). This
will provide 18% of the A^{40} in the atmosphere if total degassing of
the crust occurred 3 billion years ago. An additional 2.5% would be
supplied by a 20% leakage from the crust from that time until the
present.

4. If we abandon the closed-crust model, the locus of argon supply to the atmosphere is contingent on the modes of crust-mantle interchange and degassing.

5. To avoid specificity of mechanisms, a first-order degassing law is proposed for the earth as a whole, and a degassing constant is calculated for a chondritic earth.

6. The application of this degassing model to the degassing of He^4 from the earth may not be valid, as 67% of the earth's uranium and thorium is in the crust (assuming a chondritic model) and helium leakage from rocks at crustal temperatures is high.

REFERENCES

Bates, D. R. and M. R. C. McDowell, 1957. Atmospheric helium, *Jour. Atmospheric Terres. Phys.,* **11**, 200–208.

Damon, P. E. and J. L. Kulp, 1958. Inert gases and the evolution of the atmosphere, *Geochim. et Cosmochim. Acta,* **13**, 280–292.

Gast, P. W., 1960. Limitations on the composition of the upper mantle, *Jour. Geophys. Res.,* **65**, 1287–1297.

——————— 1962. The isotopic composition of strontium and the age of stone meteorites—I, *Geochim et Cosmochim, Acta,* **26**, 927–943.

Hedge, C. F. and F. G. Walthall, 1963. Radiogenic strontium-87 as an index of geologic processes, *Science,* **140**, 1214–1217.

Hurley, P. M., H. Hughes, G. Faure, H. W. Fairbairn, and W. H. Pinson, 1962. Radiogenic strontium-87 model of continent formation, *Jour. Geophys. Res.,* **67**, 5315–5334.

Hurley, P. M., B. C. Heezen, W. H. Pinson, and H. W. Fairbairn, 1963. K-Ar age values in pelagic sediments of the North Atlantic, *Geochim. et. Cosmochim. Acta,* **27**, 393–399.

Jacobs, J. A. and D. W. Allan, 1956. The thermal history of the earth, *Nature,* **177**, 155–157.

MacDonald, G. J. F., 1963. The escape of helium from the earth's atmosphere, *Rev. Geophys.,* **1**, 305.

Mayne, K. I., 1956. Terrestrial helium, *Geochim. et Cosmochim. Acta,* **9**, 174–182.

Nicolet, M., 1956. Sul l'origine de l'argon atmosphérique, *Bull. l'Acad. Roy. Belg. (Classe des Sciences),* 482–498.

——————— 1957. The aeronomic problem of helium, *Ann. Geophys.,* **13**, 1–21.

Rankama, K., 1954. A calculation of the amount of weathered igneous rock, *Geochim. et Cosmochim. Acta,* **5**, 81–84.

Shillibeer, H. A. and R. D. Russell, 1955. The argon-40 content of the atmosphere and the age of the earth, *Geochim. et Cosmochim. Acta,* **8**, 16–21.

Turekian, K. K., 1959. The terrestrial economy of helium and argon, *Geochim. et Cosmochim. Acta,* **17**, 37–43.

Wasserburg, G. J., E. Mazor, and R. E. Zartman, 1963. Isotopic and chemical composition of some terrestrial natural gases, pp. 219–240, in J. Geiss and E. D. Goldberg, editors, *Earth Science and Meteoritics,* North Holland Press, Amsterdam.

4

Comments on the Outgassing
of the Earth

G. J. Wasserburg

The facts at our disposal consist of measurements of the chemical and isotopic compositions of gases from various sources, such as volcanoes, fumaroles, natural gas wells, and rock gases. We can make some very specific assignment of certain juvenile components (those which have never been mixed with the atmospheric reservoir) for those nuclides which are the product of radioactive decay. There are certain observations which should be called to everyone's attention. In all samples of natural gases, the ratio A^{40}/A^{36} is equal to 296, which is equal to the present value for atmospheric argon. The observed concentrations of A^{36} indicate that the presence of this nuclide is due to the release of dissolved atmospheric argon, and is not at present being added to the atmosphere from deep-seated sources. The radiogenic component of A^{40} ($A^{40}_{rad} = A^{40} - 296\,A^{36}$) bears a regular relationship to the He^4 in these sources. The He^4 appears to be almost totally radiogenic, being produced by the uranium and thorium decay series. The ratio He^4/A^{40}_{rad} most commonly ranges between 2 and 20. This result essentially agrees with what we expect from the calculated production rates of helium and argon in "normal" crustal rocks (i.e., those with $K/U \approx 10^4$).

Starting from the time when the earth first retained an atmosphere, we may write, for the argon content of the atmosphere,

$$N_A = \int_0^T J_A(t)\,dt = \bar{J}_A T$$

where N_A is the number of argon atoms/cm^2 in the atmosphere, T is the age of the earth's atmosphere, and $J_A(t)$ the flux of argon at time t. We can place limits on $\bar{J}_A$ of $2 \times 10^{13} \leq \bar{J}_A \leq 4 \times 10^{13}$ atoms/cm^2 yr.

Since the ratio of He^4/A_{rad}^{40}, as found in natural gas samples, is a good estimate of the ratio of the fluxes of these isotopes, we can make an estimate for the present He^4 flux of $4.4 \times 10^{12} \leq J_{He^4} \leq 2.2 \times 10^{14}$ atoms/cm^2 yr, with the best estimate being $J_{He^4} \sim 10^{14}$ atoms/cm^2 yr. This yields a mean lifetime of He^4 in the atmosphere of 10^6 years. This value results from a direct calculation, which involves no assumptions about the exospheric escape mechanisms.

All of the evidence for the rare gases indicates that the flux into the atmosphere consists of a mixture of a radiogenic component and a component with atmospheric isotopic composition. This indicates that we do not observe any primordial gas. The only evidence for the contribution of primordial gas is the report of radiogenic Xe^{129} by Butler, Jeffery, Reynolds, and Wasserburg (1963).

In addition to argon and helium, a fissionogenic component in xenon has been observed in natural gases. This is a small contribution (due to spontaneous fission of U^{238}), and the flux of fission xenon may be estimated in a manner similar to that used for helium and argon.

A direct estimate of the flux of juvenile gases is difficult to obtain. If we estimate the "normal output" of volcanoes, we find that they could possibly account for the present flux as estimated before. Continuous outgassing of the crustal rocks may also account for the present flux.

It is not yet possible to state which source predominates.

REFERENCES

Clarke, W. B. and H. G. Thode, 1963. Isotope anomalies in xenon from meteorites and xenon from natural gases, in H. Craig, S. Miller, G. J. Wasserburg, editors, *Isotopic and Cosmic Chemistry*, North Holland Press, Amsterdam.

Wasserburg, G. J. and E. Mazor, 1963. Spontaneous fission xenon in natural gases, *Spoleto Conference on Nuclear Geology*, Italy.

Wasserburg, G. J., E. Mazor, and R. E. Zartman, 1963. Isotopic and chemical composition of some terrestrial gases, in J. Geiss and E. D. Goldberg, editors, *Earth Science and Meteoritics*, North Holland Press, Amsterdam.

DISCUSSION

Dr. MacDonald: Would you go along with the conclusion that the earth can't have outgassed its argon by more than a factor of two? This result is based on the thermal balance. The potassium content used in this calculation can't be off by more than a factor of ten if the thermal balance is to be maintained.

Dr. Wasserburg: Such a conclusion would not make me at all unhappy. However, it should be remembered that the calculation which you refer to assumes chondritic abundances, and none of the outgassing samples we have studied really exhibits chondritic values, with the two exceptions previously mentioned.

Dr. Whipple: There is always the possibility that part of the atmosphere was lost during the early stages of the earth's history by "splashing" due to big meteorites. This couldn't have accounted for more than a factor of two loss. This mechanism certainly couldn't have accounted for much after the first billion years or so.

5

On the Chemical Evolution of the Terrestrial and Cytherean Atmospheres

Heinrich D. Holland

The problem of the chemical evolution of the earth's atmosphere has been debated for more than a century, but only recently have the necessary data been accumulated that can lead to the formulation of a consistent model for the processes which have led to our present atmospheric composition (Holland, 1962). On the other hand, our knowledge of even the present composition of the atmosphere of Venus is still somewhat fragmentary. This paper will begin with a brief review of my ideas concerning the history of the terrestrial atmosphere, and then I will venture to make a modification of these ideas, which seems to account for the present accepted data concerning the chemical composition of the atmosphere of Venus.

The problem of the chemical evolution of the earth's atmosphere could be largely solved if we could plot as a function of time the partial pressure of all the elements and compounds that have been and are present in our atmosphere. We are obviously not in a position to do this at present. We do, however, know a great deal about the processes which control its composition.

I propose, therefore, to review very briefly some pertinent facts about the present atmosphere and then to move back in time to define the variation in the partial pressure of at least some of the important atmospheric constituents.

Table 5.1 (Mason, 1958) will serve to remind us of the relative masses of the various parts of the earth. Practically all of the mass of the earth is in the mantle and core. The crust accounts for less than

TABLE 5.1   Comparison of Various Parts of Earth

	Thickness (km)	Volume ($\times 10^{27}$ cm^3)	Mean Density (g/cm^3)	Mass ($\times 10^{27}$ g)	Mass (%)
Atmosphere	—	—	—	0.000005	0.00009
Hydrosphere	3.80 (mean)	0.00137	1.03	0.00141	0.024
Crust	30	0.015	2.8	0.043	0.7
Mantle	2870	0.892	4.5	4.056	67.8
Core	3471	0.175	10.7	1.876	31.5
Whole earth	6371	1.083	5.52	5.976	100.00

1% of the total mass; the mass of the oceans is smaller by more than three orders of magnitude than that of the earth as a whole; and the atmosphere has a mass that is smaller by six orders of magnitude than that of the earth as a whole. The fact of the extremely small mass of the atmosphere as compared to that of the whole earth is well worth keeping in mind in any discussion of the evolution of our atmosphere.

Tables 5.2 and 5.3, which were taken from one of Urey's (1959) papers, summarize the data on the abundance of the nonvariable and variable constituents of our present atmosphere. The abundance of most of these constituents is determined by complex interactions between the atmosphere, the lithosphere, the hydrosphere, the biosphere, and interplanetary space. The degree of this complexity is em-

TABLE 5.2   Nonvariable Constituents of Atmospheric Air

Constituent	Content	Stability	Spontaneous Reactions
N_2	78.084%	Stable	
O_2	20.946%	Unstable	Reacts slowly with FeO and carbon compounds
CO_2	0.033%	Unstable	Reacts slowly with silicates
A	0.934%	Stable	
Ne	18.18 $\times 10^{-6}$	Stable	
He^4	5.24 $\times 10^{-6}$	Stable	
He^3	6.55 $\times 10^{-12}$	Stable	
Kr	1.14 $\times 10^{-6}$	Stable	
Xe	0.087 $\times 10^{-6}$	Stable	
H_2	0.5 $\times 10^{-6}$	Unstable	$2H_2 + O_2 = 2H_2O$
CH_4	2 $\times 10^{-6}$	Unstable	$CH_4 + 2O_2 = CO_2 + 2H_2O$
N_2O	0.5 $\times 10^{-6}$	Unstable	$2N_2O = 2N_2 + O_2$

TABLE 5.3   Variable Constituents of Dry Air

Con-stituent	Content	Origin	Probable Destructive Reaction
O_3	0 to 0.07 ppm (summer) 0 to 0.02 ppm (winter)	Radiation	$2O_3 = 3O_2$
SO_2	0 to 1 ppm	Industrial	$SO_2 + H_2O + \frac{1}{2}O_2 = H_2SO_4$
NO_2	0 to 0.02 ppm	Industrial	To nitrates or oxygen and nitrogen
CH_2O	Uncertain	Biological or oxida- tion of CH_4	Oxidation to CO_2 and H_2O
I_2	0 to 10^{-10} g/cm^3	Industrial	Many reactions
NaCl	Order of 10^{-10} g/cm^3	Sea spray	Solution in water
NH_3	0 to trace	Industrial	$2NH_3 + \frac{3}{2}O_2 = N_2 + 3H_2O$ Solution in water
CO	0 to trace (0.8 cm atm)	Industrial	$CO + \frac{1}{2}O_2 = CO_2$

phasized by Figure 5.1 (Rankama and Sahama, 1950), which presents the major features of the geochemical cycle of nitrogen. Each of the major "spheres" of the earth can be regarded as a reservoir, and each constituent of such a reservoir is characterized by its concentration and its mean residence time. Such diagrams as Figure 5.1 lend themselves to an analysis of the processes which control the amount of a particular constituent in any given reservoir; an understanding of these processes permits us to ask how these may have varied in the past, and what the effect of such variations may have been on the partial pressure of the various constituents of the earth's atmosphere.

We would like to concentrate here on a discussion of the time variation of the oxygen content of the earth's atmosphere. The reason for this choice is the dependence of the partial pressure of a number of other important atmospheric constituents on the partial pressure of oxygen. We will take as our starting point $t = 0$ in the earth's history. The reason for starting here can be explained in terms of Figure 5.2, which has been taken from a paper by Harrison Brown (1952). Brown and Suess simultaneously started to look into the ratio of the abundances of the rare gases to silicon in the earth as compared to the ratio of the same rare gases to silicon in the cosmos as a whole (see also Signer and Suess, 1963). The ratio of

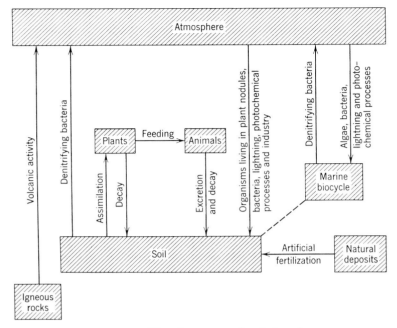

Figure 5.1   The nitrogen geochemical cycle.

xenon to silicon in the earth was found to be lower by six or seven orders of magnitude than the ratio of xenon to silicon in the cosmos. The same depletion relative to silicon was also found for krypton, neon, and for argon, if we neglect the A^{40} isotope. There are two ways to account for this depletion: either the earth was always extraordinarily poor in these elements, or they were present in larger quantities initially and were later lost.

Table 5.4 contains some data, due to Spitzer (1952), which relates the mean residence time of hydrogen, helium, neon, and oxygen to

TABLE 5.4   Mean Residence Times for Various Constituents of Earth's Atmosphere

Temperature T_x (°K)	Atom			
	H	He	N	O
500	2.4×10^7	4.2×10^{25}	10^{92}	10^{105}
1000	3.6×10^4	4.0×10^{13}	10^{45}	10^{51}
2000	1.8×10^3	2.4×10^7	3.9×10^{22}	1.0×10^{26}

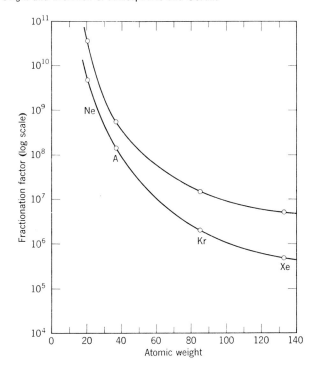

Figure 5.2   Fractionation factors for noble gases (the two curves represent estimated maximum and minimum values).

the temperature in the exosphere.   The temperature of the exosphere is apparently on the order of $2000°K$.   This means that on a geological time scale we can lose hydrogen very fast, helium reasonably fast, and nitrogen and oxygen not at all, or in extremely small amounts.

Unless conditions were very different in the earth's atmosphere at some time in the past, it is quite difficult to see how we could reduce the xenon in the earth's atmosphere by a factor of 10^6.   It is more reasonable to think that at $t = 0$ there was essentially no atmosphere present on the earth, and that the earth's atmosphere and hydrosphere have resulted from degassing of the earth's interior.   Perhaps the most important cornerstone in this argument is the very large abundance of A^{40} in the atmosphere relative to A^{36} and A^{38}.   Turekian, among others, has shown that the large quantity of A^{40} in the atmosphere can easily be accounted for in terms of the accumulation of A^{40} produced in the lithosphere by the radioactive decay of K^{40}.

We have, of course, begged the question of the anomalously low concentration of the rare gases in the earth. At present it does not seem possible to distinguish between two reasonable hypotheses. If the earth reached its present size after the loss of gases of solar composition from interplanetary space, the amount of gas that would have been captured after the earth's gravitational field had approached its present intensity would in any case have been small. On the other hand, if the earth reached its present size in the presence of large quantities of gas of solar composition, magnetic fields might have contributed to sweeping out the earth's primordial gaseous envelope (W. M. Elsasser, personal communication, 1963). Perhaps the solution of the mechanical problems of planetary accumulation will determine the choice between these two alternatives.

Let us now turn to the data presented by Rubey (1955), who was concerned with the amounts of the various elements present on the surface and in the atmosphere of the earth. From these amounts he subtracted the amounts that one could expect to have been contributed by normal rock weathering processes. He labeled the differences "excess volatiles," and these must be accounted for largely by the degassing of the earth's interior. His numerical estimates are shown in Table 5.5. Rubey suggested that the smallness of the amount of excess hydrogen indicated that the earth's atmosphere could never have been very reducing. However, hydrogen can escape from the top of the atmosphere, and if it had ever been present in large amounts, it would not now appear as an excess volatile; thus the observed hydrogen excess should really be considered merely as a residual excess, and

TABLE 5.5 "Excess" Volatile Materials in Present Atmosphere and Hydrosphere and in Buried Sedimentary Rocks (Rubey, 1955)

(in units of 10^{20} g)

H_2O	16,600
Total C as CO_2	910
Cl	300
N	42
S	22
H	10
B,Br,A,F,etc.	4

TABLE 5.6   Comparison of Rubey's "Excess Volatiles" and Eaton and Murata's (1960) Average Composition for Hawaiian Magmatic Gases

Element Abundance in g/1000 g H_2O

Element	"Excess Volatiles"	Hawaiian Gases
Total C as CO_2	55	370
Cl	18	2.5
N	2.5	25
S	1.3	155
H	0.6	0.8
B,Br,A,F,etc.	0.2	1.1

its amount need bear no relationship to the past oxidation state of the atmosphere.

Let us see how the data of Rubey compares with the composition of present day volcanic gases. In Table 5.6 the excess volatiles of Rubey, recalculated on the basis of abundance per thousand grams of water, are compared with the average composition of gases from Hawaiian volcanoes.

The correlation is not particularly good, but if we remember that the excess volatiles represent a rough time average for the earth as a whole over 4.5 billion years, and the Hawaiian gas data are for a small sample of the product of one volcano during the interval of a few years, perhaps agreement will not seem to be impossibly poor.

As we are particularly interested in the oxygen content of the atmosphere, let us consider what sort of oxidation states we might expect to have been present in the earth's atmosphere in the past. As shown above, it seems likely that at $t = 0$, no oxygen was present, i.e., that the partial pressure of oxygen was zero. A short time after $t = 0$ we probably do not yet have to be concerned about the effect of living organisms on P_{O_2}. But we do have to estimate the effect of the input of volcanic gases, whose chemistry may or may not have been closely related to that shown in Table 5.6. We also have to be concerned with the escape of material into interplanetary space, with reactions at the earth's surface, and with the capture of gases from interplanetary space.

In Table 5.7 are listed data which define the oxidation state of average Hawaiian volcanic gases. Recently Fudali has shown that this degree of oxidation is typical of a wide range of volcanic gases.

TABLE 5.7   Observed and Predicted Oxidation State of Hawaiian Volcanic Gases

	Average Hawaiian Volcanic Gases (volume %)		Predicted Ratios
H_2O	79.31	$\dfrac{P_{H_2O}}{P_{H_2}} = 137$	105
H_2	0.58		
CO_2	11.61	$\dfrac{P_{CO_2}}{P_{CO}} = 31$	37
CO	0.37		
SO_2	6.48		
S_2	0.24		
H_2S	—		
N_2	1.29		
Cl_2	0.05		
A	0.04		

If we compare the analytical results with those of Muan and Osborne (1956) on the oxidation state of gases in equilibrium with basalt melts of various kinds, we find that the agreement between the observed and predicted compositions is almost too good. In Hawaiian volcanic gases, carbon is present largely in its highest oxidation state, as CO_2; hydrogen is largely oxidized to water; there is relatively little free hydrogen and CO; and sulfur, which is present mainly in the form of SO_2, is very abundant. The escape of such gases from the interior of the earth could not of itself produce a highly oxidized atmosphere. On the other hand, very little methane could be produced by injection of such gases into the atmosphere, as too little free hydrogen is present in the initial volcanic gas mixture.

As such gases cooled, the water would largely have condensed, the hydrogen probably escaped from the top of the atmosphere, and the CO_2 reacted with surface silicates much as it does today, ultimately producing carbonates. The CO, if it was not used up in some other way, probably disproportionated into carbon and CO_2 at low temperatures. The atmosphere would thus have been characterized neither by an excess of oxygen nor by an excess of hydrogen, and we would expect P_{O_2} to have been about 10^{-7} atm.

Before we can take these thoughts seriously, we need some evidence that the oxidation state of the gases that were put into the atmosphere in the past was really similar to that of present-day Hawaiian gases. In basaltic liquids, the oxidation state of the gases that are emitted

TABLE 5.8   Comparison of FeO and Fe_2O_3 Content of Hawaiian Tholeiitic Basalt and of Triassic and Mid-Precambrian Diabases

Recent	Fe_2O_3	FeO
Hawaiian tholeiitic basalt		
A	1.95	8.96
B	1.32	9.79
Triassic		
Palisades diabase, N. J.		
Pl 1	1.25	8.91
Pl 2	1.28	8.96
Pl 3	1.02	9.10
Pl 6	1.35	8.90
Pl 9	1.70	8.51
Rocky Hill diabase, N. J.		
RH 2	1.46	8.75
Mid-Precambrian		
Nipissing diabase, Ont.		
# 312	1.60	7.95
# 166	0.85	8.70

is related to the ratio of ferrous iron to ferric iron in the melt. We can therefore use the value of this ratio in ancient basalts and diabases to obtain some idea of the oxidation state of associated volcanic gases. Some pertinent data are shown in Table 5.8.

There does not seem to be a time trend in the ratio of ferrous iron to ferric iron in these and in similar samples studied by Green and Poldervaart (1955). This suggests that there has been little, if any, change in the oxidation state of volcanic gases during the past 1.8 billion years, which is the approximate age of the Nipissing diabase.

On the other hand, we might expect that the chemistry of volcanic gases was quite different very early in the earth's history. Before the formation of the core there would have presumably been metallic iron in the upper part of the mantle, and the buffer system for the oxidation state of basalts would have been native iron–ferrous iron, rather than ferrous iron–ferric iron. Thus, very early in the earth's history, we might expect that methane, possibly ammonia, and more probably nitrogen were the dominant gases to have come out of volcanoes. This period probably lasted less than 0.5 billion years.

The only mechanisms for the production of free oxygen throughout geologic time appear to be photosynthesis and the photodissociation of water vapor in the upper atmosphere followed by the escape of hydrogen. Of these, the former is probably by far the most effective. Table 5.9 shows a rough table of the balance of the probable total oxygen production and use throughout geologic time. The main component of oxygen use, the oxidation of H_2 to H_2O, has been estimated on the basis of the present size of the oceans and a "Hawaiian" H_2/H_2O ratio for volcanic gases. The ferrous-ferric contribution is due to the oxidation of surface rocks, in which iron is the dominant element undergoing oxidation. The consumption of oxygen due to the oxidation of SO_2 and CO are calculated from Rubey's data on excess volatiles.

It seems worthwhile now to construct a graph of the partial pressure of oxygen in the atmosphere as function of time throughout the history of the earth. This is shown in Figure 5.3. At $t = 0$, there was probably essentially no atmosphere. In stage I, assuming the presence of free iron in the crust and/or upper mantle, we would expect to have had a tenuous atmosphere consisting of methane, nitrogen, ammonia, and some hydrogen, resulting from the introduction of highly reduced volcanic gases. If native iron was never present in the crust or mantle to act as an oxidation buffer, stage I would have been absent altogether.

In stage II, the introduction of Hawaiian-type volcanic gases was the dominant factor determining the composition of the atmosphere. There is still a question, however, whether the atmosphere was therefore neutral with respect to H_2 and O_2, or whether a great deal of hydrogen was lost from the top of the atmosphere following photodissociation. In the latter case, free oxygen might have been present

TABLE 5.9 Balance of Oxygen Production and Use

Total estimated production of oxygen (in units of 10^{20} g)

By photosynthesis in excess of decay	181
By photodissociation of water vapor	1
Total	182

Present distribution of produced oxygen

Free in atmosphere	12
Used in oxidation of ferrous to ferric iron	14
Used in oxidation of volcanic gases	
oxidation of CO to CO_2	15
oxidation of SO_2 to SO_3	8
oxidation of H_2 to H_2O	140
Total	189

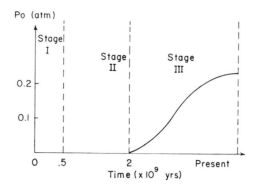

Figure 5.3   Possible course of oxygen partial pressure in the atmosphere over time.

in the atmosphere during stage II. There is some geologic evidence to indicate that oxygen was not abundant in the atmosphere during this stage. In the present-day atmosphere, Fe^{2+} in the zone of oxidation of soils very rapidly goes to Fe^{3+}; U^{4+} very rapidly goes to U^{6+}; S^{2-} very rapidly goes to S^{6+}; and similarly copper, vanadium, and manganese all change oxidation states. If free oxygen were essentially absent from the atmosphere during stage II, then, as we go back in time, we ought to find sediments in which the oxidation state of these elements has not been affected by surface oxidation. In the large uranium deposits which are 2 billion years or older—such as Blind River in Canada, or the Witwatersrand deposits in South Africa —we find small, apparently detrital grains of uraninite which would be entirely unstable in the present-day atmosphere. In the same kind of sediments we also find small pebbles of pyrite which would be rapidly oxidized today. This evidence for the absence of oxygen during stage II is not conclusive but does suggest that the partial pressure of oxygen was much smaller during this stage than it is today.

During stage III, life or, more specifically, photosynthesis determined the oxidation state of the atmosphere. We are not really sure when photosynthesis began, but it should be realized that an oxygen-rich atmosphere was not formed immediately following the onset of photosynthesis. Oxygen had to be produced at a rate faster than the rate at which the reduced gases were being put into the atmosphere. Some time during the last 3 billion years P_{O_2} rose to about its present level, although it is not certain just when or just how fast. The paleontologic evidence suggests that the oxygen content was relatively high at least as long as 0.3 billion years ago. The partial pressure of N_2, A, Ne, Kr, Xe must have been increasing gradually as volatiles leaked out of the earth. The helium content of the atmosphere has probably been roughly constant, because it is being lost from the top of the atmosphere about as fast as it is being put in. The CO_2 pressure has probably been roughly constant, because it has been taken out of the atmosphere with carbonates about as fast as it has been put into the atmosphere. The concentration of sulfur compounds in the atmosphere was presumably always quite low. The probable atmospheric composition in the three stages is summarized in Table 5.10.

It is tempting to use the lines of thought suggested above to explain what we know about the atmosphere of Venus. Gold has suggested that since there is so much water on the earth, we must also think of Venus as a somewhat watery planet. If we were to heat the surface of the earth as it is today to 400°C, a great deal of water vapor would be present in the atmosphere. Yet, water vapor seems to be virtually absent from the atmosphere of Venus. This difference is worth exploring further. The presence of water at the earth's surface must be related to the inclusion of water in the solid part of the earth during accretion, most probably as ice and as water of hydration in hydrated silicates. The relative water content of accreted planetary material is therefore surely related to the temperature during accretion. It seems likely that the temperature during accretion in the orbit of Venus was higher than the temperature in the earth's orbit; the water content of Venus could therefore be considerably smaller than that of the earth. The mean depth of the earth's oceans is about 3000 meters

TABLE 5.10 Summary of Data on the Probable Chemical Composition of the Atmosphere

	Stage 1	Stage 2	Stage 3
Major components $P > 10^{-2}$ atm	CH_4 H_2 (?)	N_2	N_2 O_2
Minor components $10^{-2} > P > 10^{-4}$ atm	H_2 (?) H_2O N_2 H_2S NH_3 A	SO_2 H_2O CO_2 A	A H_2O CO_2
Trace components $10^{-4} > P > 10^{-6}$ atm	He	Ne He CH_4 NH_3 (?)	Ne He CH_4 Kr

and is a function of the water content of the lithosphere and of the degree of degassing of the planet. If the water content of Venus were three to four orders of magnitude smaller than that of the earth, the depth of the Cytherean "oceans" or their volatilized equivalent would be negligible even if Venus is more thoroughly outgassed than the earth.

The concentrations of the other volatiles in Venus would similarly be dependent on the accretion temperature of the planet. But it is not difficult to imagine a temperature range in which water as ice is not retained as accreted material, but in which nitrogen and carbon are retained in approximately terrestrial proportions. If this indeed were the case, carbon, oxygen, sulfur, and nitrogen would be the major elements in volcanic gases on Venus.

We do not know the oxidation state of volcanic gases on Venus, but it seems most reasonable to assume that it is roughly the same as on earth, since the oxidation state is probably controlled by the same buffer system. Carbon in such gases would be present in CO_2 and CO, with the former probably more abundant than the latter. Sulfur would be present largely in SO_2. The composition of the gases would, therefore, be similar to that of terrestrial volcanic gases, but H_2O and H_2 would be virtually absent.

If such a mixture is cooled from 1500 to 600°K, a temperature apparently prevailing somewhat above the surface of Venus, two main reactions will take place. In the first and most important reaction, SO_2 and CO will react to give S_2 and CO_2:

$$2SO_2 + 4CO \rightarrow S_2 + 4CO_2$$

This reaction will go almost completely to the right, that is, until essentially all of the SO_2, or all of the CO, or both have been destroyed. The S_2 could condense at high altitudes into the slightly yellowish Cytherean clouds (Suess, 1963), and could possibly condense at the surface as well to give pools of liquid sulfur, if the sulfur content of the atmosphere is sufficiently high.

If P_{CO} is more than twice P_{SO_2} in the Cytherean volcanic gases, SO_2 will be used up before the CO is exhausted by the above reaction. But CO, being unstable at such temperatures, would largely disproportionate to graphite and CO_2:

$$2CO \rightarrow C + CO_2$$

Any graphite produced in this manner would presumably descend to the surface of Venus in a steady drizzle. This is probably not the situation, however, because the amount of CO needed to have carbon in equilibrium with one atmosphere of CO_2 at 600°K is about 10^{-3} atm, an amount that would probably have been detected in the Venus atmosphere.

Yet excess SO_2 has been unsuccessfully sought in the Venus atmosphere. Its absence is probably related to reaction largely with magnetite in surface rocks to give pyrite and hematite or pyrite and ferrous sulfate. Thus SO_2 is probably being removed continuously both by reaction with CO and with oxides in surface rocks.

Carbon dioxide also is almost certainly removed by reaction with silicates to form carbonates. If P_{CO_2} is about 1 atm and P_{N_2} about 20 atm in the atmosphere of Venus, the ratio P_{CO_2}/P_{N_2} is less by a factor of about 400 than that in terrestrial volcanic gases. There is no good reason for this large difference, unless it reflects the almost quantitative removal of CO_2 from the atmosphere of Venus by reaction with surface rocks. The high CO_2 pressure in the atmosphere of Venus as compared to that in the earth's atmosphere is probably due to the high surface temperature of Venus at which, for reactions such as

$$CaSiO_3 + CO_2 \rightarrow CaCO_3 + SiO_2$$

the equilibrium pressure is on the order of 1 atm.

REFERENCES

Brown, H., 1952. Rare gases and the formation of the earth's atmosphere, pp. 258–266 in G. P. Kuiper, editor, *The Atmospheres of the Earth and Planets*, second edition, University of Chicago Press.

Green, J. and A. Poldervaart, 1955. Some basaltic provinces, *Geochim. et Cosmochim. Acta*, 7, 177–188.

Holland, H. D., 1962. Model for the evolution of the earth's atmosphere, pp. 447–477 in *Petrologic Studies: A Volume to Honor A. F. Buddington*, Geol. Soc. Am.

Mason, B., 1958. *Principles of Geochemistry*, second edition, John Wiley and Sons, New York.

Muan, A. and E. F. Osborne, 1956. Phase equilibria at liquidus temperatures in the system MgO–FeO–Fe_2O_3–SiO_2, *Am. Ceram. Soc. Jour.* 39, 121–140.

Rankama, K. and Th. G. Sahama, 1950. *Geochemistry*, University of Chicago Press.

Rubey, W. W., 1955. Development of the hydrosphere and atmosphere, with special reference to probable composition of the early atmosphere, pp. 631–650, in A. Poldervaart, editor, *Crust of the Earth*, Geol. Soc. Am., Special Paper 62.

Signer, P. and H. E. Suess, 1963. Rare gases in the sun, in the atmosphere, and in meteorites, pp. 241–272, in *Earth Science and Meteoritics* (compiled by J. Geiss and E. D. Goldberg), North-Holland Publishing Company.

Spitzer, L. Jr., 1952. The terrestrial atmosphere above 300 km, pp. 211–247, in
G. P. Kuiper, editor, *The Atmospheres of the Earth and Planets,* University
of Chicago Press.
Suess, H. E., 1962. Thermodynamic data on the formation of solid carbon and
organic compounds in primitive planetary atmospheres, *Jour. Geophys. Res.*
67, 2029–2034.
Urey, H. C., 1959. The atmospheres of the planets, *Handbuch der Physik.*
52, 363–418.

DISCUSSION

Dr. Wasserburg: What assurance do you have that the volcanic
gases you have referred to are truly volcanic and do not represent
some chemical reactions with local ground water, carbon, and air?

Dr. Holland: I do not know whether the gases that were analyzed
are pristine mantle gases. In fact, the argon data suggests that in
general they are not. However, it really doesn't matter. First of
all, the main feeling I have about what comes out of volcanoes comes
from the sedimentary record—essentially, Rubey's data. Also, I am
mainly concerned with the total amounts, and with the oxidation
states, which I feel are controlled by the ferrous-ferric ratios in the
magmas. So it really doesn't matter whether or not any of this
material has been recycled.

Dr. Abelson: I would like to point out a common misconception;
namely, that one must not confuse photosynthesis with the emission
of oxygen. The emission of oxygen is a sophistication; there are
plenty of bacteria today that are photosynthetic but don't evolve
oxygen. Instead, they require a reducing environment to get rid of
what would be their oxygen. For example, instead of forming O_2,
they might get rid of it by a combination with sulfur compounds.

Dr. Gold: With reference to your explanation as to why there is
water on earth but not on Venus, I agree that ice will be lost, but
not the hydrated silicates. It is hard to believe that the critical
temperature for dehydrating silicates will fall right in the narrow
temperature range between the earth and Venus.

Dr. Abelson: But remember that vapor pressures are exponential.
A difference in temperature of 40 or 50 degrees could change things
by an order of magnitude.

Dr. Holland: Let's look at an alternate hypothesis—namely, that there was water present on Venus, but it is now gone. It seems to me that the only mechanism for removal is photodissociation, but then there is the problem of getting rid of the oxygen.

Dr. MacDonald: The temperature might be high enough in the Venus exosphere to boil off the oxygen.

Dr. Holland: If this is so, then there is no problem. But in choosing between these two alternatives, I prefer to believe that the amount of water was very much less to begin with.

6

The History of Growth of Oxygen in the Earth's Atmosphere

L. V. Berkner and L. C. Marshall

This paper reports on a new subject which might be classified under the general heading of "paleoatmospheres" or "fossil atmospheres." This subject involves critical quantitative study of the history of planetary atmospheres.

Studies of this kind are now feasible, in view of the substantial data from space probes on solar radiation at all wavelengths, together with reasonably complete data on the absorption of particular spectral regions by component atmospheric gases. There is at the same time a growing knowledge of the succession and rates of photochemical reactions involved in the absorption processes.

These studies are of value in understanding the composition and organization of planetary atmospheres, which are of increasing interest in view of their growing accessibility. Reasonable interpretation of the physical and biological history of a planet may be misleading, unless at the same time some reasonable estimates of accompanying atmospheres can be made.

At the moment, the analysis of the paleoatmosphere of Planet Earth is the most convenient to make, since an abundance of data is available in view of its accessibility. These data relate to the composition, distribution, and photochemistry of the present earth's atmosphere; to the behavior, composition, chemistry, and geology of its surface and interior; to related subjects of molecular biology, biochemistry, and molecular genetics of its living materials; and also to the paleontological and evolutionary evidence derived from more than a century of study. Moreover, the implications apparent from a critical study of the paleoatmosphere of the earth open new and interesting lines of inquiry and suggest reasonable solutions to many of the so-called puzzles which, in the formulation of the history of the earth, have so far remained unsolved.

In this paper, attention is directed only to the history of the growth of oxygen in the atmosphere of Planet Earth. This report is a précis, outlining only the principal methods and conclusions of a more extended study, from which a preliminary model has been formulated that awaits refinement.

From the work of Goldschmidt (1937), Brown (1949, 1952), Spencer-Jones (1950), Kuiper (1951), Urey (1952, 1959), Alfvén (1954), Fesenkov (1959), Vinogradov (1959), and many others, the current view is that upon its agglomeration, the earth was without a primordial atmosphere. The relative abundances of the rare gases, illustrated in Table 6.1 (after Brown, 1952), show that their abundances on earth range from one-millionth to one ten-billionth of their cosmic abundance.

Similarly, the relative abundances of the lighter elements, hydrogen and helium, on the sun and the more massive planets, and the paucity of these light elements on the inner planets, show that the inner planets, in the process of agglomeration, lost the greater proportion of mass attributable to the normal abundance of the gaseous elements. The accumulation of A^{40}, moreover, from decay of K^{40}, corresponds to the estimated age of the solid earth of about 5 billion years.

Thus all lines of evidence point to the absence of any primordial atmosphere and to subsequent growth of an atmosphere entirely from self-contained secondary sources. This view is consistent with the agglomeration of the earth from planetesimals whose gravitational fields were too small to retain a primordial atmosphere.

According to Urey (1952, 1959), Vinogradov (1959), and others [Kuiper (1951), Alfvén (1954)], the physical chemistry underlying retention of compounds comprising the major portion of the earth

TABLE 6.1   Fractionation Factors of Rare Gases

Element	Atomic Weight	Fractionation Factor
Neon	20	$\sim 10^{10}$
Argon (36)	40	$\sim 10^{8}$
Krypton	83	$\sim 2 \times 10^{6}$
Xenon	130	$\sim 10^{6}$

shows that the earth has never been substantially molten since its agglomeration. The earth consequently retains large quantities of gases chemically bound in various ways. These in turn provide for the source of the secondary atmosphere.

The volcanic origin of this secondary atmosphere has been developed by Rubey (1951, 1955), Urey (1959), Holland (1962), Vinogradov (1959), and others. The continents have been built at an average rate of 1 to 3 km³ per year from volcanic effluents, based on estimates of Sapper (1927), Verhoogen (1946), Bullard (1962), and Wilson (1954, 1959a,b). Wilson's (1954) estimate of a rate of average continent building of 1.3 km³ per year throughout geologic time, and down to present times, seems compatible with present estimates of the total volume of continental materials. Accompanying these solid effluents are corresponding volumes of gases—primarily primitive water vapor, presumably released from water of crystallization, together with CO_2, N_2, SO_2, SO_3, H_2, Cl_2 in substantial quantities, accompanied by traces of many other gases (Rubey, 1951; Taxieff and Fabre, 1960). No oxygen is released directly from volcanic effluents.

The absence of a significant content of oxygen in the primitive secondary atmosphere is confirmed by several lines of evidence. First, there is no suitable source, as will be shown later. Second, the incomplete oxidation of early sedimentary materials (3 billion years of age) as demonstrated by Raukama (1955), Ramdohr (1958), Lepp and Goldich (1959), and others, and summarized by Rutten (1962), suggests very early lithospheric sedimentation in a reducing atmosphere. This evidence is in concordance with the views of Holland (1962). Finally, the rapidly growing evidence on the origin of life on Planet Earth appears to forbid a significant oxygen concentration until photosynthesis has been achieved.

The work of Oparin (1953) and Bernal (1949) directed attention to the steps leading to the organization of the simple biological cell, which is now recognized as a very advanced evolutionary entity.

Oparin (1953) visualized a logical series of evolutionary syntheses starting from inorganic and very simple organic materials of non-biological origin (i.e., the simplest compounds of hydrogen, carbon, oxygen, and nitrogen), together with some traces of other elements (such as sulfur, phosphorus, and iron), finally ending with the organized cell replete with living function, which Bernal (1949) defines pragmatically as "the embodiment within a certain volume of self-maintaining chemical processes." Oparin (1953) made the interesting suggestion that each step in the achievement of the whole process was the consequence of natural experimentation on a large scale guided by natural selection.

The extensive literature on evolution leading to the simple cell is developed in work by Wald (1955), Rabinowitch (1951), Calvin (1959, 1962), Anfinsen (1961), and many others. Synthesis of amino acids and other complex elements of cell structure is demonstrable in a reducing atmosphere in the presence of ultraviolet light, which provides the energy for chemosynthesis through photoexcitation (c.f. Miller, 1959). Viable chemical precursors to the living cell were selected step-by-step from a thin soup of ever-more complex organic compounds. During this phase of primitive evolution of preliving compounds, oxygen is a powerful poison, acting to break them down as they are formed. The principal steps in evolution to the complete cell, replete with photosynthetic activity, are thus summarized in a rather elemental way in Figure 6.1.

Such evidence therefore leads to inquiry concerning the origin and concentration of oxygen in this primitive secondary atmosphere of the earth. Excellent data on solar radiation in the ultraviolet spectrum are now available from the space probes of many workers,

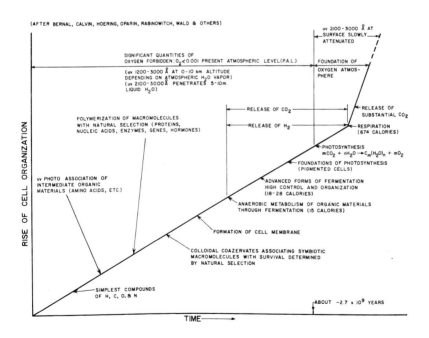

Figure 6.1   Diagrammatic visualization of evolution of the simple living cell.

including Hall, Damon, and Hinteregger (1962), and Detweiler, Garrett, Purcell and Tousey (1961), to name but a few. Available data on solar ultraviolet radiation are summarized in Figures 6.2 and 6.3 (Nawrocki and Papa, 1961), after Johnson's (1954) new evaluation of the solar constant.

Radiation down to 1400 Å arises in the upper 100 km of the solar photosphere. As shown from the studies of Wilson (1963) on the evolutionary history of stars of the main sequence similar to our

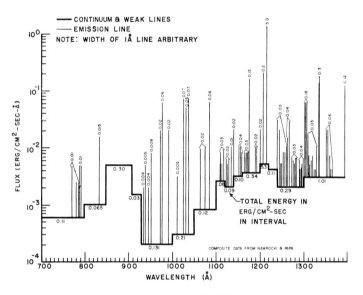

Figure 6.2   Solar intensity 700–1400 Å.

sun, this photospheric radiation above 1400 Å is extremely stable —probably self-regulating and unvarying over very long periods comparable to the age of the earth. Radiation below 1400 Å arises in the chromosphere and corona, and may have been as much as three times the present average level (this involves total average fluctuations in this spectral region of as much as 20 to 1). From the point of view of total ultraviolet energy, however, by far the major bulk (99.9%) arises from the stable photospheric radiation above 1400 Å.

Absorption of this ultraviolet spectrum by various possible component gases above 1000 Å is now well known and is summarized in Figure 6.4 after the rigorous work of Watanabe (1953, 1958) and the contribution of many others (Allen, 1963; Herzberg, 1961; Pearse,

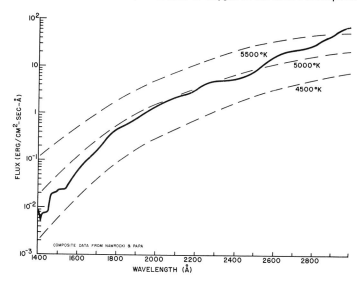

Figure 6.3   Solar intensity 1400–3000 Å.

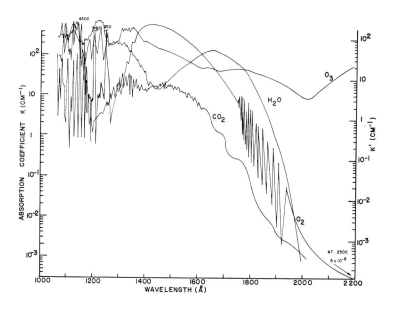

Figure 6.4   Composite of ultraviolet absorption in atmospheric gases.

1963; Pauling, 1926–1930, 1960; Nicolet and Mange, 1954; Nicolet and Marcel, 1950).

In this spectral region above 1400 Å, absorption by H_2 and N_2 and by the rare gases helium, neon, argon, krypton, and xenon is negligible. Only H_2O, CO_2, O_2, and O_3 absorb radiation strongly in this region, with only O_3 important as an absorbing gas above 2200 Å.

In order to interpret the relative importance of different concentrations of the several possible constituent gases as absorbers over the ultraviolet spectrum, these data on radiation and on absorption must be combined at each wavelength over the spectrum. To do this, the path length (expressed in centimeters NTP) required at each wavelength to reduce the incident radiation to a small selected arbitrary level is ascertained for each constituent gas in an atmosphere.

The selection of the particular reference level is not important to the subsequent interpretation, since translation to other reference levels can be made readily. The reference level in this paper is determined by the path length of the constituent gas required to reduce the incident energy at each wave band to 1 erg/cm²-sec-50 Å. This reference energy level is actually 10^{-4} of the level in a 50 Å band at the peak of solar radiation, approximately 4500 Å (i.e., the transmitted energy level after absorption, which is 0.01% of the peak

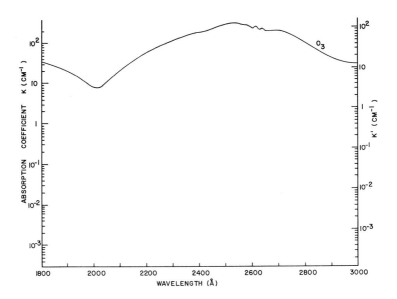

Figure 6.5   Ultraviolet absorption in O_3 (data from K. Watanabe and Vigroux).

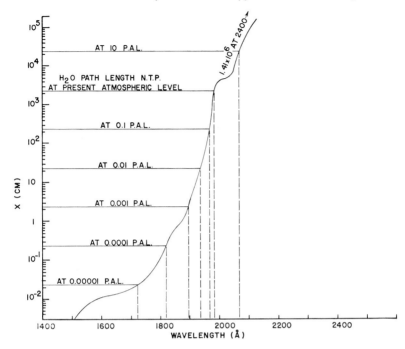

Figure 6.6 Thickness of H_2O required to absorb available ultraviolet to "extinction" (1 erg/cm²-sec-50 Å).

radiation in a 50 Å band: a transmitted level equivalent to about fifty times the brightness of the full moon). For purposes of terminology in the present discussion the path length, x, of any constituent gas required to reduce the radiation to 1 erg/cm²-sec-50 Å will be expressed as the path length required for its extinction.

The results of combining radiation and absorption data are shown in Figure 6.6 for H_2O vapor. Here it is apparent that the wavelength at which significant penetration through H_2O vapor can occur is not very sensitive to concentration. It drops only about 100 Å for a decrease of three orders of magnitude of H_2O vapor pressure.[1] In the absence of oxygen, and at low CO_2 pressures, the important photochemical reactions can be summarized by

$$H_2O + 2h\nu \rightarrow 2H + O$$

which provides a source of atmospheric oxygen.

[1] Note also that a change of reference level from 1 to 0.1 erg/cm²-sec-50 Å, for example, will simply shift the curve upward by one decade in Figure 6.6.

Urey (1959) has pointed out qualitatively, however, that production of O_2 by photodissociation of H_2O would be limited at some self-regulating concentration by the shadowing effect of the O_2 thus produced. Since oxygen is distributed exponentially above the base of the stratosphere, while water vapor is frozen out to very low concentrations at this same level, the presence of oxygen will shadow the H_2O vapor in its range of photodissociation, as seen in Figure 6.7. In the figure, it is evident that when the path length of O_2 above 10 km approaches 35 cm, water vapor is completely shadowed from the H_2O dissociative radiation-band up to 1950 Å. This path length of 35 cm of O_2 above 10 km corresponds to a total path length of O_2 above the surface of about 100 cm NTP.

This path length represents an oxygen level (Fig. 6.7) of somewhat less than 0.001 of the present atmospheric concentration. On the premises of the above discussion, *this is the upper limit of oxygenic pressure in the primitive atmosphere.*

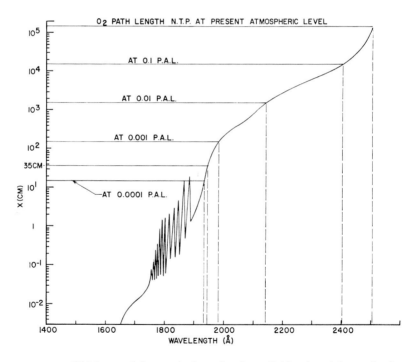

Figure 6.7 Thickness of O_2 required to absorb available ultraviolet to "extinction" (1 erg/cm²-sec-50 Å).

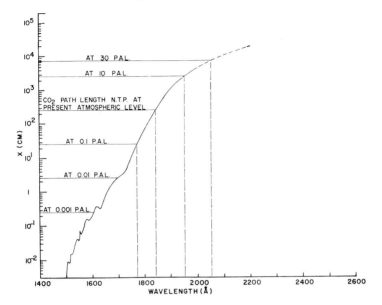

Figure 6.8   Thickness of CO_2 required to absorb available ultraviolet to "extinction" (1 erg/cm²-sec-50 Å).

The presence of significant CO_2 (Fig. 6.8) simply adds to this shadowing of H_2O vapor and lowers this upper limit of oxygenic concentration in the primitive atmosphere below this value of less than 10^{-3} PAL (present atmospheric level).

Geologists have heretofore assumed that because of the extensive oxides found in the pre-Cambrian (Proterozoic) lithosphere, the atmosphere must have been highly oxygenic. This assumption seems unnecessary, and probably improper, when the pertinent reactions are reviewed:

$$O + O + M \rightarrow O_2 + M$$

$$O_2 + O + M \rightarrow O_3 + M$$

$$O_3 + M_s \rightarrow \text{surface oxides}$$

coupled with the additional reactions

$$O + O_3 \rightarrow 2O_2$$

$$O_2 + h\nu \rightarrow O + O$$

In the primitive atmosphere the supply of O_3 is maintained close to the surface, where it is removed through surface oxidation at very high reaction rates.

Since oxygen appears in the primitive atmosphere in its most effective form for rapid oxidation of lithospheric materials, we are led to inquire into the available supply. In this study the potential oxygen supply has been calculated from the total energy available for photo-dissociation. It is found that the available energy is of the order of 100 times (or more) that which is necessary to account for existing pre-Cambrian lithospheric oxides. This leads to the realization that the oxidation rate in the Proterozoic is dependent not so much on the absolute concentration of oxygen as on its chemical form and the reaction rate in that form. Consequently, the classic assumption, that the abundance of lithospheric oxides dictates high oxygenic levels in the primitive atmosphere, seems unnecessary.

Thus in the primitive atmosphere, the oxygen balance is dominated by a rate of loss which consumes oxygen promptly upon its production. The rapid removal of oxygen from the primitive atmosphere, and its inherent self-regulation by the "Urey" process (1952), together with other geochemical and biological evidence, therefore leads to the conclusion that the oxygen level in the primitive atmosphere of the earth was $< 10^{-3}$ (i.e., $< 0.1\%$) of the present atmospheric levels.

The subsequent rise of oxygenic level can be attributed only to photosynthesis. The summary of Rabinowitch (1951) shows that in the present atmosphere all oxygen passes through the photosynthetic process in 2000 years, all CO_2 in 350 years, and all H_2O in the oceans in 2×10^6 years. These intervals are very short compared to geologic periods.

Thus photosynthesis, in oxidizing liquid water and at the same time reducing carbon dioxide to carbohydrate, is the overpowering source of oxygen in the present atmosphere.

At any time after the primitive, the oxygen balance will be determined by

Plus: Photochemical dissociation of H_2O
        Photosynthesis
Minus: O_2 and O_3 oxidation of surface materials
        Decay and respiration
        O_2 in H_2O solution

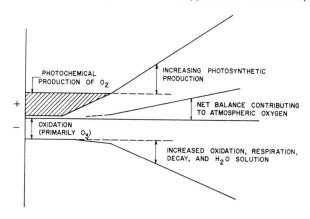

Figure 6.9   Factors in early oxygen balance.

Thus, as Holland points out, the rise of oxygen occurs as a consequence of a small differential between two much larger opposing effects, which, relatively speaking, increase simultaneously. As the initial oxygen from photosynthesis is released, moreover, it will simply substitute for oxygen from photodissociation of H_2O, because of the inherent "Urey" regulation to the level $O_2 < 10^{-3}$ PAL. This balance is illustrated qualitatively in Figure 6.9.

Not until the net rate of production of oxygen (primarily by photosynthesis) exceeds the net rate of O_2 dissociation, and its consequent loss as an active oxidant, can equilibrium values of oxygen exceed the levels in the primitive atmosphere and the building of a stable oxygenic atmosphere begin.

This leads to inquiry concerning the ecology for the rise of photosynthesis. Caspersson (1950) and Davidson (1960) have shown that cell absorption of ultraviolet radiation arises from absorption by nucleic acids primarily between 2600 and 2700 Å and by proteins between 2700 and 2900 Å. Cell absorption in these bands is highly lethal to cell function in all forms, disorganizing chemical function, and bringing growth, reproduction, and survival to a halt. Only atmospheric ozone can provide protection by shadowing the lethal radiation in these bands (Fig. 6.10).

The distribution of ozone is shown in idealized form in Figure 6.11. Ozone is distributed roughly uniformly in a column between its level of maximum production and the surface, to which it is convected and lost. The level of maximum production is lowered as the

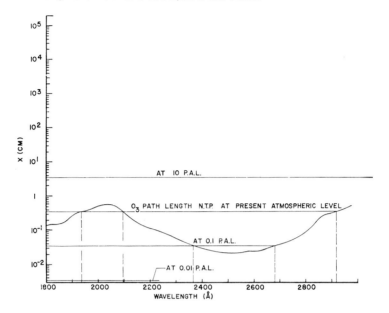

Figure 6.10 Thickness of O_3 required to absorb available ultraviolet to "extinction" (1800–3000 Å) (1 erg/cm²-sec-50 Å).

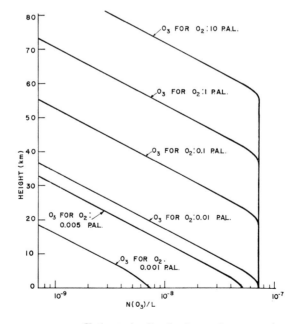

Figure 6.11 Estimated distribution of ozone for various levels of oxygen.

TABLE 6.2   Estimated Total Path Lengths of O_3 for Varying Pressures of O_2*

x (PAL)	$\sim\overline{H}$(cm)	% of atm (NTP)	$\sim x$(cm)
10.0	65×10^5	7×10^{-8}	0.5
1.0	47×10^5	7×10^{-8}	0.33
0.1	28×10^5	7×10^{-8}	0.2
0.01	12×10^5	4×10^{-8}	0.05
0.005	12×10^5	1.6×10^{-8}	0.02
0.001	12×10^5	4×10^{-9}	0.005

* The crude integration of total path length established in this table is all that present data coupled with basic assumptions will justify.

oxygenic concentration diminishes.   Therefore, the total path length of ozone in various atmospheres will diminish, as shown in Table 6.2.

Combining these data on the path lengths of ozone, the path lengths of oxygen previously derived, and the path lengths for absorption in water using the measurements of Dawson and Hulburt (1934), results in Figure 6.12, which shows the penetration of ultraviolet radiation in water in the presence of various oxygenic atmospheres.   Here it is seen that in the primitive atmosphere, lethal radiation penetrates to a depth of approximately 10 meters of water.   Therefore, the requirements for primitive photosynthesis are as follows:

1. A water depth of more than 10 meters, but no deeper than needed, to permit a maximum of visible light for photosynthesis.
2. A minimum of liquid convection to avoid circulation of primitive metazoa toward the lethal surface, but gentle convection to provide organic nutrients synthesized photochemically at the surface, in the presence of ultraviolet radiation, according to the processes described by Miller (1959).

This rigidly restrictive ecology describes bottom-dwelling organisms (green algae or their evolutionary precursors) in protected shallow lakes or seas.   In particular, life in the oceans seems unlikely.

Warm pools, associated with volcanic hot springs, which are rich in nutrient minerals and elemental compounds, seem prime candidates for the origin of life and photosynthesis.   The ancient bioherms, 2.7 billion years old and known to have supported photosynthetic or-

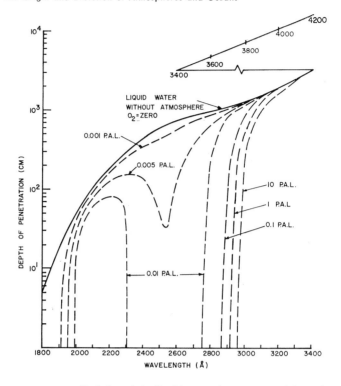

Figure 6.12   Path length in liquid water in presence of O_2 and O_3 for various concentrations of O_2 to absorb available ultra-violet to "extinction" (1 erg/cm^2-sec-50 Å).

ganisms (from the work of Hoering and Abelson, 1961), could well have been at the base of such pools, and must be very close to the seat of life. The rigid ecologic insulation between such pools suggests the possibility of multiple origins of living organisms with selection among them only at a later era when the permissive ecologic environment became more general.

Only as the continents grow with volcanic action can sufficient areas for photosynthesis be found to meet the criteria for a growing oxygenic atmosphere. With constantly changing geographic areas, and corresponding fluctuations of climatology, the growth of the oxygenic atmosphere appears to have awaited the proper combination of conditions to satisfy the critical criterion.

As oxygen rises toward the level $O_2 \sim 0.01$ PAL, several interesting potentialities arise.

1. The penetration of lethal ultraviolet (replotted in Fig. 6.13) diminishes to a few centimeters of water, opening the oceans to life. 2. The oxygen level reaches the "Pasteur point" where organisms change from fermentation to respiration. Thus the energy available for chemosynthesis jumps for $\sim$20 cal/gram-molecule to $\sim$675 cal/gram-molecule (c.f. Genovois, 1927, and Rabinowitch, 1951).

This leads one to a search of paleontologic and geologic history for a radical and explosive change in evolutionary forms, corresponding to the opening of entirely new and far more widespread evolutionary opportunities as O_2 approaches 0.01 PAL. There is, of course, just one such evolutionary explosion—the Cambrian—beginning 600 million years ago.[2] Therefore we identify the oxygenic level, $O_2 \rightarrow 0.01$ PAL, as immediately preceding the opening of the Cambrian.

Prior to the Cambrian there is utterly no evidence of any form of life advanced beyond the elementary algae, fungi, and bacteria, that is, the simplest forms of metazoa (cf. Rutten, 1962). Since Proterozoic sediments favorable to fossil preservation have been studied for more than a century by a host of workers, the utter absence of fossils prior to the Cambrian evolutionary explosion has been considered heretofore as a scientific "puzzle" (cf. Kummel, 1961).

The assumption is usually made that evolutionary pre-Cambrian precursors could have had only soft parts that were unfavorable for fossilization (although it should be noted that in subsequent ages, fossils of this general kind are not infrequent).

Under the interpretation of this paper, no advanced precursors to the Cambrian evolutionary explosion should be expected until oxygenic levels presaged the opening of the Cambrian. Thus, according to the model developing in this discussion, the geologic record should be read exactly as presented in nature.

Following the Cambrian, the complexity of life is known to have multiplied rapidly. In the next few million years more than 1200 species of different creatures appeared, many of very considerable size and variety of characters. During this time the foundations for all modern phyla were laid. In particular, complex and efficient forms of respiratory apparatus were evolved as increasing oxygen levels presented favorable opportunities for selection of such evolutionary advances. These advanced respiratory systems provided the mechanistic basis for the concurrent development of circulatory systems, digestive tracts, central nervous systems, bisexual modes of reproduc-

[2] This dating follows the most recent geologic and geochronologic conclusions (c.f. Kummel, 1961).

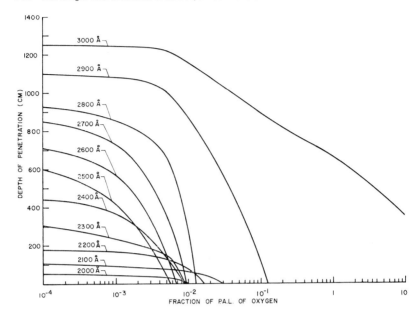

Figure 6.13 Penetration of ultraviolet in liquid water with various combinations of oxygen and ozone atmospheres (intensity at extinction $= 1$ erg/cm^2-sec-50 Å).

tion, and similar characters associated with advanced biological organisms through effective supply of oxygen and removal of oxidized carbon.

As oxygen rises with widespread marine photosynthesis to the level of 0.1 PAL (10% present concentration), lethal radiation will be largely shielded from dry land (Fig. 6.13). This will open a new ecological niche for evolution ashore. The geologic record shows no evidence of any form of life ashore until the late Silurian period, 420 million years ago. Then a number of different phyla of plants and animals exploded on dry land. By the early Devonian, 30 million years later, great forests had appeared, and, soon after, amphibian vertebrates were found ashore.

This interprets the late Silurian as the earliest stage at which plants could emerge above the surface without danger of lethal "sunburn." Therefore we identify the period 420 million years ago with an oxygenic level of $O_2 \sim 0.1$ PAL.

The explosion of evolution ashore increases photosynthesis in a step function by some 20 to 25%, again tilting the oxygen balance radically toward the plus side.

In examining the oxygen balance in the light of all factors studied to date, the relation between production rate and final equilibrium may be represented crudely by Figure 6.14. Much more refinement of this balance is, of course, necessary in future studies.

Following the late Silurian, high rates of photosynthesis are induced without corresponding quantities of organic materials immediately available ashore for decay and replenishment of CO_2. This suggests that oxygen may have "overswung" the present level to a somewhat higher value as the lush life of the Carboniferous developed. Then, with reduction of CO_2, the earth would cool, due to loss of the "greenhouse" effect of CO_2, leading to the ice ages of the Permian period. As the earth cooled, photosynthesis would sharply fall, leading to a major loss of oxygen. Thus the phase difference of production of O_2 and of CO_2 suggests that the levels of these two atmospheric components in the post-Silurian atmosphere must have been unstable, the instability being damped by the ever-improving adaptation of organisms to wider environmental ecologies. Pending more analytical study, a preliminary estimate seems justified of the order of 10^8 years

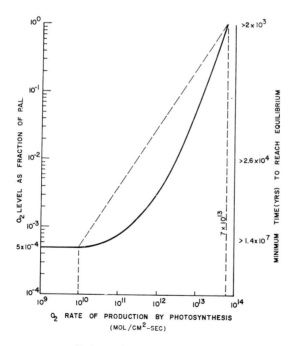

Figure 6.14 Estimated atmospheric levels of oxygen as a function of production rates.

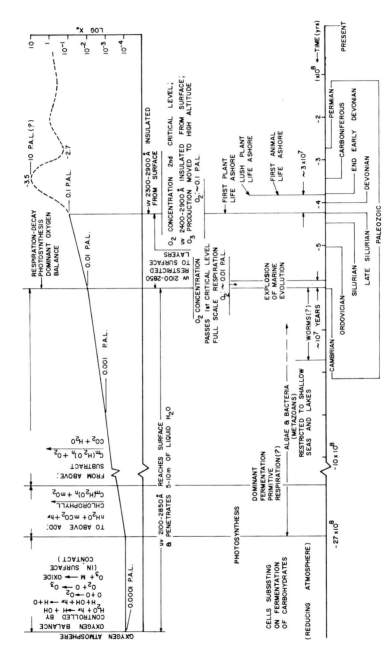

Figure 6.15 Tentative model of growth of oxygen in atmosphere. (x_0 is the penetration of atmosphere and liquid water.)

for a complete oscillation above and below the present quasi-permanent level.

A model may therefore be devised from the studies to date of oxygenic levels over geologic history, as shown in Figure 6.15.

In conclusion, a comment on the atmosphere of Mars seems in order. Because of the low gravitational field, coupled with its smaller diameter and mass, Mars has probably lost all H_2 and helium, and should be losing atomic oxygen at a rate determined by its temperature and rates of production and of diffusion or convection. In the absence of oceans, the atmosphere of Mars would otherwise appear to be somewhat similar to the primitive atmosphere of the earth, well prior to the Cambrian. Life on Mars therefore may be subject to the same restrictive ecology found for the primitive atmosphere of the earth. It seems probable, for the primitive earth, that somewhat different forms of life, arising from different initial precursors in separate and highly insulated pools, might be expected. Quite clearly, the direct study of Mars and its atmosphere should open exciting new and powerful vistas to science.

The study of paleoatmospheres involves a tremendous range of correlative information, and this précis can only present the briefest account of much more extensive analysis. The generation of a model for the earth opens vistas to a wide range of studies relating to quantitative paleoclimatology. A wide range of circulatory and convective patterns is suggested as the level of ozone production rises with increasing oxygen at different eras, and of paleoionospheres resulting from a wide difference in aeronomy. The purpose of this paper is to encourage more critical studies and discussions of the subject, and to approach the much greater refinements that are immediately apparent.

REFERENCES

Alfvén, H., 1954. *On the Origin of the Solar System,* Oxford Clarendon Press.

Allen, C. W., 1963. *Astrophysical Quantities,* second edition, University of London, The Athlone Press.

Anfinsen, C. B., 1961. *The Molecular Basis of Evolution,* John Wiley and Sons, New York.

Bernal, J. D., 1949. The physical basis of life, *Proc. Phys. Soc. (London)* **62A,** 537.

Brown, H., 1952. Rare gases and the formation of the earth's atmosphere, p. 258 in G. P. Kuiper, editor, *The Atmospheres of the Earth and Planets,* University of Chicago Press.

————————— 1949. A table of relative abundances of nuclear species, *Rev. Mod. Phys.,* **21,** No. 4, 625.

Bullard, F. M., 1962. *Volcanoes, in History, in Theory, in Eruption*, University of Texas Press.

Calvin, M., 1959. Evolution of enzymes and the photosynthetic apparatus, report in *The Origin of Life on the Earth*, Symposium of International Union of Biochemistry (Moscow, 1957), The Macmillan Company, New York, **1**, 207.

——————— and J. A. Bassham, 1962. *The Photosynthesis of Carbon Compounds*, W. A. Benjamin, Inc., New York.

Caspersson, T. O., 1950. *Cell Growth and Cell Function: A Cyto-Chemical Study*, W. W. Norton and Company, New York.

Davidson, J. N., 1960. *The Biochemistry of the Nucleic Acids*, fourth edition, John Wiley and Sons, New York.

Dawson, L. H. and E. O. Hulburt, 1934. The absorption of ultraviolet and visible light by water, *Jour. Opt. Soc. Am.*, **24**, 175.

Detwiler, C. R., D. L. Garrett, J. D. Purcell, and R. Tousey, 1961. The intensity distribution in the ultraviolet solar spectrum, *Ann. Geophys.*, **17**, 263.

Fesenkov, V. G., 1959. Some considerations about the primeval state of the earth, in *The Origin of Life on the Earth*, Symposium of International Union of Biochemistry (Moscow, 1957), The Macmillan Company, New York, **1**, 9.

Florkin, M., 1959. Selected references from *The Origin of Life on the Earth*, Symposium of International Union of Biochemistry (Moscow, 1957), The Macmillan Company, New York, **1**, 503, 578.

Genevois, L. (Bordeaux), 1927. On the respiration and fermentation in green plants, *Beochemisches Zeitschrift*, **186**, 461.

Goldschmidt, V. M., 1937. Geochemische verteilungsgesetze der elemente. IX. Die Mengen verhaltnisse der Elemente und der Atom-Arten, *Norske Videnskaps-akad. Oslo, Skr., Mat.-Nat. Kl.*, **4**, 148.

Hall, L. A., K. R. Damon, and H. E. Hinteregger, 1962. Solar extreme ultraviolet photon flux measurements in the upper atmosphere of August, 1961, paper presented at Third International Space Science Symposium, COSPAR, Washington, D. C.

Herzberg, G., 1961. *Molecular Spectra and Molecular Structure: I. Spectra of Diatomic Molecules*, D. Van Nostrand Company, New York.

Hoering, T. C. and P. H. Abelson, 1961. Carbon isotope fractionation in formation of amino acids by photosynthetic organisms, *Proc. Natl. Acad. Sci. U.S.*, **47**, 623.

Holland, H. D., 1962. Model for the evolution of the earth's atmosphere, in A. E. J. Engel, H. L. James, and B. F. Leonard, editors, *Petrologic Studies: A Volume to Honor A. F. Buddington*, Princeton University, Princeton, New Jersey.

Johnson, F. S., 1954. The solar constant, *Jour. Meteorol.*, **11**, 431.

Kuiper, G. P., 1951. On the origin of the solar system, *Proc. Natl. Acad. Sci.*, **37**, 1.

Kummel, B., 1961. *History of the Earth*, W. H. Freeman and Co., New York.

Lepp, H. and S. S. Goldich, 1959. Chemistry and origin of iron formations, *Bull. Geol. Soc. Am.*, **70**, 1637.

Miller, S. L., 1959. Formation of organic compounds on the primitive earth, in *The Origin of Life on the Earth*, Symposium of International Union of Biochemistry (Moscow, 1957), The Macmillan Company, New York, **1**, 123.

Nawrocki, P. J. and R. Papa, 1961. Atmospheric processes, *Geophysics Corporation of America*, Bedford, Massachusetts, A.F.C.R.L. Report, Contract #AF 19(604)7405.

Nicolet, M. and D. R. Bates, 1950. The photochemistry of atmospheric water vapor, *Jour. Geophys. Research*, **55**, No. 3, 301.

———————— and P. Mange, 1954. The dissociation of oxygen in the high atmosphere, *Jour. Geophys. Research*, **59**, No. 1, 15.

Oparin, A. I., 1953. *Origin of Life,* Dover Publications, New York, S213.

Pauling, L., 1926–1930. *International Critical Tables of Numerical Data, Physics, Chemistry and Technology,* prepared under the auspices of the International Research Council of the National Academy of Sciences, by National Research Council of the United States of America, McGraw-Hill Book Company, New York.

———————— 1960. *The Nature of the Chemical Bond and the Structure of Molecules and Crystals: An Introduction to Modern Structural Chemistry,* Cornell University Press, Ithaca, New York.

Pearse, R. W. B. and A. G. Gaydon, 1963. *The Identification of Molecular Spectra,* third edition, John Wiley and Sons, New York.

Rabinowitch, E. I., 1951. *Photosynthesis and Related Processes,* Interscience Publishers, New York.

Ramdohr, P., 1958. Die uran-und Goldlagerstatten Witwatersrand, Blind River District, *Abhandl. deut. Akad. Wiss. Berlin Kl. Chem., Geologie und Biologie,* No. 3, 35 pp., 19 pl.

Raukama, K., 1955. Geologic evidence of chemical composition of the pre-Cambrian atmosphere, *Geol. Soc. Am., Special Paper,* **62**, 651.

Rubey, W. W., 1951. Geologic history of sea water: an attempt to state the problem, *Bull. Geol. Soc. Am.,* **62** (2), 111.

———————— 1955. Development of the hydrosphere and atmosphere with special reference to probable composition of the early atmosphere. *Geol. Soc. Am., Special Paper,* **62**, 631.

Rutten, M. G., 1962. *The Geological Aspects of Origin of Life on Earth.* Elsevier Publishing Co., Amsterdam, New York.

Sapper, K., 1927. *Vulkankunde,* Stuttgart, Engelhorns.

Spencer-Jones, Sir H., 1950. The evolution of the earth's atmosphere, *Science Progress,* **38**, 417.

Taxieff, H. and R. Fabre, 1960. Composition of volcanic gases of the permanent lava lake of Nyiragongo (Belgian Congo), *Academie des Sciences Comptes Rendus,* **250**, 2482.

Urey, H. C., 1952. *The Planets: Their Origin and Development,* Yale University Press, New Haven.

———————— 1959. Primitive planetary atmospheres and the origin of life, in *The Origin of Life on the Earth,* Symposium of International Union of Biochemistry (Moscow, 1957), The Macmillan Company, New York, **1**, 16.

Verhoogen, J., 1946. Volcanic heat, *Amer. Jour. Sci.,* **244**, No. 11, 745.

Vinogradov, A. P., 1959. The origin of the biosphere, in *The Origin of Life on the Earth,* Symposium of International Union of Biochemistry (Moscow, 1957), The Macmillan Company, New York, **1**, 23.

Wald, G., 1955. The origin of life, p. 3, Chapter I, Part I in *The Physics and Chemistry of Life,* Simon and Schuster, New York.

Watanabe, K., 1958. Ultraviolet absorption processes in the upper atmosphere, in H. E. Landsberg, and J. Van Mieghem, editors, *Advances in Geophysics*, **5**, 153.

———————————, M. Zelikoff, and E. C. Y. Inn, 1953. Absorption coefficients of several atmospheric gases, *Geophysical Research Papers*, No. 21, A.F.C.R.C. Technical Report #52-23, *Geophysics Research Directorate*, Cambridge, Mass.

Wilson, J. T., 1954. The development and structure of the crust, rates of erosion, deposition and volcanism, p. 150 in G. P. Kuiper, editor, *The Solar System*, Vol. II of *The Earth as a Planet*, p. 150, University of Chicago Press.

——————— 1959a. Geophysics and continental growth, *Am. Scientist*, **47**, 1.

———————————, J. A. Jacobs, and R. D. Russell, 1959b. *Physics and Geology*, McGraw-Hill Book Company, New York.

Wilson, R. W., 1963. A discussion of the disk component of the galactic radio radiation, *The Astrophysical Jour.*, **137**, No. 4, 1038.

DISCUSSION

Dr. Sagan: With regard to your remark about the cold trap in the primitive atmosphere, you have assumed that there are no intermediate oxidation-state molecules.   One would expect to find such molecules as acetone and acetaldehyde in such an atmosphere.

Dr. Berkner: The difficulty is, however, that these are molecules that would be relatively low in the atmosphere and would not reach the mesosphere, because there would be very little convection as a result of the cold trap.

Dr. Sagan: Certainly in an atmosphere of methane, ammonia, water, and hydrogen, if there ever were such a thing, the molecules I mentioned would be photochemically produced at high altitudes.

Dr. Berkner: True, but these are strong absorbers.   There would be enough energy in the 2200 to 3000 Å range to simply dissociate them. This is equally true for ozone, but the life of O_3 is long compared to its rate of formation from O_2 and O.

Dr. Abelson: It is now pretty well established that there could be no metazoa without the presence of free oxygen—I would guess that about 1% of the present oxygen content would be required—and in view of the many enzyme systems of metazoa and the many building blocks that had to be made, there must have been a period in which there was free oxygen before the existence of metazoa.   I would rather interpret what happened at the beginning of the Cambrian as the completion of the last crucial building blocks necessary for the development of metazoa.

Dr. Berkner: This, then, would set the timing back some tens of millions of years. I wouldn't dispute this at this time, but I think there is something else worth considering. I don't think we've paid enough attention to the so-called prestored characteristics. If we take nearly any DNA, we find that about three-quarters of it plays no role whatsoever in reproduction. In fact, if we look at the mathematics of evolution, we notice that even lethal recessive genes may be retained in the population for many, many generations. Metazoa may very well have been acquiring prestored characteristics well before the oxygen level came to the point where they could adapt themselves to a new environmental niche, and once the niche opens, a wide variety of prestored characteristics could adapt themselves and immediately move in. So perhaps this would reduce the time scale a bit.

Voice: As I understand it, the production of oxygen by photosynthesis means that a plant will produce O_2 by pulling carbon into its cell structure and hydrolizing it. When the plant decays, the net effect will be a corresponding burial of organic carbon. Thus in the geologic record we should see a general correlation between the amount of oxygen used in the geologic period and the amount of organic carbon incorporated in the sediments. However, the Carboniferous, when a great amount of carbon was buried, is a period not characterized by excessive oxidation throughout the world sediments; also, the Triassic is characterized by the red beds and oxidation of iron everywhere, and minimal amounts of carbon.

Dr. Berkner: The Triassic is fairly late; the oxygen level would be high anyway. By the time of the Triassic, we may be well into a slowly oscillating system with a period of perhaps a hundred million years. But the oxygen levels at that time are getting fairly close to the levels we have at the present time. As far as the red beds, remember that even if the oxygen level is as low as 10^{-3} (present levels), there are two aspects to this problem. One is that all you have to do is stretch the time 10^3 years to get the same amount of oxidation from O_2. Second, the oxygen balance at low oxygenic levels is such that there is plenty of O_3 present. Then the rate of oxidation will be very much faster. In other words, what little oxygen is present in the atmosphere is disappearing rapidly through very effective oxidation.

Dr. Sagan: There is much that is attractive about the view of a reducing atmosphere in early times, with substantial penetration of ultraviolet light to produce organic reactions. In particular, we have recently succeeded in synthesizing nucleocide phosphates from other molecules which in turn are produced from other molecules which are produced from methane, ammonia, water, and hydrogen. The significance of this is that nucleocide phosphates are themselves building blocks of DNA. So it seems as if it is possible, by taking dilute solutions of simple organic molecules which we know must have been produced in such an atmosphere, to make the very molecules which are most critically implicated in biological reproduction. So even if the time scale for a reducing atmosphere is as short as Holland has suggested—only a few hundreds of millions of years—it looks as if that might be enough time to make enormous quantities of just the molecules that we need. By implication, if it is that easy to do in the laboratory, it was that easy to do in early times on the earth, and it must also have been easy to do on lots of other planets.

Dr. Berkner: Of course, you get many combinations of amino acids involved. We must bring in natural selection to decide which ones are going to perpetuate themselves.

7

The Escape of Helium from
the Earth's Atmosphere

Gordon J. F. MacDonald

ABSTRACT

The rate of influx of He^4 from the earth's crust into the atmosphere is about 2×10^6 atoms/cm^2-sec. The average rate of thermal escape averaged over the last solar cycle is 6×10^4 atoms/cm^2-sec. The present abundance of helium in the atmosphere would accumulate in about two million years. Either some nonthermal mechanism permits at present a greater rate of escape of helium, or the rate of escape has varied in time. The present paper is concerned with an examination of possible changes in the escape rate caused by variations in the earth's magnetic field.

Problems associated with the heat balance in the upper atmosphere are reviewed. Statistical analysis of drag on satellites and solar decimeter flux establishes that the 27-day variation in atmospheric density results from fluctuations in the intensity of the solar wind. It is considered likely that a heat source over and beyond that provided by ultraviolet radiation is required to account for both the day-night variations in upper atmosphere densities and the 27-day variation. Various mechanisms by which energy density in the solar wind can be transferred into the upper atmosphere are considered. It is suggested that if the additional heat source is indeed due to the solar plasma, then historical fluctuations in the earth's magnetic field could result in a greater escape rate for helium. The establishment and identification of the additional heat source is necessary for a full understanding of the escape of helium.

The terrestrial economy of He^3 is reviewed. The contribution by solar cosmic rays to the abundance of He^3 remains a major problem.

Reprinted by permission from Reviews of Geophysics, **1,** 305 (1963).

The rate of influx of He³, about 10 atoms/cm²-sec, is greater than the escape rate averaged over the last solar cycle—about 4 atoms/cm²-sec, if solar cosmic rays contain about 10% He³.

INTRODUCTION

Bates and McDowell (1957, 1959) first suggested that helium (He⁴) in the atmosphere is not in equilibrium, but instead the current rate of influx exceeds the escape flux.   Better estimates of the generation rate have been obtained in recent years and detailed investigations of the upper atmosphere provide improved limits on the rate of thermal escape.   These new data clearly show that at present the rate at which He⁴ is supplied to the atmosphere greatly exceeds the rate of thermal escape.   Bates and McDowell (1957) tentatively suggested that at some time in the past the escape rate was greater and pointed to the possibility of changes in the solar flux.   Bates and Patterson (1962) made an alternative suggestion that helium is now in equilibrium, but that the escape is nonthermal involving the dissociative recombination of HeO⁺.

Nicolet (1957) demonstrated that thermal escape could not account for the observed abundances of the two isotopes of helium, He⁴, and He³.   If the temperature were high enough to account for the loss of He⁴, then He³ would be removed at a rate far in excess of its production.   If He³ escapes thermally and is in equilibrium, then He⁴ remains trapped.   The implication of Nicolet's (1957) study is that either steady equilibrium does not hold, or else there is some nonthermal process removing helium from the atmosphere.

The escape of helium is a complex problem and, despite advances, there are many more problems than there are answers.   The complexity requires a review of many aspects of geophysics.   The escape problem forms a framework in which a number of fascinating aeronomical problems can be examined.

The rate of thermal escape of helium is a delicate function of the temperature at the escape level.   This level, defined as the height at which the mean free path of helium becomes large compared with its scale height, is at 500 to 600 km.   Small changes in the input of energy to the tenuous gas at high altitudes will make a large difference in the effective temperature.   It is known that the ultraviolet flux, which largely determines the temperatures at these heights, does undergo changes with the solar cycle and there may be longer period fluctuations.

It is also known that the earth's magnetic field undergoes a variety of fluctuations.   Indeed, of all internal fields, it is the most changeable.

The nondipole part of the field undergoes long-period changes with an average value of 5×10^{-4} gauss/year and a maximum rate of change of 1.5×10^{-3} gauss/year. The dipole field has changed over the past century at an average rate of 3.5×10^{-5} gauss/year, which implies that if the field changed linearly with time, then ten thousand years ago the field was twice its current value. Indeed, studies of remnant magnetism in Roman ceramic objects suggest that only two thousand years ago, the field had twice the present intensity (see, e.g., Hide and Roberts, 1961). These relatively rapid changes, combined with the controversial paleomagnetic evidence of a changing field on a geologic time scale, raise the problem of the effect of the magnetic field on the long-term stability of the upper atmosphere.

The long-term stability of a planetary atmosphere will certainly be influenced by variations in solar ultraviolet flux. The magnetic field may also influence the composition of the atmosphere at high altitudes. The effects of the changing solar flux can be treated in a relatively straightforward fashion. The influence of the magnetic field is complex and requires detailed examination. It is clear that on the earth an escaping neutral atom passes through the upper atmosphere much too fast for it to be ionized and trapped by the field. On the other hand, the magnetic field shields the upper atmosphere from the low-energy solar plasma and prevents this potential heat source from reaching it. The magnetic field also interacts with the solar plasma and this interaction gives rise to hydromagnetic and electromagnetic waves which may in part determine the thermal conditions near the escape layer. In addition, the interaction may produce energetic electrons which enter the magnetosphere and deposit their energy in high-latitude regions. The shielding by the field also influences the accretion rate; this rate is important in considering the economy of He^3 and tritium.

The atmospheres of Venus and of the earth present two contrasting examples of development. At present, it is widely believed that the earth's atmosphere has evolved gradually through geologic time (Rubey, 1951, 1955; Holland, 1962). The continued exhalation of the gases from the earth's interior results from gradual heating up of portions of the earth's interior. The rate of exhalation is controlled primarily by the internal thermal processes, which are as yet poorly understood. The internal structure of Venus is similar to that of the earth (MacDonald, 1962). The two planets have approximately the same linear dimensions and approximately the same mass. The bulk chemical composition of the two planets thus cannot differ to any great extent. It is also likely that the radioactive composition is similar.

Thus it is probable that Venus and the earth have had similar, though not necessarily identical, thermal histories. If this is so, there is no reason to expect that the gases, and particularly the rate at which the gases have been supplied to the outer surface of Venus, should differ from those which are found on the earth. The fact that the atmospheres apparently differ presents a number of fascinating problems.

One marked difference between Earth and Venus is that the magnetic field of Venus is weak compared to that of the earth and may well be nonexistent (Smith et al., 1963). Is this first-order striking difference between the two planets of possible importance in the divergent development of the planetary atmospheres?

The rapid advances in the understanding of the upper atmospheres make profitable a review of the current state of the theory of the escape of the atmosphere. Particular attention is given to the possibility of changes of escape rates in the past. Later in this chapter (p. 132ff.) we review the constitution of the upper atmosphere. A detailed study of atmospheric models is essential to the escape problem, since only through the model is an estimate of the temperature possible. Data on the drag of satellites provide reliable estimates of atmospheric density from 200 km up to at least 1000 km. These densities can then be used as controls on calculated models of the atmosphere. Construction of a model atmosphere would be impossible without detailed knowledge of the nature of the solar flux, since it is this flux that provides a major heat source. Rocket measurements of the extreme ultraviolet taken during the past five years have greatly clarified the position. The compositional models of the atmosphere must remain most uncertain because of the lack of knowledge of the most critical region within the atmosphere, 100 to 200 km. The convective equilibrium changes into a diffusive equilibrium with large temperature gradients. This region has only been perfunctorily explored by rockets. Conditions assumed here fix in a large part the density, composition, and temperature of the atmosphere at greater altitudes. Despite the uncertainties, it appears from model studies that ultraviolet radiation alone cannot account for the observed temporal variations in the density of the high atmosphere. Further evidence for a heat source in addition to solar radiation is found in the detailed comparison of the variation of solar radio flux and drag.

We shall review new data (p. 159ff.) on the flux of the critical constituents into the atmosphere. It appears probable that particles emitted by solar flares add substantial fractions of He^3 and tritium to the atmosphere. New studies on the chemical composition of natural gases permit a better estimate of the rate at which important constituents enter the atmosphere through its lower boundary.

The current state of the theory of escape from a planetary atmosphere is discussed on pp. 164–171. Considerable advances have been made since the early work of Jeans. Furthermore, it is clear that an important factor in determining the long-term stability of minor constituents is the rate at which a minor component diffuses through the major components. The diffusion rate is complicated by the phenomenon of thermal diffusion. A comparison of the present escape of He^4 with production rates confirms Bates and McDowell's (1959) and Nicolet's (1961c) conclusions regarding the helium balance in the atmosphere.

The effects of the magnetic field are considered later (p. 171ff.). A strong field hinders the accretion and can influence the thermal balance. The additional heat source just referred to may be due to hydromagnetic and electromagnetic radiation resulting from the interaction of the solar wind with the magnetic field. If this is so, then an increase of the field in the past would have resulted in a greater interaction cross section of the earth for the solar wind and a higher upper atmosphere temperature. Alternatively, if no heat source over that provided by the ultraviolet radiation is required, then a weakening of the field could have provided a higher temperature in the past. A weak field would allow the penetration of the plasma and the deposition of thermal energy in the upper atmosphere. If the heating of the upper atmosphere is due entirely to ultraviolet radiation, then the disappearance of the field would result in a greater rate of helium escape. Alternatively, if an additional heat source involving the interaction of the field with the plasma is important, then a strengthening of the field yields a higher escape rate. It is argued that the strengthening of the field is more likely and that over at least 10% of geologic time the field was at least twice its present strength. The many problems associated with helium balance are summarized at the end of this chapter.

Because of the complexity of the subject, a guide to the organization of the review may be helpful. The helium problem is considered explicitly on p. 159ff. and p. 169ff. The first part of this chapter is in the nature of a more general review of atmospheric constitution and can be omitted by the reader interested primarily in helium escape. A more speculative treatment is provided (pp. 171–175) of both heat sources in the upper atmosphere and of possible changes in these heat sources during geologic time. Summaries of the longer sections (pp. 132–164) are provided.

MODELS OF THE UPPER ATMOSPHERE

Data Obtained from Satellite Drag Studies

As a satellite passes through the upper atmosphere, it interacts with the neutral gas. In colliding with the neutral particles, the satellite transfers a portion of its momentum. The rate of transfer of momentum is greatest where the density of neutrals is high. Since the density in the atmosphere is approximately exponential, most of the momentum transfer takes place when the satellite dips farthest into the atmosphere. Observation of the secular change in the orbital elements permits a determination of atmospheric density in the region near perigee. A large number of studies have been carried out relating the atmospheric properties to changes in the orbits of satellites; these have been reviewed, for example, by Harris and Priester (1962a), Nicolet (1961a), Paetzold (1961), and King-Hele and Walker (1961).

The determination of the absolute value of density at a given height is complicated by the dependence of the drag parameter on the mass of a satellite, the effective cross section, and the satellite's drag coefficient. All of these parameters vary from satellite to satellite so that the absolute values of density derived from satellite observation remain in doubt. For high altitudes above 1000 to 1500 km, there is a further possible complication that interaction with ionized gas and the magnetic field may contribute to the drag. The separation of the electromagnetic contribution from the drag of the neutral molecules is difficult. A first attempt at confirming the density obtained from drag observations by direct measurement was carried out by Sharp, Hanson, and McKibbin (1962) at 500 to 600 km. They used a ribbon microphone and converted the observed ram pressure to densities. The values obtained agree well with those derived from orbits of satellites.

While there is still some uncertainty regarding the absolute densities at high altitudes, their time variation is now well established. The spectrum of variations, while complicated, includes a strong line at 24 hours corresponding to a diurnal density variation. Priester, Martin, and Kramp (1960) showed that at 200 km the variation represented a few per cent of the mean drag. At 650 km the variation reaches almost a factor of 10 (Jacchia, 1960); Priester and Martin, 1960; King-Hele and Walker, 1960). Sharp, Hanson, and McKibbin (1962) obtained a day-night variation of approximately a factor of 4 at 550 km.

High-frequency variations in the solar atmosphere are apparent by the behavior of satellites during solar events. The most dramatic of these was the series of flares of November, 1960, in which there were rapid changes in the density of the upper atmosphere (Jacchia, 1961; Groves, 1961; Bryant, 1961).

The analysis of drag of various satellites also shows a peak in the spectrum centered around 27 days and correlated with the variation in radio emission from the sun in the wavelength range of 3 to 30 cm (Jacchia, 1958, 1959, 1960; Priester, 1958, 1961). The striking correlation between the radio flux and the variation in drag is illustrated in Figures 7.1–7.4. Zadunaisky, Shapiro, and Jones (1961) carried out a detailed analysis of the orbit of Echo I. The power spectrum of the Echo drag is shown in Figure 7.1 for the period August 13, 1960 to January 11, 1961. There is a definite peak at 0.037 cycles per day (27-day period), though the spectrum climbs rapidly at the low frequencies. The very low-frequency variations have purposely not been filtered out as filtering would exaggerate the 27-day peak. In addition, there is a peak at 0.12 cycles per day corresponding to a period of about 8 days. The power spectrum for the time variations of the

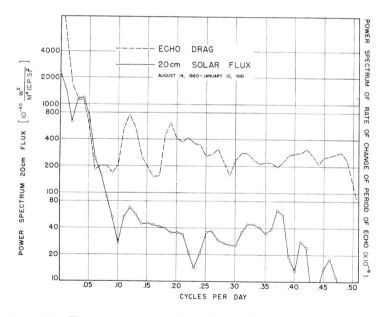

Figure 7.1   The power spectrum of the drag on Echo I and of the 20-cm solar flux. Power spectra covers the interval August 14, 1960 to January 1961. Both spectra climb at low frequencies, but the low frequency components have purposely not been filtered out so as not to exaggerate the 27-day peak.

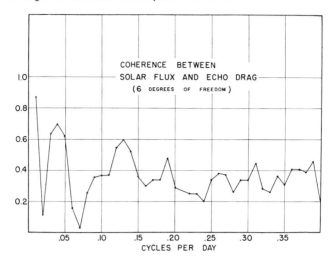

Figure 7.2   The coherence between the 20-cm solar flux and drag on Echo I.

20-cm solar flux is also shown in Figure 7.1.   Both the 27-day and the 8-day peaks appear in the spectrum.   Figure 7.2 shows the coherence between the 20-cm flux and the drag.   The coherence is 0.7 at the 27-day peak and 0.6 for the 8-day peak.

Explorer IX was a 12-foot balloon satellite launched specifically to investigate the values of atmospheric drag.   The orbital elements for the interval February 17 to October 2, 1961, have been analyzed in detail by Jacchia and Slowey (1962).   The perigee height varied between 640 and 753 km over the 7.5-month interval studied by Jacchia and Slowey.   The power spectrum of the drag after removal of radiation pressure effects is shown in Figure 7.3.   The drag on Explorer IX is highly correlated ($R^2 = 0.87$) with the variation of the 10.7-cm radio flux (see Figs. 7.3 and 7.4) at the 27-day period.   There is some evidence for the 8-day period noted in the Echo I spectra, but the peak is much weaker.

While the solar decimeter flux is well correlated with changes in drag, the solar decimeter radiation cannot be the physical cause of the fluctuations, but is merely associated with the cause.   The decimeter radiation is generally attributed to thermal emission from condensations in the solar corona.   The variations in atmospheric density are thought to be primarily the result of variations in the extreme ultraviolet radiation.   The ultraviolet radiation may arise from the coronal

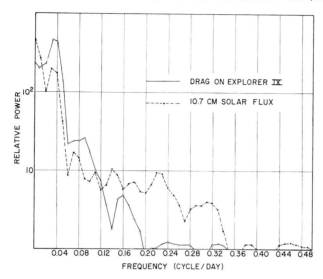

Figure 7.3 The power spectrum of the drag on Explorer IX and the 10.7-cm solar flux.

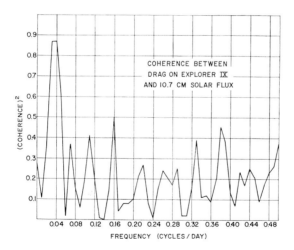

Figure 7.4 Coherence between drag on Explorer IX and 10.7-cm solar flux. The only significant coherence is at the frequency corresponding to the 27-day period.

condensations, since emission is probably due to cascades following recombination on excited levels (Harris and Priester, 1962*a*).

If the changes in drag are due to ultraviolet radiation from coronal condensations, then the time interval between an event on the sun and a variation in drag should equal the light transit time plus the response time of the atmosphere. We will later show that the response time is at most on the order of a few hours because of the short thermal time constant of the atmosphere. Thus the variation of drag should lag behind the fluctuation in decimeter flux by about two hours if the heating is due to ultraviolet radiation.

A direct determination of the phase relations would require the identification of a solar event and the measurement of the change in drag. The evaluation of drag requires determination of the change in orbital elements, and an accurate determination requires a day's observation. An alternate scheme for determining the time delay is to obtain a statistical estimate of the phase relations by measuring the cross spectra between the drag and radio flux (see, e.g., Munk and MacDonald, 1960, for a discussion of cross-spectral analysis). The phase angle at a given frequency then fixes the average time interval between the arrival of the decimeter radiation and the change in drag.

Measurements of the cross spectra show that at the 27-day period the drag on Echo I lags behind the 20-cm flux by 32 degrees, and the drag on Explorer IX lags by 31 degrees. Thus at the 27-day period there is a 56-hour delay between the emission of the solar radio flux and the response of the atmosphere.

The statistics in neither case are particularly good though they are much better for Explorer IX. Goodman (1957) shows that there is a probability p that the true phase will lie within the limits $\theta - \Delta\theta$ and $\theta + \Delta\theta$, where

$$\sin^2 \Delta\theta = \frac{1 - R^2}{R^2} [(1 - p)^{-2/\nu} - 1]$$

and where R is the coherence and ν the number of degrees of freedom. For Explorer IX, there are 8 degrees of freedom so that there is one chance in five that the true phase lies outside the interval of 20 to 40 degrees, and there is less than one chance in a hundred that the true phase is zero, provided the errors are normally distributed.

If no allowance is made for the response time of the atmosphere, the 56-hour delay corresponds to a straight line velocity from the sun of 750 km/sec. Observations of the solar wind made on Mariner II (Neugebauer and Snyder, 1962) show a quiet-time average velocity during the interval August 29, 1962 to October 31, 1962, of 560 to 690 km/sec.

The phase lag determinations thus establish that the 27-day fluctuations in atmospheric drag are associated with the plasma issuing from the sun. The long delay time rules out both ultraviolet radiation and high-energy particles traveling directly from the sun as the principal causes of the 27-day variation. The relative weakness of the statistical data is strengthened by the agreement between the two satellites. The identification of the 27-day fluctuation in drag as primarily due to interaction of the upper atmosphere with the solar wind is important in later considerations of heat sources in the upper atmosphere.

A similar analysis comparing drag on Echo and Explorer IX with the variation of geomagnetic K and A numbers shows that there is a much weaker correlation with geomagnetic activity.

The spectrum of drag variations show power both at lower and higher periods than the 27-day variation. No single satellite has been up long enough to determine in detail long-period variations of the solar atmosphere; it is clear that the 11-year solar cycle does show up in the observations of satellites (Harris and Priester, 1962b; King-Hele and Rees, 1962). Again, the density in the upper atmosphere is correlated with the long-period changes in radio flux.

Construction of Numerical Models

Satellite orbits provide abundant information regarding the density and its variations in the high atmosphere. However, there is as yet very little information regarding the chemical composition. Unless the chemical composition is assumed, the density values cannot be converted into temperature, and it is temperature that is of interest in considering problems of atmospheric escape.

The usual procedure is to compute a model of the atmosphere based on diffusive equilibrium above a certain level. The model can then be tested by comparing its predicted density with the densities derived from satellite determinations. There are many difficulties hampering such a procedure. The nature and distribution of the heat sources are not well determined. It is not clear where the region of convective equilibrium ends and diffusive equilibrium begins. As yet, satellite investigations have not probed in detail the region between 100 and 200 km; yet it is in this altitude range that the atmospheric parameters undergo the greatest change. As a result, extrapolation must be made through this region. Many of the parameters needed to describe the processes are based on incomplete laboratory data or on uncertain theoretical predictions. Despite these many difficulties, model atmospheres have been constructed that agree well with the densities and the variations in densities derived from satellite observations.

Before reviewing possible models for the upper atmosphere, we first consider methods by which models are constructed. While the physical principles that govern the distribution of the constituents in a planetary atmosphere are well known, it is essential to have in view the numerous parameters that go into establishing the vertical distribution of density, temperature, and composition.

It is usual to assume that the distribution of atmospheric pressure with height (z) is according to the hydrostatic law,

$$\frac{dp}{dz} = -\rho g \tag{1}$$

where p is the total pressure, g is the acceleration of gravity, and ρ is the density. Both pressure and density will be functions of time as well as of altitude; g varies with height. Equation (1) describes a static equilibrium.

The density is a function of the number density or concentrations of the constituents, n_i, and the molecular masses, m_i:

$$\rho = \sum_i m_i n_i \tag{2}$$

It is assumed that the atmosphere behaves like a perfect gas with an equation of state of

$$p = nkT \tag{3}$$

where k is Boltzmann's constant (1.38×10^{-16} ergs/deg), T is the absolute temperature, and n is the total concentration

$$n = \sum_i n_i \tag{4}$$

where the summation is over all constituents. From equation (3) we see that the vertical variation of pressure depends on the local values of pressure, concentration, and temperature, and on the gradients of concentration and temperature:

$$\frac{1}{p}\frac{dp}{dz} = \frac{1}{n}\frac{dn}{dz} + \frac{1}{T}\frac{dT}{dz}. \tag{5}$$

Combining equations (5) and (1) we see that the concentration gradient depends on the local values of temperature, concentration, and the gradient of temperature:

$$\frac{dn}{dz} = -\frac{\Sigma n_i m_i g}{kT} - \frac{n}{T}\frac{dT}{dz}. \tag{6}$$

On combining equations (6) and (4), the general law governing the distribution of a given constituent with height in a static atmosphere is obtained:

$$\frac{1}{n_i}\frac{dn_i}{dz} = -\frac{m_i g}{kT} - \frac{1}{T}\frac{dT}{dz}. \tag{7}$$

Integration of equation (7) yields

$$n_i(z, t) = \frac{n_i(z_0, t)\,T(z_0, t)}{T(z, t)}\exp\left[-\int_{z_0}^{z}\frac{m_i g(z)}{kT(z, t)}\,dz\right], \tag{8}$$

where z_0 is some reference height usually taken as the height at which diffusive equilibrium begins.

The variation of the gravitational acceleration with height is given by

$$g(z) = g_0(z_0)\left(\frac{R_0}{R_0 + z}\right)^2 \tag{9}$$

where g_0 is the value of the gravitational acceleration at a reference height z_0, which is at a distance R_0 from the center of the earth.

The concentration of a given constituent depends on the local temperature $T(z, t)$ and on an integral involving the temperature distribution between z_0 and z. The distribution of temperature thus enters critically in the variation in concentration of a given constituent. The concentration $n_i(z, t)$ also depends on the concentration of the constituent at z_0, as well as on the temperature at this reference height. The reference height is usually taken to be equal to the height at which diffusive separation commences and below which convective mixing prevails. A problem of importance is the determination of this level and a description of the gradation between convection and diffusion. In general, the concentration and temperature at the reference level will vary with time.

In a time-varying atmosphere, heat can be transported both by conduction and convection. The vertical transport of heat due to the mass motion resulting from changes of density adds a complication, and we shall wish to evaluate the contribution of convection to the total thermal transport. In considering the thermal balance, we shall neglect the heat flow caused by the concentration gradients (Dufour effect) as we also neglected the flow of matter caused by a temperature gradient in deriving equation (8). We shall return to the effects of thermal diffusion when considering the motion of a minor constituent, such as helium and hydrogen, through the atmosphere.

The equation for the concentration of entropy s is

$$\frac{ds}{dt} = \frac{q}{T} \tag{10}$$

where q is the net accession of heat (ergs/g-sec) (Eckart, 1960). We wish to transform equation (10) into an equation for temperature. From thermodynamics, the vertical gradient of temperature is related to the equilibrium density and entropy gradients by

$$\left| \frac{1}{T} \frac{dT}{dz} \right|_{eq} = (\gamma - 1) \left(\left| \frac{1}{\rho} \frac{d\rho}{dz} \right|_{eq} + \left| \frac{1}{nk} \frac{ds}{dz} \right|_{eq} \right), \tag{11}$$

where γ is the ratio of the specific heats. The ideal gas law has been used in obtaining equation (11). The equilibrium gradients appearing in equation (11) are time independent.

The temperature, density, and entropy can be written as the sum of the equilibrium values plus a time-varying quantity, which is assumed to be small. The validity of such perturbation expansion must, of course, be examined critically. In general, the time-varying quantities, T_1, ρ_1, s_1, will be functions of the horizontal coordinates as well as the vertical coordinates:

$$T(z, t) = T_{eq}(z) + T_1(z, t) + \cdots$$
$$\rho(z, t) = \rho_{eq}(z) + \rho_1(z, t) + \cdots \tag{12}$$
$$s(z, t) = s_{eq}(z) + s_1(z, t) + \cdots$$

Again, we shall wish to examine the effects of the horizontal gradients on the thermal balance, and it will be shown that these are relatively small. Equations (10), (11), and (12) together with the expression for the conservation of mass,

$$\frac{\partial \rho}{\partial t} + \frac{\partial}{\partial z} (\rho w) = 0 \tag{13}$$

yield

$$\frac{\partial T_1}{\partial t} + \frac{\partial T_{eq}}{\partial z} w + (\gamma - 1) T_{eq} \frac{\partial w}{\partial z} = \frac{q}{c_v} \tag{14}$$

where w is the velocity in the vertical direction and c_v is the specific heat at constant volume.   Equations (13) and (14) are valid only if the motion is strictly one-dimensional along the vertical coordinate.

Accession of Heat

The net accession of heat q is made up of a number of terms. Heat may enter a volume by ordinary thermal conduction.   Viscous dissipation associated with the motion may contribute to the net accession.   In the upper atmosphere the principal source of heat is that due to radiation from the extreme ultraviolet, and there are radiative cooling effects.

We first consider the heat due to conduction.   Heat transported into a unit volume by conduction is given by

$$\rho q_c = \frac{\partial}{\partial z} \left[K(T) \frac{\partial T}{\partial z} \right] \tag{15}$$

where K is the thermal conductivity.   The thermal conductivity of a dilute gas is related to the viscosity μ of the fluid by

$$K = f \mu c_v \tag{16}$$

(Chapman and Cowling, 1939), where f takes on a numerical value of about 2.5 for a monatomic gas and about 1.9 for diatomic molecules.   The kinetic theory of gases shows that the coefficient of viscosity can be as written as

$$\mu = \frac{5\pi}{16} \left(\frac{mkT}{\pi} \right)^{\frac{1}{2}} \frac{1}{\pi d^2} = BT^{\frac{1}{2}} \tag{17}$$

where m is the atomic mass and d is the atomic radius.   Table 7.1 lists the values for A and B, where the thermal conductivity is written in the form

$$K = AT^{\frac{1}{2}} \tag{18}$$

In a multicomponent system the total conductivity can be written as

$$K(T) = \frac{\sum_i A_i n_i}{\sum_i n_i} T^{\frac{1}{2}} \tag{19}$$

and a similar expression holds for the viscosity of a mixture.

TABLE 7.1   Numerical Values of A and B for Several Gases. A and B are Defined by Equations (18) and (17), Respectively

	A (erg/cm-sec-deg$^{3/2}$)	B (erg/sec-deg$^{1/2}$)
H	2.1×10^3	6.8×10^{-6}
He	9.0×10^2	1.1×10^{-5}
O	3.6×10^2	1.9×10^{-5}
$O_2 \cdot N_2$	1.8×10^2	1.3×10^{-5}

The magnitude of the vertical velocity can be estimated from the conservation of entropy equation specialized to one dimension,

$$\frac{\partial s}{\partial t} + w \frac{\partial s}{\partial z} = \frac{q}{T} \tag{20}$$

In the spirit of the perturbation treatment, the vertical distribution of entropy is

$$\frac{ds}{dz}\bigg|_{eq} = \frac{1}{T_{eq}} \left(c_p \frac{dT}{dz}\bigg|_{eq} + g \right). \tag{21}$$

The vertical velocity, w, for steady motion is

$$w = \frac{q}{c_p} \left(\frac{dT}{dz}\bigg|_{eq} + \frac{g}{c_p} \right)^{-1} \tag{22}$$

where g/c_p is the adiabatic gradient for an an ideal gas, and c_p is the heat capacity at constant pressure. For an ideal gas, the heat capacity at constant pressure can be written as

$$\rho c_p = \sum_i k n_i C_i \tag{23}$$

where k is Boltzmann's constant, and C_i is a constant depending on the constituent:

$$C_i = 2.5 \text{ (monatomic molecules)} \tag{24}$$

$$= 3.5 \text{ (diatomic molecules)}.$$

In interpreting equation (22), we note that q/c_p is the rate at which the temperature would increase provided the heating occurred at constant pressure and without motion. If the fluid is initially in hydrostatic equilibrium in a temperature gradient $dT/dz \big|_{eq}$ and becomes heated, it rises. If the heating occurred at constant pressure, and the fluid always remained in hydrostatic equilibrium, the velocity of rise would be

$$\frac{q}{c_{p}}\left(\frac{dT}{dz}\bigg|_{\text{eq}}\right)^{-1} \tag{25}$$

As it rises, the fluid encounters lower pressure and expands. The expansion causes a cooling because of the work done on the surroundings by the expansion. In order to remain in hydrostatic equilibrium, the fluid rises with a smaller velocity and the adiabatic gradient appearing in equation (22) takes account of the adiabatic cooling.

In order to obtain a numerical estimate, we consider conditions at 200 km where the density is on the order of 4.0×10^{-13} g/cm³ and the density scale height is about 50 km. If 1 erg/cm² is deposited over a scale height every second, then q is $\sim 3 \times 10^5$ ergs/g-sec. The vertical velocity is then of the order of 3×10^2 cm/sec. The presence of a temperature gradient will further reduce the maximum vertical velocity. In addition, we will see the estimate of 1 erg being deposited over the 50-km height range is on the high side and, therefore, the vertical velocity of 6 m/sec provides a maximum limit for this altitude. The satellite observations indicate at most a 2% diurnal change in density at this altitude. This corresponds to a vertical displacement of 1 km of the surfaces of equal density. The corresponding average value of the velocity of surfaces of equal density would be on the order of 2 cm/sec.

Estimates of the vertical velocity permit an estimate of the rate at which heat is deposited by viscous degradation of mechanical energy; the viscous contribution to the accession can then be compared with the heat accession due to conduction. In addition, we shall wish to compare heat conducted and heat transported by convection.

From dimensional considerations, we see that the rate of accession of heat due to viscous dissipation q is on the order of

$$\frac{\mu w^2}{\rho L^2} \tag{26}$$

where L is the smallest length scale involved in the motion. Setting L equal to the scale height we have

$$q_v \approx \frac{10^{-5}(10^2)^2}{4 \times 10^{-13}(5 \times 10^6)^2} \approx 10^{-2} \text{ erg/g-sec} \tag{27}$$

Since the rate of accession from other sources is on the order of 10^5 ergs/g-sec, the contribution of viscous dissipation is completely negligible. This would be true even if a much smaller scale of motion were involved.

The rate of change of temperature due to heat transported by ordinary conduction is given by

$$\frac{1}{\rho c_v} \frac{\partial}{\partial z} \left(K \frac{\partial T}{\partial z} \right) \tag{28}$$

The order of magnitude of the ratio of heat carried by conduction to that transported by convection is

$$\frac{K}{\rho c_v L w} \tag{29}$$

where L can again be taken as equal to the scale height. At 200 km, the temperature is on the order of $1000°K$ and the total number density is on the order of 10^{10}. The ratio of the heat transported by conduction compared to that convected is then on the order of 30. Conduction thus outweighs convection by an appreciable amount, although the total heat transported by convection may not be negligible.

Influence of Horizontal Temperature Gradients

In calculating the net accession of heat, account is taken of the vertical flux of heat. The difference in temperature between day and night hemispheres will lead to a horizontal flow of heat.

The difference in temperature between the dark and sunlit side is on the order of $600°K$ at 1000 km, corresponding to an average temperature gradient of 3×10^{-7} K°/cm. The corresponding heat flow is on the order of 1×10^{-2} erg/cm²-sec. This heat flow is small compared with the vertical heat input, but may measurably affect the details of the temperature distribution, particularly in the upper level where the vertical gradients are only slightly larger than the horizontal gradients. The effect of the horizontal flow of heat will be to reduce the maximum temperatures.

The high thermal conductivity of the upper atmosphere will prevent large permanent temperature gradients not maintained by external conditions. The time required for a temperature anomaly having a scale length L to decay is given by

$$t \approx \frac{\rho c_v}{K} L^2 \tag{30}$$

(Carslaw and Jaeger, 1959). At 400 km, a temperature disturbance with a scale length of 1000 km would decay in about 9 hours. At 1000 km height, the same disturbance would decay in a few minutes.

The large horizontal temperature gradients required by the day-night effect will also produce horizontal velocities. In order for the horizontal mixing to be effective, velocities on the order of 10^4 cm/sec would be required for the horizontal mass motion to transport appreciable thermal energies. From considerations similar to those which led to an estimation of vertical velocity, we can show that the horizontal velocities are much too small to give rise to any appreciable horizontal thermal transport.

The small time scale for the vertical flow of heat implicit in equation (30) assures that the atmosphere will respond to changes in thermal input with a time scale of a few hours at most.

Ultraviolet Heat Source

So far we have considered both the magnitudes of conducted and convected heat and the contribution of viscous dissipation to the thermal budget. Convection is minor compared with conduction, and the effects of viscosity can be neglected. The most important heat source is due to the absorption of solar ultraviolet radiation. The heat source due to the absorption of the solar ultraviolet radiation can be written as

$$\rho q_{uv} = \sum_{\lambda} \sum_{i} \epsilon_{i\lambda} n_i(z, t) F_\lambda \sigma'_{i\lambda} \exp\left[-\tau_{i\lambda}(z, t)\right] \tag{31}$$

The summations are over all constituents, i, and over all wavelengths, λ; F_λ is the time-dependent incident flux of wavelength λ at the top of the atmosphere; $\sigma'_{i\lambda}$ is the photoionization cross section of the ith constituent at wavelength λ; $\tau_{i\lambda}$ is given by

$$\tau_{i\lambda} = \int_{z}^{\infty} \sigma_{i\lambda} \frac{n_i(z, t)}{\cos \theta(t)} \, dz \tag{32}$$

where $\sigma_{i\lambda}$ is the total absorption cross section, θ is the zenith angle of the sun, and $\epsilon_{i\lambda}$ is an efficiency factor for the conversion of the ultraviolet absorbed by the ith constituent into heat.

A determination of the ultraviolet heat source requires a measurement of the ultraviolet radiation F_λ outside the earth's atmosphere;

the number densities n_i must be calculated for a particular model. Hinteregger and Watanabe (1962) have given the most detailed review of the values of the solar flux outside the atmosphere. Table 7.2 is a summary of their results for the energy flux in various wavelength regions.

Molecular oxygen has the lowest ionization potential among all the major constituents of the atmospheric gas. Radiation at wavelengths shorter than 1027 Å will ionize O_2. Radiation in the wavelength region of 1350 to 1027 Å is important in the formation of the D layer of the ionosphere and through its interaction with the minor constituent NO. Atomic oxygen is ionized by radiation below 911 Å while molecular nitrogen is ionized below 796 Å. The ionization threshold for helium is 504 Å.

There are various uncertainties in the other parameters that enter into the discussion. In particular, the efficiency of the conversion of ultraviolet radiation into heat involves a large uncertainty.

Before considering the detailed application of equation (31), we note that the heating is proportional both to the number density and to the ionizing flux. As the ionizing flux passes through the highest portions of the atmosphere, it is lightly attenuated because of the limited number of absorbers. As it enters into somewhat denser atmosphere, the attenuation goes up and the heating rate will be a maximum for a given wavelength at an intermediate region in the atmosphere. The detailed calculations suggest that most of the heating is between 150 and 300 km. This is also the region where the number density of ionized particles reaches a maximum.

Of interest is the heat source at altitudes well above the region of maximum heat production. Hinteregger and Watanabe (1962)

TABLE 7.2   Flux of Solar Radiation at Short Wavelengths

Wavelength Interval, in Å	Energy Flux in Wavelength Interval (ergs/cm²-sec)
1350–1027	6.0
1027– 911	0.2
911– 630	0.3
630– 370	0.3
370– 280	0.6
280– 170	0.8[1]
170– 10	0.3
10–1027	2.5

estimate that the heat sources due to the ionization of oxygen, helium, and hydrogen are approximated by

$$\rho q_O \approx 1.4 \times 10^{-17} \epsilon_0 n_0 \ \text{erg/cm}^3\text{-sec}$$

$$\rho q_{He} \approx 1.4 \times 10^{-18} \epsilon_{He} n_{He} \ \text{ergs/cm}^3\text{-sec} \tag{33}$$

$$\rho q_H \approx 4.0 \times 10^{-17} \epsilon_H n_H \ \text{ergs/cm}^3\text{-sec}$$

In writing equation (33), we make the assumption that the attenuation by absorption is not sufficient to bring about a first-order change in the incoming radiation. The values listed refer to an overhead sun.

The absorption and ionization coefficients in equation (31) are still poorly known. Detailed theoretical calculations have been carried out for atomic oxygen by Dalgarno and Parkinson (1960). The cross section is a function of wavelength, varying from about $2.5 \times 10^{-18} \ \text{cm}^2$ at 900 Å to $1.3 \times 10^{-17} \ \text{cm}^2$ at 500 Å. The ionization cross section for N_2 is most complicated and varies greatly, with an average value of about $1 \times 10^{-17} \ \text{cm}^2$. The lack of secure data on the photoionization and absorption cross sections is one of the weaknesses in the construction of any model of the upper atmosphere. In addition, the efficiency of transfer of absorbed photons into thermal energy is even more uncertain (Nicolet, 1959, 1960, 1961a). Some of the absorbed solar energy goes into the excitation of atmospheric particles, in which case the energy may be lost in the form of radiation. The energy which goes into the dissociation of molecules into atoms is lost as far as the upper regions of the ionosphere are concerned, since recombination does not occur in these regions; instead, the atoms must diffuse down into a region where the density is high enough so that three-body collisions take place. The energy which is absorbed in exciting metastable atomic or molecular states is not available if the atom radiates the energy instead of becoming deactivated by collision. The number of possible metastable states is large and the evaluation of the definite processes is a complicated matter. Hanson and Johnson (1961) estimate that some 15 to 30% of the total energy absorbed in the upper regions of the ionosphere goes into heat.

Radiative Loss of Heat

In determining the net accession of heat it is necessary to consider radiation out of the region of interest. The principal infrared radiator in the upper atmosphere is atomic oxygen (Bates, 1951a), which radiates at 63 μ according to

$$O(^3P_1) \to O(^3P_2) + h\nu(\lambda = 63 \ \mu) \qquad (34)$$

The net accession due to radiation in atomic oxygen can be written as

$$\rho q_O = n_O A_{12} E_1 \left(\frac{W_1 \exp \ (-E_1/kT)}{W_2 + W_1 \exp \ (-E_1/kT) + W_0 \exp \ (-E_0/kT)} \right) \qquad (35)$$

which is

$$\rho q_O = \frac{-1.68 \times 10^{-18} e^{-228/T}}{1 + 0.6 e^{-228/T} + 0.2 e^{-325.3/T}} n_O \qquad (36)$$

where n_0 is the concentration of atomic oxygen; E_1 is the energy difference between the $^3P_1$, and $^3P_2$ levels of atomic oxygen; E_0 is the energy difference between the $^3P_0$ and $^3P_2$ levels of atomic oxygen; W_0, W_1, W_2 are the statistical weights at the various levels; and A_{12} is the Einstein coefficient for the transition $^3P_1 - ^3P_2$.

The numerical coefficient multiplying the concentration of oxygen in (36) will be less than 10^{-18} ergs/cm³-sec. For the radiative losses to equal 1 erg/sec about 10^{18} atoms of atomic oxygen are required. At a concentration of 10^{11} atoms/cm³, a column 100 km thick would be required to radiate 1 erg/cm²-sec. As we shall see, the concentration of atomic oxygen in the upper atmosphere is far less than this. However, the infrared radiation from atomic oxygen can contribute substantially to the heat balance in the height interval of 120 to 160 km.

Numerical Models of the Upper Atmosphere

Numerous models for the upper atmosphere incorporating the satellite-derived densities and ultraviolet fluxes obtained from rocket measurements have been calculated. The most detailed analysis has been carried out by Harris and Priester (1962a). Combining equations (8) and (14), Harris and Priester have determined the time variation of a model atmosphere by taking into account the gain of heat through ultraviolet flux and the loss through radiation by atomic oxygen, and by approximating the vertical motion within the atmosphere. In this way they derive the daily and solar cycle (Harris and Priester, 1962b), variation of the density concentration, and temperature of the upper atmosphere. We present a review of their work in order to illustrate certain of the problems inherent in such calculations, and also to indicate the current estimates of the constitution of the upper atmosphere.

Boundary Conditions at 120 Kilometers. The simultaneous integration of equations (8) and (14) requires boundary values of the number density of the relevant constituents and the temperature at the level at which diffusive equilibrium replaces convective mixing. The two problems are to determine the height of this level and to estimate the constitution of the atmosphere at this level.

Early attempts to determine the composition and height of the diffusion level through the use of mass spectrometers were made by Townsend, Meadows, and Pressly (1954). During the IGY, successful flights through the critical regions were made (Townsend and Meadows, 1958). The method of determining the region of diffusive separation involved the determination of the A/N_2 ratio. These flights and Russian flights (Pokhunkov, 1962) showed a decrease of A/N_2 ratio with altitude compatible with the onset of diffusive separation in the 100 to 120-km region.

An alternative method of determining the level at which diffusive separation sets in is through the use of artificial injections of alkali metals by rockets. Blamont and deJager (1961), through the study of alkali vapor trails, show that below about 100 km, motion is intense with a strong shearing. Above 100 to 105 km, the alkali vapors diffuse into the atmosphere. A remarkable feature of the observations is that the transitional region is very sharp. There are seasonal variations in the intensity of the motion and also in the height of the transition layer. Since the alkali-vapor technique is limited to the twilight and dawn hours, it is impossible to investigate the daily variations in the height of the transitional layer. Observations on meteor trails (Greenhow, 1959) show a similar transition, although the upper height of the turbulent motion has been found at altitudes greater than 100 km.

A major advance has been the determination of the O/O_2 ratio in the 100 to 135 km region by Schaeffer (1963), who ejected the spectrometer from the rocket to minimize the effects of rocket exhaust. The instrument was designed to minimize the probability of surface recombination of atomic oxygen. Schaeffer found at 127 km a ratio of O/O_2 equal to two. The values are in good agreement with the ultraviolet determination of the O/O_2 ratio (Byram et al., 1955; Kupperian et al., 1960) but disagree markedly with earlier mass spectrometer results.

Table 7.3 lists the values of the constituents at 120 km altitude used by Harris and Priester and derived from the study of Nicolet

TABLE 7.3   Concentration of Constituents
at 120 Kilometers

Constituent	Number Density (particles/cm^3)
N_2	5.80×10^{11}
O_2	1.20×10^{11}
O	7.60×10^{10}
He	2.50×10^7
H	4.36×10^4

(1961a).   The structure of the atmosphere depends particularly on the ratio adopted for atomic to molecular oxygen.   As has been noted before, atomic oxygen is a radiative cooling agent, and if a high abundance of atomic oxygen is used, then the maximum temperatures obtained are less.   Harris and Priester estimate that a change of a factor of 10 in the ratio O/O_2 decreases the maximum temperature reached at high altitudes by about 250 K°.   The ratio used is consistent with Schaeffer's (1963) measurements.

Required Heat Sources.   Using the above boundary conditions, Harris and Priester (1962a) carried out detailed calculations of the temperature and composition for various heat sources.   A remarkable feature of their study was that an ultraviolet heat source symmetrical in time about local noon, vanishing before 6 o'clock in the morning and after 6 in the evening, does not yield density variations compatible with satellite observations.   The peak value of the heat source depends on the thermal efficiency, ϵ.   Harris and Priester assigned a thermal efficiency of 0.37 and used Hinteregger's estimate of 2.5 ergs/cm²-sec for wavelengths less than 911 Å.   However, the observed response of the atmosphere demands an additional heat source with a maximum in the midmorning and a minimum in the early afternoon, with a small amount of heating during the night and an average magnitude comparable to that provided by the ultraviolet flux.   Only if such a heat source is assumed can the calculated densities, assuming the time-independent boundary values given in Table 7.3, be brought into agreement with the observed variations in density derived from satellite observations.   The critical point is that the discrepancy is in the phase of the heat source rather than its absolute magnitude.   If the magnitude were off, then the discrepancy could be attributed to incorrect values for the thermal efficiency or for the ionization cross sections.   The phase relations cannot be explained in such a fashion.   The model does not take into account the depletion of the neutral population through the ionization.   The percentage population of the ionized particles is so small that the effects associated with the ionized particles can be neglected.   However, there is a possibility of an additional heat source lagging behind the maximum in the solar flux due to the nighttime recombination.

Numerical Models.   The basic parameters produced by the models which can be compared directly with satellite observations are the density and the variation of density with height.   We recall that the absolute values of the density derived from satellites are uncertain, but the variation with time is much clearer.   Figures 7.5 and 7.6

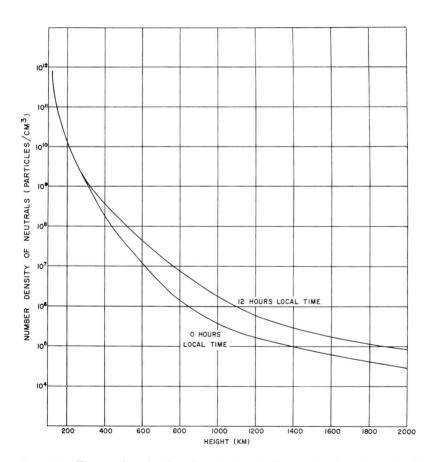

Figure 7.5   The number density of neutral molecules at 0 and 12 hours local time as a function of altitude.   The number densities have been derived from the models of Harris and Priester (1962a) and correspond to solar conditions during the years 1956 and 1959 during the last solar cycle.

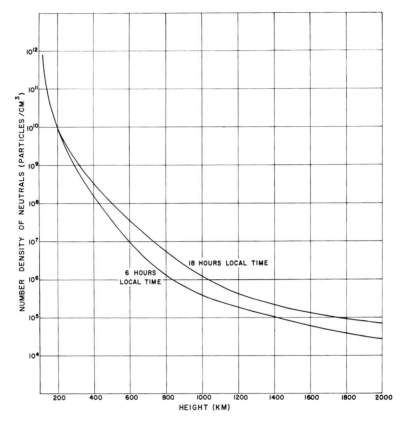

Figure 7.6 The number density of neutral particles in the high atmosphere at 6 and 18 hours local time.

show the variation of the number density of the neutrals between 0 and 12 hours and 6 and 18 hours. The total number densities are useful in association with Figures 7.7–7.10, which give the relative proportion of the constituent atoms within the upper atmosphere.

Figures 7.5 and 7.6 show that the major fluctuations in density take place at altitudes above 300 km. At 1000 km, the maximum change in density is about a factor of 8.

Figures 7.7–7.10 show the variation of the relative proportions of the major constituents. Three distinct regions in the atmosphere between 120 and 2000 km can be outlined. At noon, between 120 and 250 km, molecular nitrogen dominates. Between 250 and 1150 km, atomic oxygen is the principal constituent, and above 1150 km helium dominates. Nicolet (1961b,c) first showed that the slow decrease in atmospheric density with altitude between 750 and 1500 km as derived from satellite observation indicated that helium was the major constituent in the region concerned.

Nicolet's prediction is strikingly confirmed by observations of Bourdeau et al. (1962), who found that at an altitude of 1630 km the He^+ to O^+ ratio was on the order of unity. The ratio of the ionized particles cannot be directly converted into ratios of the neutral particles but the observations do indicate the importance of helium in the upper atmosphere. Hanson (1962) also showed that

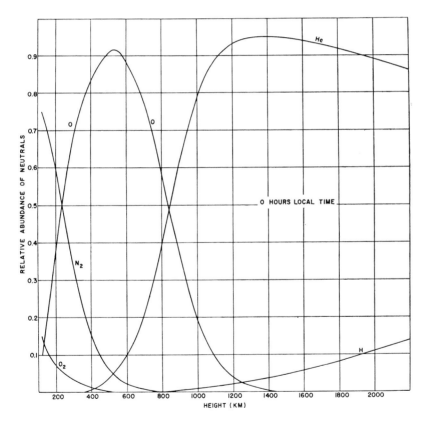

Figure 7.7   The relative abundance of neutral particles as a function of altitude at 0 hours local time. The absolute abundances can be derived by using Figure 7.5.

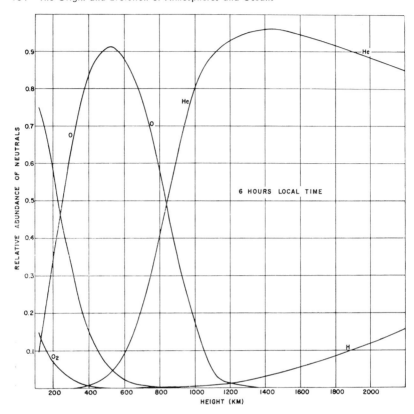

Figure 7.8 The relative abundance of neutral particles at 6 hours local time. The absolute abundance can be derived by using Figure 7.6.

an ion probe experiment by Hale (1961) can be interpreted as indicating that the helium atoms are indeed present, as suggested by Nicolet. The composition of the atmosphere derived by Hanson is in general agreement with those obtained by Harris and Priester.

The variations in composition during the day-night cycle are illustrated in Figures 7.7–7.10. During the nighttime, the peak concentration of oxygen is at a lower level than during the day. As the atmosphere expands due to the heating, the maximum in the concentrations of both oxygen and helium moves outward.

The variation with temperature, time, and altitude in the model atmosphere is shown in Figures 7.11 and 7.12. The temperature at midnight is about 1200°K at heights above 400 km while the temperature at noon is on the order of 1715°K during 1956 and 1959 of the last solar cycle.

Solar Cycle Variations. Harris and Priester (1962b) have attempted to estimate the variation in the parameters of the atmosphere during the solar cycle. The basis of their estimates is in the correlation of the postulated heat source with the long-term averages of the 10.7-centimeter solar flux. The derived densities are then compared with the densities obtained from satellites for the period 1958–1961. The models just discussed and represented in Figures 7.5–7.12 correspond to the years 1956 and 1959 during the last solar cycle. The peak in the solar cycle would be in the period 1957–1958. The maximum, mean, and minimum daily temperatures obtained by Harris and

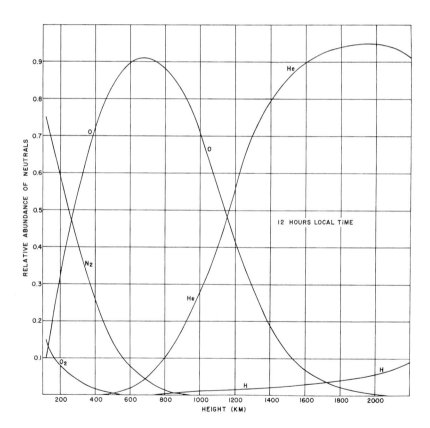

Figure 7.9 The relative abundance of neutral particles at 12 hours local time. The absolute abundances can be derived by using Figure 7.5.

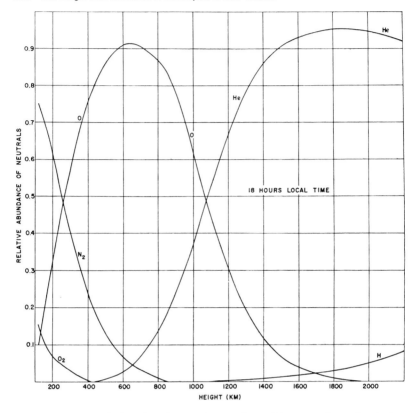

Figure 7.10 The relative abundance of neutral particles at 18 hours local time. The absolute abundances can be derived by using the number densities given in Figure 7.6.

Priester for solar maximum and solar minimum are shown in Table 7.4. For comparison, King-Hele and Rees (1962) obtain, by using a somewhat simplified model of the atmosphere, an average maximum temperature in 1958 of 1600°; in 1959, 1350°; in 1960–1961, 1150°K. Again, the agreement with the estimates of Harris and Priester is quite good.

TABLE 7.4 Maximum, Mean, and Minimum Daily Temperatures (°K)

Period	Minimum	Mean	Maximum
Solar maximum	1400	1775	2150
Solar minimum	590	730	870

Harris and Priester have assumed that the conditions at 120 km do not vary either daily or over the solar cycle. The time dependence of conditions at 100 to 120 km is an important problem on which there is yet little evidence. There is no doubt that the O/O_2 ratio varies, probably by a factor of 3 to 4, over the day-night cycle. Such a variation complicates the heat source distribution since the abundance of oxygen determines the radiative cooling.

Summary of Atmospheric Constitution

The principal results of the satellite studies, when combined with theoretical investigations, show that the temperature of the upper

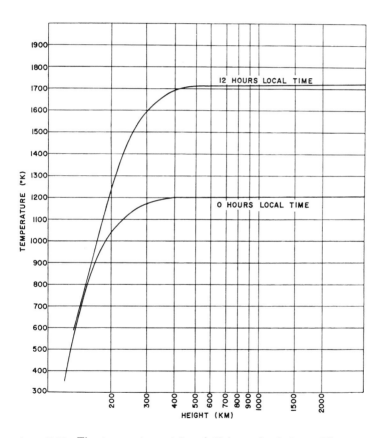

Figure 7.11   The temperature at 0 and 12 hours local time. The temperature corresponds to conditions during 1956 and 1959 of the last solar cycle (Harris and Priester, 1962a).

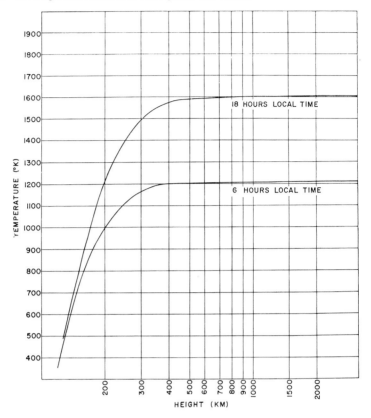

Figure 7.12   Temperatures at 6 and 18 hours local time. Temperatures correspond to solar conditions prevailing during 1956 and 1959 of the last solar cycle.

atmosphere varies on a daily basis and with the solar cycle. The details of this variation are still somewhat uncertain and the absolute temperature assigned at any given time may be in error by as much as 100 K°. During the maximum of the solar cycle, the daily maximum temperature is of the order of 2150°K. During the minimum of the solar cycle, the maximum temperature may be only 900°K. During most of the solar cycle, the maximum daily temperature will be no more than some 1700°K. These conclusions have a profound effect as far as any consideration of escape of helium from the upper atmosphere is concerned.

There is uncertainty about the detailed nature of the composition of the upper atmosphere, as well as the variation of composition with the solar cycle, and diurnally. However, it appears that the atmosphere between 200 and 1000 km is, on the average, dominated by atomic oxygen. At higher altitudes, helium is the principal constituent, and at still greater altitudes, perhaps on the order of 4000 km, hydrogen becomes the principal constituent.

The major uncertainties in the construction of a model for the upper atmosphere are concerned both with the nature of the heat source and with conditions prevailing at 100 to 120 km. Detailed investigations such as those carried out by Harris and Priester indicate that the ultraviolet heat source is inadequate to account for the phase of the observed diurnal fluctuations. An additional heat source, peaking in the midmorning and with a minimum in the midafternoon, is required to supplement the ultraviolet heat source, which is a maximum at local noon. Since it is the phase of the heat source that is involved, possible underestimates of the thermal efficiency or errors in the photoionization cross section cannot account for the observed density fluctuations in the atmosphere. However, possible variations in composition at 120 km may account for the phase relations; these effects have not been investigated largely because of the lack of data on the atmosphere in the 100 to 200 km interval. Harris and Priester suggest that high-energy particles may provide this additional energy source. We will later return to the detailed consideration of possible heat sources and their long-term variations.

FLUX OF CONSTITUENTS INTO THE ATMOSPHERE

In considering the escape of gases from the earth's atmosphere, it is necessary to make an estimate of the rate of influx of these gases into the atmosphere. We will be principally concerned with the two isotopes of helium, He^4 and He^3. However, it is necessary to consider the influx of argon, since knowledge of the argon flux permits an estimate of the flux of helium from the crust into the atmosphere (Birch, 1951; Damon and Kulp, 1958; Turekian, 1959). The atmospheric content of neon is also of interest since it sets a limit to the amount of gas that has been accreted from outer space.

The estimation of the rate of release of radiogenic helium and argon from the crust is very complex. It may be that not all of the relevant factors have been taken into account. It is important that this point be appreciated, since the conclusion that is to be reached is that the present rate of release of helium into the atmosphere greatly exceeds the rate at which helium is presently escaping.

Advances in knowledge of the influx of important constituents into the atmosphere have come from two directions. First of all, the studies on the abundances of gases in natural waters permit a new method of estimating the influx. Prior to recent work, the influx has followed from estimates based only on the measured heat flows and ages of rocks. In addition, advances in the understanding of the interaction of the magnetosphere with the interplanetary medium and measurements of the particle fluxes in solar flares allow an estimate of the rate at which certain elements are being accreted.

The content of the various constituents in the atmosphere in particles per square centimeter is given in Table 7.5. These values are derived primarily from the discussion of Glauckauf (1951) (see also Nicolet, 1957; and Urey, 1959).

The Flux of He^4

The radioactive decay of K^{40} produces A^{40}, and He^4 results from the radioactive decay of both uranium and thorium. A rough estimate of the maximum amount of helium and argon that can have entered the atmosphere follows from general considerations of the heat balance of the earth (Nicolet, 1957; Birch, 1951). Potassium, uranium, and thorium are the principal radioactive elements and certainly produce most of the heat that is now reaching the surface of the earth. The present heat flow is 62.8 ± 4.3 ergs/cm²-sec (MacDonald, unpublished). If the earth had the composition of chondritic meteorites (1.1×10^{-8} g/g uranium, 4.4×10^{-8} g/g thorium, and 8.0×10^{-4} g/g potassium), the surface heat flow would be 59.4 ergs/cm²-sec provided all heat being produced reached the surface. If only the mantle had chondritic composition, the equilib-

TABLE 7.5   Concentration of Rare Gases in the Earth's Atmosphere

Gas	Concentration (particles/cm²) at Sea Level
He^3	1.41×10^{14}
He^4	1.13×10^{20}
Ne	3.84×10^{20}
A	1.93×10^{23}
Kr	2.0×10^{19}
Xe	1.6×10^{18}

rium surface heat flow would be 40.1 ergs/cm²-sec. Several factors contribute to a present heat flow greater than the equilibrium heat flow. These include the higher rate of heat production in the past, the long thermal time constant of the earth, and the contributions from initial heat (MacDonald, 1959). The close agreement between the equilibrium heat flow from a chondritic earth and the observed heat flow is usually taken as evidence for the chondritic composition of the earth as far as the radioactive elements are concerned.

If, indeed the earth has a chondritic composition and if the gases produced in the radioactive decay of potassium and argon are reaching the surface, then the present-day flux into the atmosphere should be 2.6×10^6 He^4 atoms/cm²-sec and 3.24×10^6 argon atoms/cm²-sec. The relatively short half-life of K^{40} means that 4.5×10^9 years ago argon was produced at approximately 10 times the present rate, so that the average flux of argon over geologic time would be 1.3×10^7 argon atoms/cm²-sec. If all the argon produced in a chondritic earth had reached the atmosphere, the total content of argon would be 1.8×10^{24} argon atoms/cm². This is a factor of 10 greater than the observed abundance. It is therefore clear that not all the argon that has been produced has reached the surface. The validity of the last assertion depends on the potassium abundance of the earth. However, it is extremely unlikely that a consistent thermal model of the earth can be constructed with a potassium concentration one-tenth of that of chondritic meteorites.

The ratio of argon produced to argon in the atmosphere, 0.9, permits an estimate of the present-day retentivity of the earth to argon provided that the outgassing process has been a continuous one. If 90% of the helium is also retained within the earth, then the current flux of helium to the atmosphere would be 2.6×10^5 particles/cm²-sec. In a sense, this is a lower limit to the flux of helium for an earth having a chondritic composition, since helium is retained within rocks to a far lesser extent than is argon.

The estimates of the flux of argon and helium into the atmosphere suffer from the fact that they are based on compositional models for the earth, which, though reasonable, are still uncertain. Wasserburg et al. (1963) have attempted to obtain an estimate based on the observed content of argon in the atmosphere and on the ratios of helium to argon in natural gases. Measurement of natural gases (Zartman et al., 1961) shows that the He/A ratio varies from 2 to 200 with a value of about 10 being the most frequent. On this basis, Wasserburg, et al. conclude that the ratio of the present flux of helium to argon lies between 2 and 20. The present flux of argon is estimated to lie between 7×10^4 and 3.5×10^5 atoms/cm²-sec, where the factor of 2 uncertainty arises from the possibility that half of the argon present in the atmosphere is primeval. The estimated flux of helium obtained by Wasserburg et al. is then between 1.4×10^5 and 7×10^6 atoms/cm²-sec. Assuming that all the argon in the atmosphere originated from outgassing, the most frequent ratio of helium to argon in natural gases would yield a present-day flux of 3.5×10^6 atoms/cm²-sec. This estimate lies close to the estimate derived from the arguments based on the present thermal conditions.

The Flux of He³

The two possible sources of He³ in the atmosphere are direct production resulting from the interaction with cosmic rays and the injection of He³ into the atmosphere from the sun.

A detailed analysis by Fireman (1953) shows that He³ may be produced by collision of cosmic-ray neutrons with nitrogen leading to the formation of tritium, which then decays to He³. Tritium can also be produced by direct ejection in cosmic-ray stars, as can He³. Numerious other studies have been carried out evaluating the production of tritium by galactic cosmic rays and the spallation production of He³ (Craig and Lal, 1961; Wilson and Fergusson, 1960; Begemann and Libby, 1957; Dostrovsky, Fraenkel, and Winsberg, 1960). These estimates indicate that the galactic cosmic rays produce on the order of 2 He³ atoms/cm²-sec.

Direct evidence of the accretion of tritium and He³ from the sun was obtained by Fireman et al. (1961) and Schaeffer and Zahringer (1962) from a study of the tritium and He³ in the casing of the earth satellite, Discoverer XVII, which was flown following the solar flare of November 12, 1960. The amounts of tritium and He³ recovered from the satellite are 2 orders of magnitude too large to be accounted for by spallation of the casing material. The results show that the solar flare radiation intercepted by the satellite consisted of 0.4% tritium and 10% He³. The average yearly integrated intensity of solar cosmic rays with energies above 30 Mev for the years 1956–1961 is about 1.1×10^2 particles/cm²-sec (McDonald, 1963). Thus the sun may inject on the average some 10 He³ atoms/cm²-sec (Flamm et al., 1962).

The accretion rate remains uncertain, since Biswas et al. (1962) did not report He³ in emulsions flown shortly after the November 12 flare. Three hundred tracks were examined carefully for the presence of deuterons and tritons. In the energy range accepted by the emulsion, some 3 or 4 particles should have been He[3] if the ratios obtained from the analysis of the Discoverer satellite are correct.

The Accretion of Neon

The abundance of neon is important since it sets an upper limit to the gases that may have been accreted from the sun. Neon, like argon, is too massive to have escaped from the earth's atmosphere unless the upper atmosphere temperatures were an order of magnitude greater than they are today. The abundance of neon in the sun's atmosphere is not known directly from spectroscopic observations. Biswas et al. (1962, 1963) obtained estimates of the ratio of neon to hydrogen and helium in solar cosmic rays. The hydrogen to neon ratio is 1×10^4 and the helium to neon ratio is 6.7×10^2. The numbers are uncertain because of the statistics, but the results are consistent with estimates of cosmic abundances.

The solar cosmic-ray flux of 100 particles/cm²-sec is far too low to supply the neon now present in the atmosphere if the rate were maintained over geologic time. A second possible source is the low-energy plasma streaming from the sun. Measurements of the flux (Neugebauer and Snyder, 1962) yield a quiet-time value of 1×10^8 particles/cm²-sec. If the cosmic-ray abundances are the same for the low-energy flux, then this corresponds to a flux density of 1×10^4 neon atoms/cm²-sec. The total number of neon atoms that would be accreted, assuming constant flux over geologic time, would be 1.4×10^{21}, or a factor of 3 larger than the observed abundance. As will be discussed later, the magnetic field effectively shields the atmosphere from the solar wind and, as a result, only when the field is much weaker than it is at present will solar plasma penetrate into the atmosphere. The neon content of the atmosphere could be accreted if the field were much weaker than its present value on the average of about one-third of geologic time.

The maximum number of accreted hydrogen and helium can be calculated using the present abundance of neon and the observed ratios of neon to the lighter isotopes. The maximum flux of 2.7×10^7 hydrogen atoms/cm²-sec and 7.2×10^5 helium atoms/cm²-sec. The validity of these maximum figures depends on the assumption that all the neon has been introduced into the atmosphere.

Summary of Flux of Gases into Atmosphere

Table 7.6 summarizes the present information regarding the flux of He[3], He[4], and argon into the atmosphere. The range of values

TABLE 7.6   Flux of Gases into the Atmosphere

	Flux from Earth (particles/cm^2-sec)		Flux from Space (particles/cm^2-sec)	
Constituent	Range	Preferred Value	Range	Preferred Value
He^3	—	—	2–12	12
He^4	1.4×10^5–7.0×10^6	2.0×10^6	6–6 $\times 10^6$	6
A	7.0×10^4–3.5×10^5	2×10^5	—	—

permitted for the influx of He^4 from space results from the uncertainty in the proportion of the solar wind that can penetrate the magnetosphere. If only solar cosmic rays contribute to the upper atmosphere, then the lower values are appropriate. If a substantial fraction of the solar wind does indeed penetrate into the magnetosphere, then a higher value is required.

Using the preferred values given in Table 7.6, the present abundance of He^4 would accumulate in 1.8×10^6 years. Only 3.7×10^5 years would be required to supply the atmosphere with its present content of He^3, provided that solar cosmic rays make the contribution to the influx indicated in Table 7.6. If only galactic cosmic rays contribute to the production of He^3, then a time scale of 2.2×10^6 years is required.

THERMAL ESCAPE OF GASES

The density of the atmosphere decreases with height. At some level the mean free path of the constituent particles becomes large in comparison with the scale height, and collisions above this level are infrequent. The region in which collisions are negligible is termed the *exosphere*. The atmosphere grades into the exosphere; however for the purposes of the escape theory it is usual to speak of a given level as the base of the exosphere. Below this level collisions are frequent enough so that the particles assume a Maxwell distribution. From the base of the exosphere, some particles are ejected upward with velocities less than that required for escape. These particles describe elliptic, ballistic orbits and return to the base of the exosphere. Some fraction of the particles describing ballistic orbits have a velocity greater than the escape velocity. These particles will leave the exosphere in hyperbolic orbits. In addition, there is a component in elliptical orbits circling the planet and not passing through regions where the density is high enough for collisions to take place.

A basic problem in the theory of planetary escape is the calculation of what fraction of atoms have a velocity such that their kinetic energy is greater than the gravitational potential energy. The classical theory of escape has been developed by Jeans (1916) and Lennard-Jones (1923). A discussion that has influenced much of the later work is given by Spitzer (1949). These models assume an iso-thermal atmosphere with a gas in equilibrium having a Maxwellian velocity distribution up to the base of the exosphere. Above this level collisions are sufficiently infrequent as to be unimportant in slowing down outwardly traveling particles.

The problem of escape is complicated by the fact that for a minor constituent, the base of the exosphere must be supplied through dif-fusion from below. If the thermal conditions are such that the escape rate of a particular constituent is large compared with the diffusion rate, then diffusion effectively controls the escape of that constituent. Diffusion thus effectively limits escape during short intervals in which locally the temperature may rise much above the average temperature. The region between 100 and 200 km has a very large temperature gradient, and diffusion through this region is complicated by the phe-nomenon of thermal diffusion.

Classical Theory of Escape

The two necessary conditions for escape to take place are that the velocity of an outgoing particle is greater than a critical velocity, v_c, and that the atom with this velocity has a negligible chance of undergoing a collision. The critical velocity is defined by the require-ments that the particle's kinetic energy is greater than the gravitational potential,

$$\tfrac{1}{2}mv_c^2(z) = mg(R_0)\frac{R_0^2}{(R_0 + z)} \tag{37}$$

m is the mass of the particle, g is the gravitational acceleration at an arbitrary distance R_0 from the center of the earth, and z is the height measured from R_0 at which the particle has a velocity v. For a gas in thermal equilibrium, the number of particles having a velocity between v and $v + dv$ in an element of solid angle is

$$4\pi r^2 n\left(\frac{m}{2\pi kT}\right)^{3/2}\exp\left(-\frac{mv^2}{2kT}\right)v^2\sin\theta\,d\theta \tag{38}$$

where

$$r = R_0 + z$$

and θ is the angle between the velocity vector and the radial coordinate. The flux dF in particles/cm²-sec follows by multiplying equation (38) by the radial component of the velocity, $v \cos \theta$.

$$dF = 4\pi r^2 n \left(\frac{m}{2\pi k T} \right)^{3/2} \exp\left(-\frac{mv^2}{2kT} \right) v^3 \sin\theta \cos\theta \, d\theta \qquad (39)$$

Integration over the angular coordinate yields the number of molecules crossing the unit area of a hemisphere per unit time, and integration over velocities from the critical velocity to the infinite velocity yields the flux of particles having velocities which exceed the local velocity of escape.

$$F(r) = n(r) \left(\frac{kT}{2\pi m} \right)^{1/2} \left[1 + \frac{mg(r)r}{kT(r)} \right] \exp\left[-\frac{mg(r)r}{kT(r)} \right] \qquad (40)$$

Defining the scale height $H(r)$ by

$$H(r) = \frac{kT(r)}{mg(r)} \qquad (41)$$

the flux of escaping particles per unit area per second is

$$F(r) = n(r) \left[\frac{g(r)H(r)}{2\pi} \right]^{1/2} \left[1 + \frac{r}{H(r)} \right] \exp\left[-\frac{r}{H(r)} \right] \qquad (42)$$

The expression for $F(r)$ gives the outward radial flux at a level r of the particles whose total velocity exceeds the critical escape velocity defined by equation (37). If there are no further collisions at distances greater than r, $F(r)$ equals the escape loss; otherwise it is just the outward flux. The physical interpretation of equation (42) thus depends critically on the relative frequency of collisions beyond a given level.

The conditions for the validity of equation (42) have been discussed in great detail by Opik and Singer (1959, 1960), Brandt and Chamberlain (1960), Herring and Kyle (1960), and Aamondt and Case (1962). Within the region of the atmosphere where collisions are frequent, the Maxwellian distribution on which equation (42) is based holds quite accurately, and it gives a direct estimate of the outward flux. However, part of this outward flux is balanced by an inward flux due to the fact that a certain fraction of the particles in their upward paths collide and return. The net outward flux is then less than that given by equation (42). As the base of the exosphere is approached, the total net flux is more closely approximated by equation (42), but because of the absence of collisions, the Maxwellian distribution holds less exactly.

It should be noted that the scale height refers to the particular escaping component. For the case where the scale height is much less than the distance to the center of the earth, equation (42) simplifies to

$$F(r) = n(r) \left(\frac{g(r)}{2\pi}\right)^{\frac{1}{2}} H(r)^{-\frac{1}{2}} \exp \left\{ - \frac{r}{H(r)} \right\} \tag{43}$$

For a minor constituent, the escape level r_c can be defined as the height at which

$$\sigma \int_{r_0}^{\infty} n(r)\, dr = \tfrac{1}{2} \tag{44}$$

where n is the total number density, and σ is the effective collision cross section. For the escape of a minor constituent, equation (44) can be approximated by

$$H_c n_c \sigma = \tfrac{1}{2} \tag{45}$$

where H_c is the scale height at the critical level and n_c is the number density at the escape level. For an atmosphere dominated by oxygen atom, σ is about 7×10^{-16} particles/cm^2 so that the condition at escape level is

$$H_c n_c \approx 7 \times 10^{14} \tag{46}$$

For the models discussed earlier (pp. 148–159), at a scale height of 100 km, the number density is on the order of 7×10^7. The escape level is thus on the order of 500 to 600 km depending on the time of day. It is also to be noted that the escape level is in a region in which the atmosphere is nearly isothermal.

Theory of Diffusion of a Minor Component

We next consider the laws governing the diffusion of a constituent through the atmosphere. As has been noted, the rate of diffusion may control the rate of escape when the rate of escape is high. The diffusion of one gas through another in the presence of a temperature gradient has been treated in detail by Chapman and Cowling (1939). For simplicity, we assume a mixture of two gases, A and B, where the number density of gas A is much less than the number density of gas B

$$n_A \ll n_B \qquad n = n_A + n_B \approx n_B \qquad (47)$$

We denote the flow of particles in the positive z direction across unit area per unit time by F_A. The relation between the flow and the gradients of composition and temperature can be described by linear relationships, provided that the gradients are not too high.

$$F_A(z) = -nD \left\{ \frac{d(n_A/n)}{dz} - \frac{n_A n_B \alpha}{n^2 T} \frac{dT}{dz} \right\} \qquad (48)$$

D is the ordinary coefficient of diffusion, while α is the thermal diffusion factor. In general, α is positive. This means that in the steady state the lighter gas tends to concentrate toward the higher temperatures.

Since the concentration of the constituent A is small compared with the bulk composition, the diffusion will not upset the hydrostatic equilibrium of the bulk gas. In view of this, equation (48) may be rewritten in terms of the vertical concentration of the constituent A as

$$\frac{dn_A}{dz} = -n_A(z) \left[\frac{1}{H_A(z)} + \frac{\{1 - \alpha\}}{T} \frac{dT}{dz} \right] - \frac{F_A(z)}{D} \qquad (49)$$

H is the scale height for the major constituent. The first term on the righthand side of the equation gives the equilibrium distribution for a diffusing component, where no account is taken of the sink corresponding to the escaping gas.

If the last term in equation (49) is neglected, the ratio of the minor constituent A at two levels, z_1, z_2, is given by

$$\frac{n_A(r_1)}{n_A(r_2)} = \left(\frac{T(r_2)}{T(r_1)} \right)^{1-\alpha-\beta} \left(\frac{n_B(r_1)}{n_B(r_2)} \right)^{\beta} \qquad (50)$$

where β is the ratio of the molecular masses of A and B:

$$\beta = \frac{m_A}{m_B} \qquad (51)$$

(Bates and McDowell, 1957).

Equations (43) and (49) can be combined to yield the expression for the vertical distribution of a minor escaping component:

$$\frac{dn_A}{dz} = -n_A(z) \left[\frac{1}{H_A(z)} + \frac{(1 - \alpha)}{T} \frac{dT}{dz} \right]$$
$$- \frac{n(z)}{D} \left[\frac{g(z)}{2\pi} \right]^{\frac{1}{2}} H_A(z)^{-\frac{1}{2}} \exp \left\{ -\frac{r}{H_A(z)} \right\} \qquad (52)$$

For a two-component gas with collision cross-section σ, the coefficient of diffusion D is

$$D = \frac{3}{32} \frac{1}{n\pi a^2} \left(1 + \frac{m_A}{m}\right)^{\frac{1}{2}} \left(\frac{8kT}{\pi m_A}\right)^{\frac{1}{2}} \tag{53}$$

where a is the atomic radius (Chapman and Cowling, 1939). The diffusion coefficient thus varies inversely with the total concentration of the gas and directly as the square root of the temperature.

Equations (43) and (50) can be combined to yield the escape flux at the critical level in terms of the concentration of the minor constituent at the level at which diffusive separation begins, provided that the back effect of the diffusion on the vertical distribution of the minor constituent is neglected. Alternatively, we can calculate the escape flux for a given component using equation (43) and the concentrations derived for various model atmospheres discussed earlier (pp. 148–159). The differences in the results arise from the fact that thermal diffusion is neglected in calculating model atmospheres. We note from equation (50) that the effect of thermal diffusion is to increase the concentration of the minor constituent at the escape level since α is positive. The proportional increase of the number density of the minor constituent at the escape level due to thermal diffusion is equal to

$$\left[\frac{T(z_0)}{T(z_c)}\right]^{-\alpha} \tag{54}$$

where z_0 is the height at which diffusive separation begins, and z_c is the critical height. The magnitude of α is uncertain, but it is customary to take values of about 0.4 (Grew and Ibbs, 1952). The escape flux can thus be calculated for a model atmosphere using equation (43), making the correction for thermal diffusion given in equation (54). The calculated flux will then be a maximum flux since no account is taken of the effect of escape on the diffusion. Bates and McDowell (1957) show that the back effect of diffusion is negligible except when the escape rates become large.

Escape of Helium from the Earth's Atmosphere

Using the model for the atmosphere described earlier (p. 148ff.), we find that at a temperature of $1700°K$ at the critical level, the escape rate for He^4 is 7×10^4 atoms/cm²-sec. At the same temperature, the escape rate for He^3 is 6 atoms/cm²-sec. At $2100°K$, the escape rate of He^4 is 1.2×10^6 particles/cm²-sec, and the corresponding escape rate of He³ is 50 particles/cm²-sec. The numerical values obtained using this model atmosphere are somewhat greater than those obtained by Bates and McDowell (1959) because the models assume a higher concentration of helium at the beginning of the diffusive layer.

Consideration of the solar cycle and diurnal fluctuations in temperature at the escape level indicates that the temperature at the escape level is 2100°K less than 1% of the time. The temperature would be at 1700° or above less than 10% of the time. An integration in time over a solar cycle yields an average rate of escape of He⁴ of 6×10^4 particles/cm²-sec. This rate of escape corresponds to a rate of escape of He³ of 4 particles/cm²-sec. Both these values are less than the estimated rates of influx into the atmosphere. The rate of influx of He⁴ is at least a factor of two greater than the indicated escape rate, and may be an order of magnitude greater. It is thus clear that He⁴ cannot be in a steady state at present if thermal escape is the mechanism for He⁴ leaving the atmosphere. This point was first noted by Bates and McDowell (1957), and newer data fully confirm their suggestions.

Since the present content of helium would accumulate at a time on the order of 2×10^6 years, it is clear that either some mechanism by which helium could escape has been overlooked, or that conditions in the past differed from those holding at present. For the second suggestion what is needed is an effective heat source that will raise the average temperature of the escape level to about 2200°.

The additional heat flux needed to raise the average temperature to 2200° would require detailed investigation since the number of competing effects is large. However, a rough estimate follows from equation (14) and substituting numerical values appropriate for the models discussed earlier (pp. 148–159). An increase in the total heat flux of 1 erg/cm²-sec increases the average temperature about 900 K°. The average temperature over the last solar cycle has been about 1400°K. An additional heat flux of about 1 erg/cm²-sec is required in order for helium to escape at a rate sufficient to keep up with the present production. An additional heat source of 2 ergs/cm²-sec would result in an escape flux of He⁴ greater than 10⁷ atoms/cm²-sec. These estimates must necessarily be crude, since we assume that the conditions at the beginning of the diffusive layer remain constant while the conditions at greater heights change in response to the changing energy input.

At present, He³ is also out of equilibrium, with a production rate slightly greater than the escape rate if only galactic cosmic rays contribute to the production of He³. If, in addition, there is an influx from solar cosmic rays, then the excess of the input over the escape rate is about 10 atoms/cm²-sec. The content of He^3 has built up in a time of about 5×10^5 years. Since the content of He^4 can be built up in a time of about 2×10^6 years, it can be concluded that within the last 10^5–10^6 years conditions in the upper atmosphere have been radically different, if thermal escape is the loss mechanism.

The comments of the foregoing paragraphs depend on the assumption that thermal processes alone are responsible for the escape of helium. Bates and Patterson (1962) made the important suggestion that the recombination of HeO^+ produces helium atoms with a kinetic energy in excess of the 2.4 ev that are required for escape from the exosphere into interplanetary space. A nonthermal process for the escape provides a neat solution to the helium problem but the relevant rates of reactions and energy relations are most uncertain.

EFFECT OF THE MAGNETIC FIELD

The direct effects of the magnetic field on escaping particles are well understood. There is no interaction between the magnetic field and the neutral particles. As far as ionized particles are concerned, the magnetic field restricts their motion to a direction tangent to the field so that ionized particles cannot escape except where the field lines open out into outer space. The indirect effects of the magnetic field are complicated. The magnetic field acts as a shield to the onrushing solar plasma, effectively fending off the low-energy particles and preventing these particles from entering and heating the atmosphere. In addition, the magnetic field also interacts with the plasma; the plasma generates magnetohydrodynamic and low-frequency electromagnetic waves which penetrate into the ionosphere where they are attenuated. Dessler (1959) first pointed out the possible importance of magnetohydrodynamic waves as a heat source in the upper atmosphere. In addition, the interaction of the field with the plasma will result in a disordered electric field. The electric fields may accelerate electrons into the kilovolt range. The energized electrons provide an additional heat source, provided they can penetrate the magnetic field.

The behavior of ionized particles in the upper atmosphere differs from the behavior of the neutral particles principally because of the long-range Coulomb force interaction between ionized particles and the interaction of the ionized particles with the magnetic field. As a result of the Coulomb interaction, a charged particle exchanges its momentum not by single collisions, but in small bits through distant interaction. Because of the small but frequent exchanges of momentum, a particle may transfer an appreciable portion of its momentum in distances short compared with the distances a particle must travel to exchange all of its momentum. The effective collision cross section is thus not easily defined, but for temperatures on the order of $1000°K$, the cross section for the interaction between ions is about 10^5 as great as the cross section for interaction between neutral particles. In the exosphere the gas is partially ionized, and there are several mean free paths corresponding to neutral-charged particle collisions, neutral-neutral collisions, and charged particle interactions. In addition, the inelastic processes, such as ionization-recombination charge exchange, introduce further complications. The difference between the neutral-neutral mean free path and the neutral-charged particle mean free path is small. Over the entire exosphere, the neutral gas mean free path is in excess of 10 km, and is large compared with other lengths except for the scale height that characterizes the motion of the charged particles. It is because of this large difference in the representative length scale of neutral and charged particle gas that it is usually assumed that the two gases act independently. However, for large disturbances in the lower exosphere, this no longer holds true and the neutral gas exerts a heavy influence in damping the organized motion of the ionized gas.

Because of the interaction of the magnetic field with the charged particles, it is possible to treat the ionized gas as a continuum even for processes where the length scales are short compared to the effective mean free path. Because of the magnetic field, the charged particles spiral around the lines of force. The motion of the charged particles in directions at right angles to the line of force is greatly restricted, while the motion along the line of force is largely independent of the magnetic field.

Direct Effect of the Field

The magnetic field will exercise a controlling influence on the escape of particles if a particle leaving the exosphere with a velocity greater than the escape velocity became ionized prior to leaving the region dominated by the earth's magnetic field. The escape velocity at 600 km is 10.7 km/sec. The boundary of the magnetosphere is at about 10 earth radii on the sunlit side (Cahill and Amazeen, 1963). It would thus take an escaping particle less than two hours to pass out of the region where the earth's magnetic field might interact with the particle. The outgoing particle can become ionized either by charge exchange or by photoionization. Assuming an average atmospheric density of 10^3 ionized particles/cm^3 and multiplying by the mean velocity and the charge exchange cross section, we obtain the result that a particle would have to spend about a week in the outer exosphere before becoming ionized. The time scale for ionization due to interaction with extreme ultraviolet is even longer; it is on the order of a year. It is thus clear that on the average an escaping neutral atom will pass through the magnetosphere without becoming ionized.

Thermal Processes Associated with the Magnetic Field

The indirect effects of the magnetic field on the temperature in the high atmosphere are speculative, and no attempt will be made to present a quantitative theory.

In considering the indirect effect of the magnetic field, we need to review data on the solar wind and the theory of the interaction of the solar wind with the earth's magnetic field. Flights of Explorer X and Mariner II established certain of the properties of the low-energy particle radiation from the sun. Neugebauer and Snyder (1962), from observations on Mariner II, find that for quiet, nonstorm conditions, the plasma flux was 1.2×10^8 particles/cm^2-sec, with an energy density of 4.4×10^{-9} ergs/cm^3 and a magnetic field energy density of 1.0×10^{-10} ergs/cm^3. For a velocity of 600 km/sec, the energy flux is then 0.26 ergs/cm^2-sec. These values are in general agreement with data obtained by Explorer X (Rossi, 1962).

The interaction of the plasma with the earth's magnetic field will lead to a distortion of the field. This problem has been studied in great detail by Beard (1960, 1962), Dungey (1961, 1962), Hurley (1961), and Slutz (1962). In these models, the dynamic pressure of the plasma with n particles of mass m_p and velocity v is nm_pv^2, and is balanced by the magnetic pressure $B^2/8\pi$ interior to the bounding surface. The magnetic pressure includes contributions both from the dipole and from the current field associated with the cavity surface.

The calculations of the boundary shape are most appropriate along the sun-earth line, while the shape of the magnetic cavity in the downwind direction remains most uncertain. Equating the magnetic and dynamic pressure yields the distance r_0 from the center of the earth to the bounding cavity, along the sun-earth line:

$$r_0 = \left[\frac{\mu_0}{32\pi^2} \right] \frac{M^{\frac{1}{3}}}{p_0^{\frac{1}{6}}} \tag{55}$$

where M is the magnetic moment, and p_0 is the dynamic pressure. The linear dimensions of the cavity thus vary as a one-third power of the surface field, and inversely as the one-sixth power of the plasma pressure. The interaction cross section of the earth varies as $B^{2/3}$.

Using values for the interplanetary flux and the surface field, we see that the radius of the cavity in the direction toward the sun is on the order of 9 earth radii (Cahill and Amazeen, 1963). The interaction cross section of the earth with the solar plasma is thus on the order of 300 times the cross-sectional area of the solid earth. If all steady energy of the solar plasma intercepted by the magnetosphere could be funneled into the atmosphere, then the energy flux into the atmosphere would be about 100 ergs/cm²-sec.

Most of the studies of the magnetospheric cavity have been concerned with the steady-state shape. The plasma streaming by undergoes a wide variety of fluctuations (Neugebauer and Snyder, 1962). The observed low-frequency fluctuations in pressure will interact with the bounding surface and give rise to hydromagnetic waves. In addition, higher frequency fluctuations associated with the disordered electric field will give rise to low-frequency electromagnetic radiation.

The generation and transmission of hydromagnetic waves is a complicated problem (MacDonald, 1961). Under conditions where the magnetic field pressure is large compared with the thermal pressure, one mode is propagated almost spherically at the Alfvén wave velocity. Another mode propagates the vorticity of the fluid motion one-dimensionally along the magnetic lines of force, again at Alfvén velocity. The third mode is a perturbed sound mode and is unimportant for conditions where the mean free path along the line of force is very large.

As the plasma streams past the bounding surface of the magnetosphere at velocities greater than the local Alfvén velocity, waves can be generated in the surface of the magnetosphere either through shear instability or by the fluctuations in the dynamic pressure (Dessler and Fejer, 1963). The action of the fluctuations in dynamic pressure can be visualized in a straightforward fashion. We suppose that there is a pressure fluctuation with a certain length scale, L. This fluctuation will tend to produce longitudinal waves of the same scale, L, traveling at various angles to the solar wind. In general, the wind speed will be different from the phase velocity of the waves. However, if the component of the wind speed, resolved in the direction of the wave, just equals the velocity of the wave, then there is a matching between the fluctuation in pressure and the mode of oscillation. A kind of resonance takes place, and the wave amplitude builds up. The local Alfvén velocity at the bounding surface is on the order of one-tenth the streaming velocity of the plasma. Since the rate of buildup is greatest when the resolved component of the velocity equals the phase velocity, we should expect that the fluctuations in pressure would be most effective on the circular region on the bounding cavity where the circular region subtends an angle of about 10 degrees.

Waves generated along the bounding surface will be transmitted inwardly with a longitudinal mode propagating spherically, while the transverse mode is guided along the lines of force. Both modes are trapped within the magnetosphere. These modes then pass into a region where the density of neutral particles becomes so high that the collisions of the ionized particles with the neutral particles remove energy from the wave at a high rate (Dessler, 1959; Francis and Karplus, 1960; Karplus, Francis, and Dragt, 1962). However, part of the energy can be converted into electromagnetic energy and propagated through the earth's neutral atmosphere as ordinary electromagnetic waves. Observations at ground level can thus provide some estimate of the intensity of hydromagnetic waves in the upper atmosphere. For example, Ness et al. (1962), in a power spectral analysis of geomagnetic fluctuations at Fredericksburg, Virginia, find, in the frequency interval 0 to 0.5 cycles/sec, an energy of 0.1 ergs/cm³. The spectrum peaks at about 0.1 cps with a Q of about 6. Similar values for a Q for giant pulsations have been obtained by Sugiura (1961). Q is related to the rate of energy dissipation by

$$\frac{\overline{dE}}{dt} = 2E\pi f Q^{-1} \tag{56}$$

where E is the peak energy, and the left-hand side is the energy dissipated averaged over a cycle. The quiet-time rate at which energy is dissipated in the frequency range from 0 to 0.5 cps is then of the order of 1×10^{-14} ergs/cm³-sec. With an Alfvén velocity on the order of 10^9 cm/sec, the energy flux into the ionosphere due to hydromagnetic wave dissipation in this frequency range is 10^{-5} ergs/cm²-sec.

The fluctuations in the plasma at the bounding surface contain sufficient energy to account for the extra heating required by the satellite data. It is apparent both from ground observations and from satellite measurements that the energy available in the plasma fluctuations is not radiated into the ionosphere by the hydromagnetic waves, at least in the frequency range of 0 to 1 cps. This raises the intriguing question as to the energy density within the frequency range 1 to 1000 cps. In this range, observations both at ground level and in space are inadequate to give a proper estimate of the energy flux.

SUMMARY AND CONCLUSIONS

The high degree of correlation between the solar activity as measured by the 10.7-cm flux and the change in density of the atmosphere as measured by the satellite drag, coupled with the phase relations, strongly suggests that the solar wind is involved in heating the ionosphere. However, this heating cannot take place in the low-frequency end of the hydromagnetic wave spectrum. The additional energy may be transferred by higher-frequency waves or by high-energy electrons. However, neither mode of energy transfer from the plasma to the ionosphere has definitely been identified.

Until the present-day additional heat source is clearly identified, considerations of the possible change of the thermal conditions in the upper atmosphere must remain speculative. However, a few comments appear appropriate. If high-frequency hydromagnetic and low-frequency electromagnetic radiation is an appropriate heat source, then this heat source would increase with an increase in the cross-sectional area of the magnetosphere and with an increase in the fluctuations in the particles emitted from the sun. The cross-sectional area varies as $B^{2/3}$. An additional heat source in the past averaging 1 erg/cm²-sec would require that the cross-sectional area should double, and this in turn would require a magnetic field 2.8 times the strength of the present field. This assumes, of course, that the energy in the high-frequency hydromagnetic wave is proportional to the cross-sectional area. If this is so, then even the historical fluctuations in the magnetic field must have produced rather major changes in the temperature of the upper atmosphere.

An alternative suggestion might be that the magnetic field has been much weaker in the past than it is at present. This would then allow the solar flux to enter. The protons would deposit their energy at heights above about 200 km since the mean energy of the solar wind is on the order of 1 to 10 kev. The energy flux of 0.3 ergs/cm²-sec would be appropriate, since the cross-sectional area for interaction with the plasma would not be enlarged by the magnetic field. In this case, the mean energy of the plasma rather than the fluctuations are used to heat up the atmosphere. The present quiet-time flux would not be sufficient to raise the temperature to that required for helium to escape. However, the active-time solar flux may be a factor of 4 to 5 times greater than the quiet-time flux if the solar wind is proportional to the 10.7-cm radial flux. However, this increase in flux would hold only over a short part of the solar cycle and the temperatures on the average would not be great enough to provide the required escape of helium.

It thus seems clear that the removal of the magnetic field is not sufficient by itself to provide the required escape of helium. An increase of the field by a factor of 2 or 3 would give rise to the required escape flux provided that the energy in the fluctuating plasma can be transmitted from the boundary of the magnetosphere and deposited within the ionosphere. Over geologic time, on the average, the field would have had to be twice the present field 10% of the time.

Alternatively, it may be assumed that the ultraviolet part of the solar spectrum undergoes long-period variations that are of the same order as its mean value. This again could account for the loss of helium. One additional source of energy which has not been considered is the radiation of gravity waves from the surface into the atmosphere. Calculations coupled with observation of the ground level pressure spectrum (MacDonald, unpublished data) indicate that this source is not sufficiently strong to produce the required extra heating of the upper atmosphere. Furthermore, it is difficult to imagine, on time scales on the order of a million years, large-scale changes in the source of the gravity waves, since they are generated by motions in the lower atmosphere.

REFERENCES

Aamondt, R. E. and K. M. Case, 1962. Density in a simple model of the exosphere, *Phys. Fluids,* **5,** 1019–1021.

Bates, D. R., 1951. The temperature of the upper atmosphere, *Proc. Phys. Soc.,* **B64,** 805–821.

Bates, D. R. and M. R. C. McDowell, 1957. Atmospheric helium, *Jour. Atmos. and Terrestrial Phys.,* **11,** 200–208.

——————— 1959. Escape of helium, *Jour. Atmos. and Terrestrial Phys.,* **16,** 393–395.

Bates, D. R. and T. R. L. Patterson, 1962. Helium ions in the upper atmosphere, *Planetary and Space Science,* **9,** 599–605.

Beard, D. B., 1960. The interaction of the terrestrial magnetic field with the solar corpuscular radiation, *Jour. Geophys. Res.,* **65,** 3559–3568.

——————— 1962. The interaction of the terrestrial magnetic field with the solar corpuscular radiation, 2: Second-order approximation, *Jour. Geophys. Res.,* **67,** 477–483.

Begemann, F. and W. F. Libby, 1957. Continental water balance, ground water inventory and storage times, surface ocean mixing rates, and world-wide water circulation patterns from cosmic-ray and bomb tritium, *Geochim. et Cosmochim. Acta,* **12,** 277–296.

Birch, F., 1951. Recent work on the radioactivity of potassium and some related geophysical problems, *Jour. Geophys. Res.,* **56,** 107–126.

Biswas, S., C. E. Fichtel, and D. E. Guss, 1962. Study of the hydrogen, helium, and heavy nuclei in the Nov. 12, 1960, solar cosmic-ray event, *Phys. Rev.*, **128**, 2756–2771.

Biswas, S., C. E. Fichtel, D. E. Guss, and C. J. Waddington, 1963. Hydrogen, helium and heavy nuclei from the solar event on Nov. 15, 1960. Goddard Space Flight Center, NASA, X-611-62-235.

Blamont, J. E. and C. deJager, 1961. Upper atmospheric turbulence near the 100 km level, *Annales Geophysique*, **17**, 134–144.

Bourdeau, R. E., E. C. Whipple, Jr., J. L. Donley, and S. J. Bauer, 1962. Experimental evidence for the presence of helium ions based on Explorer VIII satellite data, *Jour. Geophys. Res.*, **67**, 467–475.

Brandt, J. C. and J. W. Chamberlain, 1960. Density of neutral gas in a planetary exosphere, *Phys. Fluids*, **3**, 485–486.

Bryant, R., 1961. A comparison of theory and observation of the Echo I satellite, *Jour. Geophys. Res.*, **66**, 3066–3069.

Byram, E. T., T. A. Chubb, and H. Friedman, 1955. Dissociation of oxygen in the upper atmosphere, *Phys. Rev.*, **98**, 1594–1597.

Cahill, L. J. and P. G. Amazeen, 1963. The boundary of the geomagnetic field, *Jour. Geophys. Res.*, **68**, 1835–1843.

Carslaw, H. and J. C. Jaeger, 1959. *Conduction of Heat in Solids*, Oxford University Press.

Chapman, S. and T. G. Cowling, 1939. *The Mathematical Theory of Non-Uniform Gases*, Cambridge University Press.

Craig, H. and D. Lal, 1961. The production rate of natural tritium, *Tellus*, **13**, 85–105.

Dalgarno, A. and D. Parkinson, 1960. Photoionization of atomic oxygen and atomic nitrogen, *Jour. Atmos. and Terrestrial Phys.*, **18**, 335–337.

Damon, P. E. and J. L. Kulp, 1958. Inert gases and the evolution of the atmosphere, *Geochim. et Cosmochim. Acta*, **13**, 280–292.

Dessler, A. J., 1959. Ionospheric heating by hydromagnetic waves, *Jour. Geophys. Res.*, **64**, 397–401.

———— and J. A. Fejer, 1963. Interpretation of K_p index and M-region geomagnetic storms, *Planet. and Space Sci.*, **11**, 505.

Dostrovsky, I., Z. Fraenkel, and L. Winsberg, 1960. Monte Carlo calculations of nuclear evaporation processes, IV: Spectra of neutrons and charged particles from nuclear reactions, *Phys. Rev.*, **118**, 781–793.

Dungey, J. W., 1961. The steady state of the Chapman-Ferraro Problem in two dimensions, *Jour. Geophys. Res.*, **66**, 1043–1047.

———— 1962. The interplanetary field and auroral theory, *Jour. Phys. Soc. Japan*, **17**, Suppl. A-2, 15–18.

Eckart, C., 1960. *Hydrodynamics of Oceans and Atmospheres*, Pergamon Press, New York.

Fireman, E. L., 1953. Measurement of the (N, H^3) cross section in nitrogen and its relationship to the tritium production in the atmosphere, *Phys. Rev.*, **91**, 922–926.

———— J. de Felice, and D. Tilles, 1961. Solar flare tritium in a recovered satellite, *Phys. Rev.*, **123**, 1935–1938.

Flamm, E., R. E. Lingenfelter, G. J. F. MacDonald, and W. F. Libby, 1962. Tritium and helium-3 solar flares and loss of helium from the earth's atmosphere, *Science*, **138**, 48–59.

Francis, W. E. and R. Karplus, 1960. Hydromagnetic waves in the ionosphere, *Jour. Geophys. Res.,* **65,** 3593–3600.

Gluckauf, E., 1951. The composition of atmospheric air, *Compendium of Meteorology,* Am. Meteor. Soc. (March 10), Boston, Mass.

Goodman, N. R., 1957. On the joint estimation of the spectra, cospectrum, and quadrature spectrum of a two dimensional stationary Gaussian process, *Scientific Paper No. 10,* Engineering Stabsl. Laboratory, New York University.

Greenhow, J. S., 1959. Eddy diffusion and its effect on meteor trails, *Jour. Geophys. Res.,* **64,** 2208–2209.

Grew, K. E. and T. L. Ibbs, 1952. *Thermal Diffusion in Gases,* Cambridge University Press.

Groves, G. V., 1961. Correlation of upper atmosphere air density with geomagnetic activity, Nov. 1960, in H. Kallmann-Bijl, editor, *Space Research,* Vol. 2, North Holland Press, Amsterdam, 751–753.

Hale, L. C., 1961. Ionospheric measurements with a multigrid potential analyzer, Abstract, *Jour. Geophys. Res.,* **66,** 1554.

Hanson, W. B., 1962. Upper-atmosphere helium ions, *Jour. Geophys. Res.,* **67,** 183–188.

————— and F. S. Johnson, 1961. Electron temperatures in the ionosphere, *Memoires Soc. R. Sc. Liege,* **4,** 390–424.

Harris, I. and W. Priester, 1962a. Time-dependent structure of the upper atmosphere, *Jour. Atmos. Sci.,* **19,** 286–301.

————— 1962b. Theoretical models for the solar-cycle variation of the upper atmosphere, *Jour. Geophys. Res.,* **67,** 4585–4591.

Herring, J. and L. Kyle, 1961. Density in a planetary exosphere, *Jour. Geophys. Res.,* **66,** 1980–1982.

Hide, R. and P. H. Roberts, 1961. The origin of the main geomagnetic field, pp. 27–98 in L. H. Ahrens, F. Press, K. Rankama, and S. K. Runcorn, editors, *Physics and Chemistry of the Earth, 4,* Pergamon Press, New York.

Hinteregger, H. E. and K. Watanabe, 1962. Photoionization rates in the *E* and *F* regions, 2, *Jour. Geophys. Res.,* **67,** 3373–3392.

Holland, H. D., 1962. Model for the evolution of the earth's atmosphere, pp. 447–477 in A. E. J. Engel, H. L. James, and B. F. Leonard, editors, *Petrologic Studies: A Volume to Honor A. F. Buddington,* The Geological Society of America.

Hurley, J., 1958. Interaction of a streaming plasma with the magnetic field of a two-dimensional dipole, *Phys. Fluids,* **4,** 854–859.

Jacchia, L. G., 1958. The erratic orbital acceleration of 1957 beta, *Sky and Telescope,* **17,** 278.

————— 1959. Recent advances in aeronomy. Reduction of orbital data of the satellites to yield atmospheric densities at heights up to 700 km, *Nature,* **183,** 327.

————— 1960. A variable atmospheric-density model from satellite accelerations, *Smithson. Astrophys. Obs. Spec. Rept. No. 39.*

————— 1961. A working model of the upper atmosphere, *Nature,* **192,** 1147–1148.

————— and J. Slowey, 1962. Preliminary analysis of the atmospheric drag of the twelve-foot balloon satellite (1961 1), *Smithson. Inst. Astrophys. Obs., Research in Space Science, Spec. Rept. No. 84.*

Karplus, R., W. E. Francis, and A. J. Dragt, 1962. The attenuation of hydro-magnetic waves in the ionosphere, *Planet. and Space Sci.,* 9, 771–786.

King-Hele, D. G. and J. M. Rees, 1962. Scale height in the upper atmosphere, *Proc. Roy. Soc.,* 270, 562–585.

King-Hele, D. G. and D. M. C. Walker, 1960. Density of the upper atmos-phere and its dependence on the sun as revealed by satellite orbits, *Nature,* 186, 928–931.

—————————— 1961. Upper-atmosphere density during the years 1957–1961 determined from satellite orbits, in H. Kallman-Bijl, editor, *Space Research, Vol. 2,* North-Holland Press, Amsterdam, 918–957.

Kupperian, J. E., E. T. Byram, H. Friedman, and A. Unzicker, 1960. Molecular oxygen densities in the mesosphere over Fort Churchill, *Ann. Intern. Geo-phys. Yr.,* 12, 440–444.

Lennard-Jones, E., 1923. Free paths in a non-uniform rarefied gas with an application to the escape of molecules from an isothermal atmosphere, *Trans. Cambridge Phil. Soc.,* 22, 535–556.

McDonald, F., 1963. *Solar Proton Manual,* NASA-X-611-62-122, Goddard Space Flight Center.

MacDonald, G. J. F., 1959. Calculations on the thermal history of the earth, *Jour. Geophys. Res.,* 64, 1967–2000.

—————————— 1961. Spectrum of hydromagnetic waves in the exosphere, *Jour. Geophys. Res.,* 66, 3639–3670.

—————————— 1962. On the internal constitution of the inner planets, *Jour. Geophys. Res.,* 67, 2945–2974.

Munk, W. H. and G. J. F. MacDonald, 1960. *Rotation of the Earth, A Geo-physical Discussion,* Cambridge University Press.

Ness, N. F., T. L. Skillman, C. S. Scearce, and J. P. Heppner, 1962. Magnetic field fluctuations on the earth and in space, *Jour. Phys. Soc. Japan,* 17, Suppl. A-II, International Conference on Cosmic Rays and the Earth Storm, Part II, 27–33.

Neugebauer, M. and C. W. Snyder, 1962. Solar plasma experiment, *Science,* 138, 1095–1096.

Nicolet, M., 1957. The aeronomic problem of helium, *Annales Geophysique,* 13, 1–21.

—————————— 1959. Constitution of the atmosphere at ionospheric levels, *Jour. Geophys. Res.,* 64, 2092–2101.

—————————— 1960. Les variations de la densite et du transport de chaleur par conduction dans l'atmosphere superieure, in H. Kallman-Bijl, editor, *Space Research, Vol. 1,* North Holland Press, Amsterdam, 46–89.

—————————— 1961a. Structure of the thermosphere, *Planet. and Space Science,* 5, 1–32.

—————————— 1961b. Les modeles atmospheriques et l'helium, *Space Re-search, Vol. 2,* North Holland Press, Amsterdam, 896–901.

—————————— 1961c. Helium, an important constituent in the lower exo-sphere, *Jour. Geophys. Res.,* 66, 2263–2264.

Opik, E. J. and S. F. Singer, 1959. Distribution of density in a planetary exo-sphere, *Physics of Fluids,* 2, 653–655, 1959.

—————————— 1960. Distribution of density in a planetary exosphere, *Phys. Fluids,* 3, 486–488.

Paetzold, H. K., 1961. A preliminary model for the variations of upper air densities, *Nature*, **190**, 35–36.

Pokhunkov, A., 1962. Mass-spectrometer investigations of the structural parameter of the earth's atmosphere at altitudes from 100 to 210 km., *Planetary Space Sci.*, **9**, 269–279.

Priester, W., 1959. Sonnenaktivitaet und Abbremsung der Erdsatelliten, *Mitt. Univ. Sternwarte Bonn*, **24**, 4 pp.; and *Naturwissenschafter*, **46**, 197–198.

———————— 1961. Solar activity effect and diurnal variation in the upper atmosphere, *Jour. Geophys. Res.*, **66**, 4143–4148

———————— and H. A. Martin, 1960. Solare und tageszeitliche effekte in der hochatmosphaere aus beobachtungen kunstlicher erdsatelliten, *Mitt. Univ. Bonn.*, **29**, 53 pp. Engl. translation: Royal Aircraft Establishment Farnborough Library translation No. 901, 20 pp.

———————— and K. Kramp, 1960. Diurnal and seasonal density variations in the upper atmosphere, *Nature*, **188**, 202–204.

Rossi, B., 1962. *The Interplanetary Plasma*, paper presented at American Physical Society Meeting, New York.

Rubey, W. W., 1951. Geologic history of sea water. An attempt to state the problem, *Geol. Soc. Am. Bull.*, **62**, 1111–1148.

———————— 1955. Development of the hydrosphere and atmosphere, with special reference to probable composition of the early atmosphere, pp. 631–650 in A. Poldervaart, editor, *Crust of the Earth*, Geol. Soc. Am. Spec. Paper 62.

Schaeffer, E., 1963. The dissociation of oxygen measured by a rocket-borne mass spectrometer, *Jour. Geophys. Res.*, **68**, 1175–1176.

Schaeffer, O. A. and J. Zahringer, 1962. Solar flares. Helium in satellite materials, *Phys. Rev. Letters*, **8**, 389–390.

Sharp, G. W., W. B. Hanson, and D. D. McKibbin, 1962. Atmospheric density measurements with a satellite-borne microphone gage, *Jour. Geophys. Res.*, **67**, 1375–1382.

Slutz, R. J., 1962. The shape of the geomagnetic field boundary under uniform external pressure, *Jour. Geophys. Res.*, **67**, 505–513.

Smith, E. J., L. Davis, Jr., P. J. Coleman, Jr., and C. P. Sonett, 1963. Magnetic field, *Science*, **139**, 909.

Spitzer, L., 1949. The terrestrial atmosphere above 300 km., pp. 211–247 in G. P. Kuiper, editor, *The Atmospheres of the Earth and Planets*, University of Chicago Press.

Sugiura, M., 1961. Evidence of low-frequency hydromagnetic waves in the exosphere, *Jour. Geophys. Res.*, **66**, 4087–4095.

Townsend, J. W., Jr. and E. B. Meadows, 1958. Density of the winter nighttime Arctic upper atmosphere, *Annales de Geophysique*, **14**, 117–130.

———————— and E. C. Pressly, 1954. A mass spectrometric study of the upper atmosphere, *Rocket Exploration of the Upper Atmosphere*, Pergamon Press, London, 169–188.

Turekian, K. K., 1959. The terrestrial economy of helium and argon, *Geochim. et Cosmochim. Acta*, **17**, 37–42.

Urey, H. C., 1959. The atmospheres of the planets, pp. 363–418 in S. Flügge, editor, *Encyclopedia of Physics, Vol. 52*, Springer-Verlag, Berlin.

Wasserburg, G. J., E. Mazor, R. E. Zartman, 1963. Isotopic and chemical composition of some terrestrial natural gases, pp. 219–240 in J. Geiss and E. D.

Goldberg, editors, *Earth Science and Meteoritics,* North Holland Press, Amsterdam.

Wilson, A. T. and G. J. Fergusson, 1960. Origin of terrestrial tritium, *Geochim. et Cosmochim. Acta,* **18**, 273–277.

Zadunaisky, P. E., I. I. Shapiro, and H. M. Jones, 1961. Experimental and theoretical results on the orbit of Echo I, *Smithson. Astrophys. Obs. Spec. Rept. No. 61,* **22** pp.

Zartman, R. E., G. J. Wasserburg, and J. H. Reynolds, 1961. Helium, argon, and carbon in some natural gases, *Jour. Geophys. Res.,* **66**, 277–306.

DISCUSSION

Dr. Whipple: In all of your calculations you have been using average values. But the peaks in solar flares can be very sharp, and often there is an overlapping of two incoming flares. I don't see how you have a basis for setting limits on the heights of these peaks.

Dr. MacDonald: We try to account for this in our weighting procedure. However, it's not that significant, because with sharp peaks, say of less than a day duration, the time interval is short compared with the diffusion rate, and particles will not escape in appreciable amounts.

Dr. Gold: I am troubled by the fact that the heating is very peaked both in terms of time and space, and that we are really not sure about the effects of these peaks. You have been using the average temperature that the atmosphere settles down to as a result of a flare. But the peak temperature over a short period of time and over a small area of atmosphere will be much higher. So it may be that in some places, the exosphere will be momentarily made so hot that all the gases in the small area will escape. This would have the effect of decreasing the average fractionation.

Dr. Wasserburg: How reliable are Nicolet's values for the upper atmosphere helium density?

Dr. MacDonald: There is some uncertainty in these figures but not enough to negate the conclusions. One could be off by an order of magnitude in the helium abundance at 700 km, and yet it would mean very little.

8

Primordial Rare Gases
in Meteorites

Peter Signer

Gerling and Levskii (1956) reported rare gas concentrations in the Pesjanoe achondrite greatly exceeding the concentrations which could be attributed to radioactive decay of uranium, thorium, and potassium, or cosmic ray interactions.[1] Zähringer and Gentner (1960) found similar high rare gas concentrations in the achondrite Kapoeta, and the group at Mainz, Germany, has since discovered three more meteorites containing large amounts of helium and neon (Koenig et al., 1961; Hintenberger et al., 1961; Koenig et al., 1962*a,b*). They have also found that the excess gas in these meteorites (Pantar, Tabor, and Breitscheid) is always contained in material of a dark appearance which surrounds nodules of a distinctly lighter appearance. The latter are essentially free of primordial gases. This fact is very puzzling with respect to the origin and history of the primordial gases; however, it allows for the determination of the composition of the primordial gases in a most ideal way. We extended the study of these meteorites to include the investigation of argon, krypton and xenon and found that the excess argon also resides only in the dark phase. Krypton and xenon, however, are found in both components, with only a relatively small excess of each in the dark component. Furthermore, we found that Kapoeta contains two phases and that the

---

[1] To distinguish these gases from the radiogenic and cosmogenic rare gases, they are called primordial rare gases. The relative abundances of the primordial rare gases do not necessarily reflect the rare gas abundances at the time of the condensation of matter. Here the latter shall be called primeval abundances.

primordial rare gases are confined to the dark component. Most recently we have investigated the Fayetteville meteorite on the recommendation of Suess, who noted that this meteorite showed a dark-light structure similar to Pantar. The result of this investigation is particularly surprising inasmuch as Fayetteville was found to contain concentrations of primordial helium, neon, and argon about three times higher than in any other meteorite known to contain excess rare gases.

In the following, we would like to present a summary of the presently available data on primordial gases in meteorites, point out what we believe to be a systematic pattern, and give a possible explanation for this pattern.

The data summarized in Figure 8.1 include reports of virtually all laboratories working in this field (see also Stauffer, 1961; Merrihue et al., 1962; Zähringer, 1962a,b; Signer and Suess, 1963).   The mete-

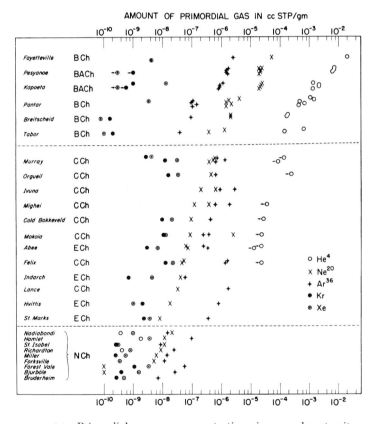

Figure 8.1   Primordial rare gas concentrations in several meteorites.

orites are listed in order of decreasing Ne^{20} concentrations and can be divided into three groups according to the abundance patterns of the rare gases. In the first group, the He^4 is most abundant and exceeds the Ne^{20} concentration by a factor of 100 to 400, whereas the Ne^{20}/A^{36} ratio is of the order of 10 to 20. All meteorites in this group show the dark-light structure just discussed, and invariably the primordial gases listed were found in the dark component. The cosmogenic and radiogenic gas in the light phase has been used to correct the rare gas measured in the dark component, and the values given in Figure 8.1 are, even for Breitscheid and Tabor, very reliable.

The meteorites in the second group (carbonaceous chondrites and enstatite chondrites) show a distinctly different abundance pattern of primordial gases. The Ne^{20}/A^{36} ratios are consistently smaller than unity and have a spread from about 0.7 to as low as 0.02. The He^4/A^{36} ratios may also be well below those of the first group. However, due to generally smaller concentrations of primordial gas and the absence of a light material free of such gases, no monitoring of the cosmogenic and particularly the radiogenic components is possible. This leads to an uncertainty in the correction, which is especially serious in the case of He^4. The abundance values given for this nuclide are the total He^4 values and are to be regarded as upper limits as indicated in Figure 8.1 by arrows. The listed total concentrations may be far too high, particularly for meteorites with He^4 concentrations of 3000×10^{-8} cc He^4/g and less.

The third group contains some chondrites with small concentrations of primordial argon, krypton, and xenon as reported by Zähringer (1962a). We have taken the liberty to compute an upper limit for the primordial neon assuming the cosmogenic Ne^{20}/Ne^{21} to be 0.90. There is no doubt that these meteorites contain small amounts of primordial neon. However, they are difficult to evaluate precisely and not much significance can be attributed to the fine structure of the abundance pattern.

The krypton and xenon concentrations do not reveal a systematic pattern except that the carbonaceous chondrites and enstatite chondrites generally contain more krypton and xenon than either the dark phase of the brecciated meteorites in the first group or the normal chondrites in the third group.

After this summary of the presently available data, we would like to offer an explanation for the differences between the primordial rare gases in the dark phase of the brecciated meteorites and in the meteorites listed in Groups 2 and 3. This scheme has recently been proposed (Signer and Suess, 1963); we feel that the discovery that the Fayetteville meteorite has a primordial gas concentration higher than any other meteorite supports the two-component system.   It is to be noted that the abundance pattern of the light rare gases in the meteorites in the second group resembles, to a certain extent, the atmospheric abundances, whereas the relative abundances in the first group are similar to cosmic abundances.

In Figures 8.2 and 8.3, we have plotted the same data as was shown in Figure 8.1 in a different manner.   This facilitates the presentation of the idea that the primordial gas found in brecciated meteorites may be understood as an admixture of rare gases of a certain composition with rare gases as found in meteorites such as those listed in Group 3 of Figure 8.1.

In Figure 8.2 the meteorites are plotted on a logarithmic neon-argon field.   We note immediately a certain correlation between the meteorite location in Figure 8.2 and the three groups distinguished in Figure 8.1.   The helium- and neon-rich meteorites (black dots in Fig. 8.2) lay in a narrow band of Ne^{20}/A^{36} ratios in spite of the wide range in their helium and neon concentrations.   The other two groups have much wider Ne^{20}/A^{36} ratios and the values are distinctly lower.

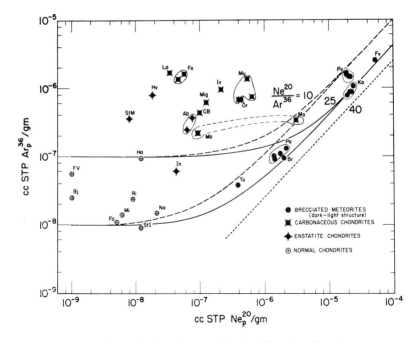

Figure 8.2 Distribution of meteorites by Ne^{20}–A^{36} abundances.

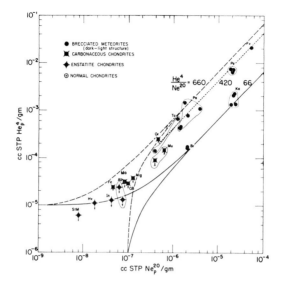

Figure 8.3 Distribution of meteorites by Ne^{20}–He^4 abundances.

This figure suggests the following history of the meteorites with respect to the primordial rare gas concentrations. The carbonaceous chondrites represent, as has been suggested on other grounds, the most ancient material, with rare gas concentrations closest to the primeval abundances. Diffusive loss may have altered these concentrations further to what we now find in the enstatite chondrites or the normal chondrites. According to the present statistics, about 1 out of 15 chondrites has undergone an additional transformation of the rare gas concentration which produced the helium- and neon-rich meteorites with their dark-light structure. This process, we believe, consists of an addition of rare gases, particularly helium, neon and argon, with relative abundances close to cosmic abundances (indicated by the dotted line). Such an addition could shift the position of a normal chondrite from the lower left to the upper right of Figure 8.2, the final location depending on the abundance ratio and amount of the admixed gas, as indicated in Figure 8.2.

Figure 8.3 shows the meteorites' locations in the neon-helium field. The same trends are found, but due to the intrinsic uncertainty in the He^4 concentrations, Figure 8.3 is not as illustrative as Figure 8.2. Nevertheless, all features recognized in Figure 8.2 are also contained in Figure 8.3.

Whether the rare gas concentrations represent the maximum ever present in these meteorites, or are affected by diffusion during the meteorites' history after the admixture, cannot be evaluated with certainty. However, we note that the He^4 concentration in the dark material of the Fayetteville meteorite corresponds to a He^4 partial pressure of the order of 0.1 atm., and it seems unlikely that it was ever substantially higher. In this context, it is of interest to note that our investigations indicate similar A^{40} concentrations in the dark and the light materials of Fayetteville, Pantar, Kapoeta, and Breitscheid. This leads to similar apparent A/K ages for the light and dark materials which are well within the range found for normal chondrites. We conclude that the thermal history of the helium- and neon-rich meteorites after the admixture of these gases did not differ drastically from that of the normal chondrites. The proposed admixture leads immediately to two questions:

1. What has been the source of the admixed rare gas?
2. By what process have these gases been injected into the meteoritic minerals?

At present, neither of the questions can be answered with certainty. As possible gas sources we may consider the solar wind, cometary impact, and gases lost by diffusion from some other region of the parent body. The dark-light structure may very well contain a secret key to the process of injection, since this structural feature seems to be a necessary, but not sufficient, requirement for the occurrence of large concentrations of helium and neon.[2] However, at present the mineralogical aspects of the dark-light structure do not appear to be fully understood (Frederiksson and Wlotzka, private communication).

Frederiksson, DeCarli, and Aaramäe (1962), have given evidence for a correlation between veins in veined meteorites and the occurrence of intense shocks. It may be that such shocks have played an essential part in the formation of the helium- and neon-rich meteorites and their rare gas concentration patterns.

Finally, it has to be pointed out that there is no clear evidence that the helium- and neon-rich meteorites are indeed the ones with the most altered rare gas patterns and that the carbonaceous chondrites are the ones closest to the primeval matter. However, we do not expect to find the true primeval light, rare gases, and the

[2] The rare gas concentrations in the dark and light component of Pantar II, another fragment of several Pantar fragments, were found to be indistinguishably similar to the concentrations in the light component of Pantar I.

carbonaceous chondrites are to be understood as closest to them, albeit possibly affected by diffusive loss. The observed spread in their concentrations and abundances can be attributed to different diffusion properties and different thermal histories. On the contrary, it seems unlikely that the rare gases in the helium- and neon-rich meteorites are the closest representatives of the primeval abundances. Only very similar diffusion losses of helium, neon, and argon could explain the small variations in the relative abundances, in spite of the great range in concentrations. However, the Group 2 and 3 meteorites, if they are to be thought of as descendants of the Group 1, would alternatively require dissimilar diffusion losses in order to fit this assumed genetic relationship. The latter would also encounter great difficulties accounting for chemical and mineralogical facts.

It is hoped that further studies, in particular investigations of the diffusion properties, will yield a deeper understanding of the primordial rare gas patterns, and that we may gain more insight into the origin and history of the solar system and of the atmospheres.

REFERENCES

Frederiksson, K., P. S. DeCarli, and A. Aaramäe, 1962. Shock-induced veins in chondrites, *Space Science III*, North Holland Publishing Co., Amsterdam.

Gerling, E. K. and L. K. Levskii, 1956. On the origin of the rare gases in stony meteorites, *Dok. 1 Akad. Nauk. SSSR*, **110**, 750.

Hintenberger, H., H. Koenig, and H. Waenke, 1962. Uredelgase im Meteoriten Breitscheid, *Z. Naturforsch.*, **17a**, 306–309.

Koenig, H., K. Keil, H. Hintenberger, F. Wlotzka, and F. Begemann, 1961. Untersuchungen an Steinmeteoriten mit extrem hohem Edelgasgehalt, I. *Der Chondrit Pantar, Z. Naturforsch.*, **16a**, 1124.

Koenig, H., K. Keil, and H. Hintenberger, 1962a. Untersuchungen an Steinmeteoriten mit extrem hohem Edelgasgehalt, II. *Der Chondrit Tabor, Z. Naturforsch.*, **17a**, 357–358.

Koenig, H. and F. Wlotzka, 1962b. Untersuchungen an Steinmeteoriten mit extrem hohem Edelgasgehalt, III. Ueber den Sitz der leichten Uredelgase im Chondriten Pantar, *Z. Naturforsch.*, **17a**, 472–476.

Signer, P., 1962. Rare gas concentration in the Pantar meteorite, *43rd Ann. Meeting AGU; J. Geophys. Res.* **67**, 3599.

————— and H. E. Suess, 1963. Rare gases in the sun, in the atmosphere and in meteorites, in J. Geiss and E. D. Goldberg, editors, *Earth Science and Meteoritics*, North Holland Publishing Company, Amsterdam.

Stauffer, H., 1961. Primordial argon and neon in carbonaceous chondrites and ureilites, *Geochim. et Cosmochim. Acta*, **24**, 70–82.

Zähringer, J. and W. Gentner, 1960. Uredelgase in einigen Steinmeteoriten, *Z. Naturforsch.*, **15a**, 600.

Zähringer, J., 1962a. Isotopie-Effekt und Häufigkeiten der Edelgase in Steinmeteoriten und auf der Erde, *Z. Naturforsch.*, **17a**, 460–471.

———————— 1962b. Ueber die Uredelgase in den Achondriten Kapoeta und Staroe Pesjanoe, *Geochim. et Cosmochim. Acta*, **26**, 665–680.

DISCUSSION

Dr. Dicke: One possibility with these brecciated chondrites is that there initially was material with an enormous surface area that gathered up the gases, and then it was compressed. It could very easily trap a lot of such gases on the surface.

Dr. Signer: That is absolutely right; this is another possibility.

Dr. Holland: Do you know where the rare gases are located in the meteorite?

Dr. Signer: There has been a considerable amount of work done on this problem. Zähringer and his group have investigated the location of the rare gas in Kapoeta, and they reported that the biggest amount is in something which they call a glassy material. It is revitrified glassy material, not closely described in their paper. According to a private communication by Waenke, he has tried to separate Pantar, among other meteorites, on a chemical basis and has come up with extremely impressive results. He finds that most of the primordial rare gas must be located somewhere on the surface of the grains, since during the first few minutes of dissolving time large amounts of gas are released.

Dr. Whipple: Would you give the background for your belief that shock will make rare gases stay in the matrix, rather than making them come out?

Dr. Signer: I will refer your question to Dr. Pepin, since the belief is based on an experiment which has been performed in collaboration between Frederiksson, deCarli, and the group at Berkeley.

Dr. Pepin: The first shock experiment was done in the absence of any sort of an atmosphere, and it was simply noted that the light material changed to dark when it was shocked. The second time, the experiment was done in a bomb-like affair with a fairly high partial pressure of atmospheric argon. We found, on subsequently running a temperature experiment on the meteorite, that the meteorite had absorbed in the process of shock a very large amount of argon, and the diffusion coefficients indicated that the argon was held as tightly as the primordial argon in the unshocked phase.

9

Isotopic Analyses of Xenon

R. O. Pepin

The rare gases in a sample of meteoritic or terrestrial material can be extremely sensitive indicators of various physical processes occurring within the sample, and of the nature of its environment, throughout its history. Important radioactive species, both long and short lived, decay to rare gas daughters. Spontaneous and induced fission of uranium and the transuranic elements produce substantial percentage yields of the heavy rare gases. External particle bombardment can cause nuclear spallation events yielding rare gas atoms. For xenon and krypton in particular, the natural or "primordial" abundances of the rare gas isotopes are so low that with present-day techniques very low level abundance anomalies due to production by these or other processes are detectable. Detailed studies of the abundance and isotopic composition of the rare gases in such samples in the past few years have provided an important basis for specific and far-ranging inferences concerning the origin and early history of the meteorites, the earth, and the solar system in general.

This research was supported in part by the U. S. Atomic Energy Commission. In addition, large sections of this review are due to J. H. Reynolds (1963) and W. A. Butler and associates, (1963). I wish to thank Dr. William B. Clarke for permission to discuss his very interesting experiments at this conference prior to the publication of his paper. Dr. Grenville Turner and Mr. Craig Merrihue have very kindly allowed me to present as yet unpublished data obtained by them at the Berkeley laboratory. The sized chondrule fractions from Bjurböle were supplied by Dr. John Wood.

The investigations carried out by the Berkeley group, under the direction of Dr. John Reynolds, have been concerned primarily with xenon isotope abundances in meteorites and in various terrestrial materials. This discussion is a general review of our results and present ideas. Much of this material has been published elsewhere; some represents current work that has not yet been described. In particular, parts of this presentation are taken from the review paper "Xenology" (J. H. Reynolds, 1963).

We begin with a discussion of isotopic analyses of xenon within the framework of theories of the origin of heavy elements in the galaxy (Reynolds, 1963). These theories, due principally to Burbidge, Burbidge, Fowler, and Hoyle (1957) and to Cameron (1958), hold that element formation takes place in stellar interiors by fusion and by neutron addition on a slow time scale, with transfer of material from stellar interiors to interstellar space by evaporation or explosion, or both. In addition, high mass isotopes and elements heavier than lead and bismuth (including the transuranic elements), which cannot be formed by the slow process, are created by neutron addition on a fast time scale (the r-process) in the extreme environment of supernovae, with injection into the interstellar medium by the explosion. This galactic nucleosynthesis probably began about 10^{10} years before the formation of the solar system; a choice of $T_{eff} \cong 2 \times 10^{10}$ years for the duration of uniform synthesis is made to compensate for the probable exponential decrease in element synthesis over the history of the galaxy.

If two elements, one stable and one unstable, are produced at the same rate in nucleosynthesis, it is easily shown that after 2×10^{10} years (or at the instant when the elements are isolated from further buildup by nucleosynthesis),

$$N_u/N_s = \tau/2 \times 10^{10}, \qquad \text{provided that } \tau \ll 2 \times 10^{10} \text{ years}$$

where N_u, N_s are the abundances of the unstable and stable elements, respectively, and τ is the mean life of the unstable element. If both elements are unstable, then

$$N_{u_1}/N_{u_2} = \tau_1/\tau_2, \qquad \text{provided that } \tau_1, \tau_2 \ll 2 \times 10^{10} \text{ years}$$

Two examples we shall need are

$$(I^{129}/I^{127})_0 \cong 0.00125$$

since $I^{129} \xrightarrow{\beta^-} Xe^{129}$, $\quad \tau = 25 \times 10^6$ years; and

$$(Pu^{244}/U^{238})_0 \cong 0.017$$

since both Pu^{244} and U^{238} are unstable. The subscript 0 refers to the time at which the abundances are closed off from nucleosynthesis.

A rough time line indicates a possible sequence of events leading to the present solar system:

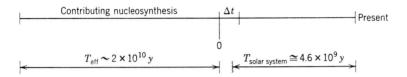

where we define Δt, the formation interval, as that period after the cessation of contributing nucleosynthesis during which the material under consideration (a meteorite or a terrestrial sample) evolves and cools to the point where it can quantitatively retain xenon. $T \cong 4.6 \times 10^9$ years is the approximate age of the solar system measured from some point within Δt.

Considering the particular decay $I^{129} \xrightarrow{\beta^-} Xe^{129}$ ($\tau = 25$ million years), it is evident that if Δt is not longer than a few mean lives of iodine, we might expect to see, in an appropriate object, evidence of the daughter Xe^{129} produced by the decay of this now-extinct radioactivity. Brown (1947) suggested that meteorites might contain evidences of this and other extinct radioactivities; circumstances are particularly favorable for the detection of a radiogenic xenon isotope, since the natural xenon abundance in meteorites is so low. Over the next thirteen years, several investigators searched for excess Xe^{129} in various stone meteorites without success. However, experimental techniques and spectrometer sensitivities were continually being improved, and Reynolds (1960) reported the first positive result—an excess of Xe^{129} in the Richardton chondrite. The xenon mass spectrum for Richardton is reproduced in Figure 9.1.

On this spectrum, horizontal lines have been drawn near the peak tops to indicate where the peaks would have been if the sample were a sample of terrestrial xenon normalized to the meteoritic sample at mass 132. The excess at mass 129 is conspicuous. This excess, called the *special xenon anomaly*, appears on the basis of subsequent investigation by several laboratories to be present in all chondritic meteorites. It has been detected in both the troilite and iron phases of the Sardis iron meteorite, and the possibility exists that it may be a general property of meteoritic xenon. The magnitude of the effect, however, varies widely with the meteorite under consideration. The Xe^{129}/Xe^{132} ratios determined to date range in value from 9.6, in a

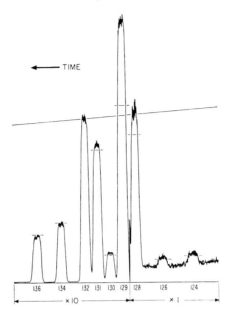

Figure 9.1 Mass spectrum of xenon extracted from the Richardton stone meteorite (from Reynolds, 1960). The peak heights for isotopes 129 through 136 have been scaled down by a factor of 10.

gas fraction from chondrules from the hypersthene chondrite Bruderheim (Merrihue, 1963), to less than 1.1 in xenon from the gas-rich carbonaceous chondrites. This ratio is 0.98 in terrestrial xenon.

Other anomalies, in addition to the excess at mass 129, are present in Richardton xenon. There are small but real differences in the mass spectrum at all other mass numbers: negative at 134 and 136, and positive at 124, 126, 128, 130, and 131. These *general xenon anomalies* also seem to be a general property of meteoritic xenon, although the differences are not always of the same magnitude or direction as those of Richardton.

INTERPRETATION OF THE XENON ANOMALIES

Let us consider, in very general terms, the origin and early history of the solar system. Suppose that at the time "0", an interstellar cloud was effectively isolated from the interstellar medium by the onset of gravitational instability (Cameron, 1962). Subsequent collapse and fragmentation resulted in the formation of a protosun and, at some evolutionary stage, an associated solar nebula. Condensation and accretion led to the appearance of small solid bodies in the nebula. It appears probable that these primary condensates interacted in a complex manner with each other, with electromagnetic and particle irradiation from the protosun, and with the material in the dissipating solar nebula to form the highly evolved and differentiated matter represented by the meteorites.

If we assume that the elemental abundances in the interstellar cloud were those derived from uniform galactic nucleosynthesis, then at the time of isolation from the interstellar medium, $(I^{129}/^{127})_0 \cong$ 0.00125. We interpret the special xenon anomaly as resulting from the survival of a fraction of this "galactic" I^{129} through the formation interval, its incorporation into premeteoritic matter, and the subsequent accumulation of daughter Xe^{129} in the iodine-bearing minerals of the meteorites. If this accumulation began at a time Δt after the isolation of the original cloud from galactic nucleosynthesis, then

$$\left(\frac{Xe^{129*}}{I^{127}}\right)_{met} = \left(\frac{I^{129}}{I^{127}}\right)_0 e^{-\Delta t/\tau} = 0.00125 e^{-\Delta t/\tau}$$

where Xe^{129*} is the excess Xe^{129} in the sample, Δt is the formation interval in millions of years, and $\tau = 25$ million years. The right-hand side of this expression gives the I^{129} abundance at the end of Δt; this will have all decayed into Xe^{129} by the present time.

It is now possible to determine Δt for any meteorite with a Xe^{129} excess. We determine the quantity $(Xe^{129*}/I^{127})_{met}$ by irradiating a meteorite sample with thermal neutrons in a pile. Part of the iodine is converted to excess Xe^{128} by the reactions $I^{127}(n, \gamma)I^{128} \xrightarrow{\beta^-} Xe^{128*}$. The sample is heated in 100 C° stages, and the gas evolved at each temperature is analyzed. $I^{127} - Xe^{129*}$ correlation in the sample appears as a correlated $Xe^{128*} - Xe^{129*}$ release pattern as a function of temperature. By a simple linear regression technique, due to Fish and Goles (1962), Δt is calculated from the ratio of *correlated* I–Xe only. This method of analysis has a number of important advantages. It does not require any assumption as to the amount of ambient Xe^{129} incorporated into the meteorite at the time of its formation; in fact, the linear regression determines this quantity. Surface iodine contamination and low temperature diffusive loss of Xe^{129*} during the history of the sample both result in the appearance of Xe^{128*} unaccompanied by Xe^{129*} in the low temperature fractions of the gas evolved from the sample; correlation is therefore absent, and these fractions are excluded in the calculation of Δt.

TABLE 9.1   Formation Intervals for Several Meteorites as Determined from Xenon 129 Excess.

Meteorite	Type	Formation Interval Δt ($\times 10^6$ years)
Bruderheim	Hypersthene chondrite	$34 \pm 6 \pm 17$
Abee	Enstatite chondrite	$52 \pm 2 \pm 17$
Richardton	Bronzite chondrite	$52 \pm 2 \pm 17$
Sardis	Troilite in coarse octahedrite	250 (tentative)

Formation intervals determined thus far are shown in Table 9.1. The values for Bruderheim (Merrihue, to be published), Abee, and Richardton were determined by the I–Xe correlation technique just described. The larger errors are due to uncertainties in the calibration of pile irradiation monitors. The tentative value for Sardis troilite was calculated directly from the total excess Xe^{129} content and the iodine content reported by Goles and Anders (1962).

The rather short formation intervals obtained for the chondrites in this model of the production of I^{129} by uniform galactic nucleosynthesis require a fast time-scale for the evolution of the solar system. Another model, assuming production of the I^{129} in a sudden synthesis of the elements just prior to the isolation of the interstellar cloud, so that $(I^{129}/I^{127})_0 \cong 1$, adds 166 million years to the values of Δt in Table 9.1. In both cases the formation interval Δt is of direct chronological significance: it is the interval between the isolation of the interstellar cloud and the final cooling of meteoritic material.

The fast evolutionary time-scale required by these formation intervals has led to the proposal of alternative models for the production of the special anomaly. Eberhardt and Geiss (1960) suggested that the decay of galactic I^{129} produced local variations in Xe^{129} abundance, which may have been maintained for long periods of time in the primitive solar nebula. The special anomaly would then be due to the direct incorporation of excess ambient Xe^{129} during the formation of the meteorites, rather than to *in situ* decay of I^{129}, and the "formation interval" would have no chronological significance. However, Jeffery and Reynolds (1961), working with an irradiated sample of the enstatite chondrite Abee, presented convincing evidence for *in situ* decay of I^{129}. They showed that an extremely close correlation exists in the release patterns of I^{127} ($Xe^{128}*$) and $Xe^{129}*$ as a function of temperature, and that such a correlation does *not* exist in the release of Xe^{132} and $Xe^{129}*$; therefore, it appears that $Xe^{129}*$ and Xe^{132} were not both present in ambient xenon, and that the $Xe^{129}*$ is located within the iodine-bearing minerals of the meteorite. The case for $Xe^{129}*$ production in Abee by *in situ* decay of an iodine isotope is very strong indeed. Similar I–Xe correlations are present in the meteorites Bruderheim and Richardton; in fact, the present method of calculating formation intervals depends on the existence of such a correlation.

Fowler, Greenstein, and Hoyle (1962) have proposed a model for the synthesis of deuterium, lithium, beryllium, and boron during the early history of the solar system by a *local* nucleosynthesis in the solar nebula, in which I^{129} is also produced. This model postulates a stage in solar system evolution in which primitive material had accreted in the solar nebula in the form of small icy "planetesimals" containing silicates and metallic oxides. Metric-sized planetesimals separated from the solar nebula were bombarded by high energy charged particles accelerated from the solar surface by intense magnetic flares. Element synthesis occurred through direct spallation reactions on planetesimal targets by the primary incident particles, principally protons; and by capture of secondary neutrons produced in spallation and thermalized by the surrounding ice. From present lithium and boron abundances in "terrestrial" material (including the meteorites), we calculate that the outer layers of the planetesimals must have received an integrated thermal neutron irridation of roughly 4×10^{21} neutrons/cm², or an effective flux $\cong 10^7$ neutrons/cm²-sec assuming major flare activity over the contraction time for the sun, approximately 10^7 years.

Under these conditions, I^{129} is produced directly in the planetesimals. Assuming solar abundances for the nongaseous elements in these bodies, the synthesis of I^{129} is $\sim 20\%$ by spallation of heavier nuclei and $\sim 80\%$ by thermal neutron capture in Te^{128}; then $(I^{129}/I^{127})_0 \cong 2 \times 10^{-4}$, where time "0" now refers to the termination of the irradiation and the end of synthesis. It is evident that formation intervals calculated on this model establish a time-scale for the formation of meteorite parent bodies from the raw material of the primitive planetesimals; the chronology of the development of the planetesimals from the original interstellar cloud is indeterminate, provided only that sufficient time elapsed for the I^{129} produced in the principal galactic synthesis to decay to a very low ambient abundance.

Examining this model in detail, we can say at once that if the bulk of the parent I^{129} responsible for the special anomaly has been formed, as postulated, by the reactions $Te^{128}(n, \gamma)Te^{129} \xrightarrow{\beta^-} I^{129}$, then there should be an *in situ* meteoritic Te-$Xe^{129}*$ correlation. It is possible to examine a sample for evidence of this correlation by exactly the same technique used to establish the existence of the I-$Xe^{129}*$ correlation, since pile irradiation of a meteorite produces, in addition to $Xe^{128}*$ from iodine, excess Xe^{131} by the neutron and decay reactions:

$$Te^{130}(n, \gamma)Te^{131} \xrightarrow{\beta^-} I^{131} \xrightarrow{\beta^-} Xe^{131}*$$

We find, for Abee and Richardton, a very much better correlation of $Xe^{129}*$ with iodine than with tellurium; for Bruderheim, a sample possibly suffering from surface iodine contamination and/or low-temperature diffusive loss of $Xe^{129}*$, the $Xe^{129}*$-I correlation is still superior if only the high-temperature gas fractions are considered (see Reynolds, 1963, for release patterns of $Xe^{128}*$, $Xe^{129}*$, and $Xe^{131}*$ evolved from Abee, Richardton, and Bruderheim as a function of temperature).

However, the absence of $Xe^{129}*$-Te correlation does not absolutely preclude the possibility that the I^{129} was originally produced, all or in part, by neutron capture in tellurium, provided that sufficiently strong fractionation processes operating during the formation of the meteorite parent bodies almost completely separated iodine, including I^{129}, from tellurium.

In summary, *in situ* decay of I^{129} appears firmly established as the source of the special anomaly, but on the basis of the present experimental evidence the question of the origin of the I^{129} remains open. The galactic nucleosynthesis model of I^{129} production appears to us to be more in accord with our results for Abee and Richardton. This model seems considerably less dependent on the operation of specific processes in the evolution of the solar system than the planetary irradiation model; yet there is little doubt that the history of meteoritic material has in fact been extremely complex, involving a large variety of complicated physical and chemical processes.

We now consider the general xenon anomalies. Since these are usually small, we use a permil notation to describe them:

$$\delta_M{}^{(132)} = 1000 \left[\frac{(Xe^M/Xe^{132})_{\text{met}}}{(Xe^M/Xe^{132})_{\text{atm}}} - 1 \right]$$

Here M refers to a particular mass number, and we normalize to mass 132. Other normalizations, especially to mass 130, are frequently employed, but they are less accurate.

In our early work with meteorites, the total meteorite samples were heated at once to above the melting point; all of the gases were driven off and then examined. The xenon from these samples showed a recurrent or "orthodox" pattern of anomalies for the various isotopes. This pattern was established with the first three carbonaceous chondrites studied at Berkeley: Murray, Mighei, and Orgueil. Carbonaceous chondrites are very gas-rich; they contain about 40 times as much xenon, gram for gram, as do such ordinary chondrites as Richardton, and 400 times as much as the earth. For this reason carbonaceous chondritic xenon is often considered to most closely approximate the "primordial" xenon incorporated into the solar system at the end of galactic nucleosynthesis.

Figure 9.2 shows the average general anomaly pattern for carbonaceous chondrites. The superimposed anomalies as determined for Richardton demonstrate the strong similarity. Figure 9.3 shows anomalies for xenon from the gas-rich dark fraction of the veined chondrite Pantar; again, the pattern is seen to be very similar to that of carbonaceous chondritic xenon.

Explanations for the general xenon anomalies have been advanced by Kuroda (1960), Cameron (1962), and Fowler, Greenstein, and Hoyle (1962). Kuroda and Cameron, noting that xenon is considerably less abundant terrestrially than in the meteorites, take the point of view that meteoritic xenon, represented by carbonaceous chondrite xenon, is primordial or "normal," and that terrestrial xenon is anomalous. Kuroda suggests that the heavy terrestrial xenon isotopes may have been enriched by spontaneous fission. If the special anomaly is attributed to I^{129} produced in r-process galactic synthesis, then another extinct radioactivity, 75 million-year Pu^{244}, also synthesized in the r-process, would have been extant in the early history of the solar system and would consequently have been incorporated

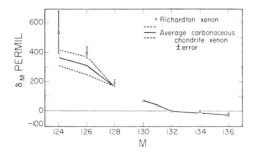

Figure 9.2 General xenon anomaly pattern for average carbonaceous chondrite.

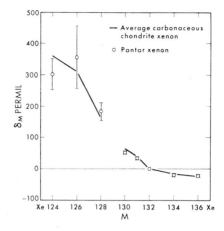

Figure 9.3 Comparison of general xenon anomalies for dark fraction of Pantar with that of average carbonaceous chondrite

into preplanetary matter. This nuclide decays in part by spontaneous fission; if the earth began to retain xenon before the Pu^{244} decayed away, the effect would be to enrich the terrestrial 131, 132, 134, and 136 xenon isotopes. Enrichment of the heavy isotopes of *meteoritic* xenon by the same mechanism might well escape detection because of the much higher Xe/Pu ratio in the meteorites, especially the carbonaceous chondrites.

Kuroda's theory does not account for the observed anomalies in those isotopes shielded from production by fission: 124, 126, 128, and 130. In an expanded treatment of the problem, Cameron (1962) points out that a second mechanism may have operated to alter the isotopic composition of terrestrial xenon: transfer of xenon from the sun to the earth in the solar wind. In Cameron's view, primordial material in the sun was exposed to heavy neutron irradiation during the deuterium-burning phase in solar evolution. Xenon, if unfractionated from neighboring elements, would have had its isotopic composition altered from primordial values principally by neutron absorption in the odd nuclei I^{127}, Xe^{129}, and Xe^{131}, resulting in depletion of Xe^{129} and Xe^{131}, and enrichment of Xe^{128} and Xe^{130}. Even-mass number isotopes of xenon and tellurium are thought to have considerably smaller cross sections, so that depletion of the even xenon isotopes and enrichment of Xe^{129} and Xe^{131} by capture in tellurim would have been negligible. Cameron suggests that this modified primordial xenon, streaming from the sun as a component of the solar wind, is captured by the earth, and that over the span of geologic time a considerable fraction of terrestrial xenon has accumulated from this source.

The total effect of all mechanisms proposed by Kuroda and Cameron is qualitatively summarized in Figure 9.4. Xe^{124} and Xe^{126} abundances are unaffected. It can be seen from Figures 9.2 and 9.3 that if the meteoritic anomaly pattern, now actually an anomaly pattern in *terrestrial* xenon, were normalized to the average of the Xe^{124} and Xe^{126} anomalies, all other isotopes would display negative anomalies. This is roughly what is predicted by the Kuroda-Cameron theory.

The relative fission yields of Pu^{244} are unknown, and are unlikely to be directly determined for some time; the amount of fission xenon in the atmosphere is unknown, as is the degree to which the non-fission primordial atmospheric component has been modified by neutron reactions in "solar" xenon. Nevertheless, the available data— the isotopic compositions of primordial (meteoritic) xenon and terrestrial xenon—permit us to make a quantitative study of this model (Krummenacher et al., 1962). The analysis shows that the amount of fission-produced xenon now in the atmosphere must be 22% of the primordial component with meteoritic isotopic composition. In addition, conclusions can be drawn as to the relative yields of xenon isotopes from the fission of Pu^{244}. The theory does not uniquely specify the Xe^{131} and Xe^{132} yields, but does specify the sum of the two yields, and that the Xe^{131} yield be more than twice that of Xe^{136}. This situation is depicted in Figure 9.5, where the family of possible fission yield curves for Pu^{244} is shown. For reference, the spontaneous fission yield curves for U^{238}, Cm^{242}, and Cf^{252} have been plotted.

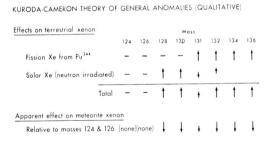

Figure 9.4 Effects on xenon isotopic abundances of mechanisms proposed by Kuroda and Cameron for abundance modification.

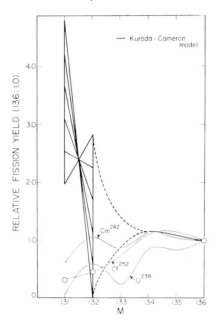

Figure 9.5 Possible fission yield curves for Pu[244] on the basis of the Kuroda-Cameron theory.

It is clear from this diagram that in order to fit the Kuroda-Cameron model to the observed isotopic anomalies, the Pu[244] fission yield curve is required to have an extremely high fine structure at masses 131 and 132. Fine structure of this magnitude, particularly at mass 131, is unprecedented.

In this connection, the results of some recent diffusion experiments with fission-produced xenon carried out by Clarke (1962) are of considerable interest. He examined the isotopic composition of xenon evolved at progressive temperature stages from samples of uranium compounds which had been exposed to a high thermal neutron flux in a pile. The xenon in these samples was that produced by neutron-induced fission of the U[235] in the uranium, so its isotopic composition was known. After 100-hour irradiations, the samples were allowed to "cool" for various times ranging from 10 days to 21 months. They were then heated in 150 C° steps to about 1100°C, with the gases evolved at each step collected separately for analysis.

Results for a uranium oxide, $UO_{2.175}$, are shown in Table 9.2, taken from Clarke's paper. Note that there are substantial augmentations of mass 131 and 132 abundances for the gas released at low temperatures over those expected for xenon from U^{235} neutron fission. The effect is large only in the first very small fractions of the total gas driven off; after a release of about 2% of total, the cumulative enrichment effectively disappears. The data have not been corrected for production of Xe^{136} by neutron capture in Xe^{135}, but Clarke predicts on theoretical grounds that there will be practically no enrichment of Xe^{136} (and very little of Xe^{134}) in the low-temperature fractions.

Another uranium oxide, $UO_{2.241}$, showed an even more pronounced low temperature enrichment of Xe^{131} and Xe^{132}, but for $UO_{2.005}$ the effect was almost absent. There seems to be a clear dependence on oxygen excess relative to the stoichiometric formula. Enrichment was also present to a marked degree in samples of U_3O_8, but was not detected in either uranium hydride or uranium nitride.

Clarke has developed what seems to be an adequate theory, based on the diffusion properties and half-lives of the radioactive, fission-produced precursors of xenon, to explain the anomalous isotopic composition of the xenon diffusing at low temperatures from the uranium oxide samples. He suggests that this same mechanism may have been operating in the earth, and that it may in fact be responsible for the anomalously high Xe^{131} and Xe^{132} fission yields of Pu^{244} required by the Kuroda-Cameron model. The apparent fine structure on the

TABLE 9.2   The Isotopic Composition and Amount of Fission Product Xenon Evolved from $UO_{2.175}$ as a Function of Temperature

Temperature Plateau, °C	Relative Isotopic Abundances				Xenon Atoms Released	Cumulative Xenon Atoms Released
	131	132	134	136		
130	1.910	1.290	1.100	1.209	3.4×10^{11}	3.4×10^{11}
240	2.020	1.070	1.110	1.209	9.8×10^{11}	1.32×10^{12}
375	3.920	2.250	1.130	1.209	5.08×10^{11}	1.83×10^{12}
540	1.510	1.110	1.060	1.209	9.79×10^{11}	2.81×10^{12}
710	0.446	0.595	1.008	1.209	1.78×10^{13}	2.06×10^{13}
850	0.383	0.597	1.005	1.209	9.26×10^{13}	1.13×10^{14}
1015	0.370	0.565	0.997	1.209	2.28×10^{14}	3.41×10^{14}
Cumulative abundances	0.384	0.578	1.000	1.209		
Expected abundances	0.364	0.544	1.000			

yield curve would then be due to diffusive fractionation in the out-gassing of terrestrial fission xenon.

If Clarke's suggestion is correct, a strong criticism of the Kuroda-Cameron theory—that it requires unreasonable spontaneous fission yields—no longer applies. There is, however, at least one important additional consequence involved in applying this mechanism to the earth. The xenon content of the earth, assumed outgassed, is $\sim 6 \times 10^{-11}$ cc STP/g; from our previous analysis of the Kuroda-Cameron model, $\sim 1.5 \times 10^{-12}$ cc/g of this is fission-produced Xe^{136}. The average uranium content (crust + chondritic mantle) is about 25 ppb. It is easily shown that all the Xe^{136} produced in the earth over the last 4.6 aeons by U^{238} spontaneous fission, even if completely out-gassed, amounts to $< 5\%$ of the fission Xe^{136} in the atmosphere. Of the extinct transuranium radioactivities, only Pu^{244} appears to have favorable decay parameters for the efficient production of fission xenon in the early history of the earth. Attributing this to production in the r-process of galactic synthesis, with $(Pu^{244}/U^{238})_0 = 0.017$, and again assuming the earth to be completely outgassed, we compute a tentative Pu-Xe formation interval of ~ 270 million years for the earth within the framework of the Kuroda-Cameron model. This is close to the figure of ~ 250 million years obtained by Cameron (1962) for the I-Xe formation interval of the earth, based on the total terrestrial iodine abundance and the amount of Xe^{129*} in the atmosphere as determined by I/Xe ratio comparisons between the Murray and Richardton meteorites, and involving a somewhat more complicated model of galactic nucleosynthesis.

Now suppose we assume that the isotopic composition of the fission xenon in the atmosphere is the result of the type of diffusion mecha-nism studied by Clarke. This requires that there has been a low temperature release of only a very small fraction of Pu^{244} fission gas to the atmosphere, and that the great bulk of all such fission gas must still be in the body of the earth. We can obtain an approximate figure for the fraction retained by a few simple—and highly tentative—calculations. It was noted by Krummenacher et al. (1962) in dis-cussing the Kuroda-Cameron theory that a typical Xe^{131}/Xe^{136} yield ratio in spontaneous fission is 0.33; if we include data for neutron fission (Hyde, 1962), the average is about 0.40. The Kuroda-Cameron model requires the Xe^{131} fission yield to be more than twice that of Xe^{136}, a discrepancy of a factor 5 to 6. An examination of Clarke's data for the uranium oxides reveals that enrichment factors of 5 to 6 for 131 relative to 136 are attained in the cumulative xenon release only when that release is much less than 1% of total. If we assume—without, as yet, any supporting evidence—that the same rules apply to the diffusion of fission gases from natural minerals with very low uranium contents, then considerably more than 99% of Pu^{244} fission xenon has been retained in the earth, and no major outgassing could have occurred after the earth began to retain its atmosphere. The total amount of fission Xe^{136} attributed to Pu^{244} is now $>1.5 \times 10^{-10}$ cc/g; assuming 6% Xe^{136} fission yield, this is more than ten times as much as can be accounted for from the Pu^{244} synthesized in our model of uniform galactic nucleosynthesis, even if the earth formed and began retaining xenon at time 0. We are therefore apparently required to adopt a model of sudden synthesis for the r-process elements in the solar system, in which abundance ratios at time 0 are essentially production ratios; under these circumstances $(Pu^{244}/U^{238})_0 \sim 0.75$, and $(U^{235}/U^{238})_0 \sim 1.5$ (Cameron, 1962). With a fission Xe^{136} content $>1.5 \times 10^{-10}$ cc/g, the Pu–Xe Δt for the earth is now <190 million years, while for the stone meteorites the I–Xe formation intervals are about 200 million years. This value of the formation interval for the earth certainly cannot be taken very seriously in view of the assumptions used in deriving it, but it does illustrate that an extreme model of nucleosynthesis would indeed be required to account for a large amount of fission xenon still retained in the interior of the earth. An immediate consequence of such a model would be the incorporation of substantial amounts of Pu^{244} into the meteorites as well; more than 50% of the Xe^{136} in Richardton, but less than 2% of that in Murray, would derive from Pu^{244} spontaneous fission. The fact that the Xe^{136}/Xe^{130} ratios (Xe^{130} is shielded in fission) are identical within experimental error in total xenon samples from these two meteorites argues strongly against this.

We can consider the possibility of a sudden synthesis of all or a large fraction of the elements in the solar system from a more general point of view. It can be shown, from present meteoritic and terrestrial abundances of Th^{232}, U^{235}, and U^{238}, their decay constants, and current estimates of their relative production rates in stellar synthesis, that a model with sudden synthesis of the elements about 6.5×10^9 years ago is chronologically concordant (Clayton, 1963). This is not, of course, the only model which can be derived from the same data—others, involving uniform and exponentially decreasing rates of synthesis over long periods of time, are perhaps more realistic since they utilize more probable values for relative production rates— but it is a possible model. However, Patterson (1956) has shown that U–Pb fractionation appears to have occurred in the earth and the meteorites about 4.55×10^9 years ago. Krypton–argon ages for the meteorites tend to be shorter, perhaps due to diffusive loss of radiogenic argon over geologic time; most of the chondrites group between 4.0 and 4.4×10^9 years (Goles, Fish, and Anders, 1959). If we assume that extinct radioactivities such as the I^{129} responsible for the special xenon anomaly were produced in galactic nucleosynthesis, and therefore that formation intervals for solar system material were short, the isolation of the presolar interstellar cloud must have occurred shortly before the primordial Pb-U ratio was established in solid bodies, or $\sim 4.6 \times 10^9$ years ago. In this case the "pure" sudden synthesis model is badly discordant. In fact, such a model requires formation intervals on the order of 2 billion years; extinct radioactivities could not survive from the principal synthesis, and would have to be made in late local events, such as the planetesimal irradiation proposed by Fowler et al. (1962). Certain unstable nuclides made only in the r-process and with half-lives short compared to 2×10^9 years—for example, Pu^{244}—would therefore be incorporated into planetary material only in very small relative abundance.

It seems that there is little to be gained in postulating a sudden synthesis of the elements in order to explain apparent large abundances of the daughter products of short-lived radioactivities. We conclude that large amounts of fissiogenic gases probably do not presently exist in the earth's interior, and therefore that the unusual isotopic composition of atmospheric fission xenon in the Kuroda-Cameron model is unlikely to be due to diffusive fractionation. It is important to stress at this point that Clarke's mechanism may be found to operate in nature, in spite of profound differences between the terrestrial regime and the laboratory conditions under which the effect has been detected. We are planning multi-stage temperature experiments with natural uranium minerals in a effort to detect this effect in the low-temperature release fraction of U^{238} spontaneous fission xenon. However, on the basis of this discussion, substantial enrichment of Xe^{131} and Xe^{132} would have to be present in cumulative release fractions of at least 10% of total before this mechanism could operate in the context of the Kuroda-Cameron model without requiring an unreasonable amount of Pu^{244} in the primitive earth.

Fowler, Greenstein, and Hoyle (1962) adopt quite a different point of view in their consideration of the general xenon anomalies. They point out that spallation and neutron reactions occurring in their model of a local nucleosynthesis within the solar nebula would be expected to modify the isotopic composition of primordial rare gases incorporated in the planetesimals. Under the postulated conditions of high energy solar proton and simultaneous secondary thermal neutron irradiation of the outer layers of the planetesimals, the principal reactions influencing the xenon isotopes are (1) production of Xe^{124} and Xe^{126} by spallation of targets with A ~ 127, primarily cesium to samarium; (2) production of Xe^{128} by neutron capture in I^{127}, with a slight contribution from spallation;   (3) enrichment of Xe^{130} and and Xe^{132} and depletion of Xe^{129} and Xe^{131} by neutron capture; (4) production of Xe^{134} and Xe^{136} by thermal neutron fission of U^{235}. Certain of the parameters of this planetesimal irradiation model are determined by terrestrial and meteoritic abundances of the light nuclei H^1, D^2, lithium and boron: for example, the total thermal neutron irradiation appears to have been $\sim 4 \times 10^{21}$ neutrons/cm^2, as mentioned in the discussion of the special anomaly, and the fraction of the total volume of planetesimal material irradiated by the thermal neutrons is estimated to be $\sim 10\%$—although this estimate has recently been sharply revised downward by Fowler (Clayton, 1963). In order to determine the xenon irradiation products quantitatively, these numbers are used in conjunction with two important assumptions: that elements in the xenon region are present in the planetesimals in abundances characteristic of primitive solar system material, and that the isotopic composition of primordial xenon is that of present-day terrestrial xenon. Under these conditions they find that their calculated anomalies for the light isotopes 124, 126, and 128 are far smaller than those observed in Richardton xenon. They suggest, in view of the properties of the rare gases, that xenon probably was not incorporated in the planetesimals in full primordial abundance, but was fractionated with respect to neighboring elements by an unknown factor. The enrichment of a particular isotope of xenon by spallation or neutron reactions in nuclides other than xenon is clearly proportional to such a fractionation factor. Normalization of the calculated Xe^{126} anomaly to the observed δ_{126} for Richardton indicates a depletion of xenon by a factor of about 20; that is, about 5% of primitive xenon, relative to silicon, was retained in the formation of the planetesimals. With this assumption, the calculated anomaly pattern in planetesimal xenon after irradiation and complete mixing is in close quantitative agreement with the orthodox pattern of the general anomalies at every mass number except 124 and 131. The most serious discrepancy is for δ_{131}, where the computed value of ~ -60 permil is considerably less than the average observed anomaly of $+40$ permil. The calculated 124 anomaly is less than half that of 126; this does not agree with the orthodox pattern, but it is interesting to note that a recent examination of xenon from Bruderheim chondrules shows $\delta_{126}/\delta_{124} = 1.5$ for the total sample, with values for individual temperature fractions as high as 1.7 (Merrihue, 1963).

In this theory of the origin of the general anomalies, the isotopic abundances of *meteoritic* xenon have been altered by various nuclear processes, while terrestrial xenon is considered to be primordial; the point of view is thus directly opposite to that taken by Kuroda and Cameron. A basic assumption of the planetesimal synthesis model is that the meteorites *and* the terrestrial planets formed from material which received the same irradiation in the planetesimal stage. Xenon irradiation products must therefore have been preferentially lost from the pre-earth planetesimals. Since at some stage prior to the formation of the earth these planetesimals must have been concentrated in orbits closer to the sun than the premeteoritic planetesimals, it is suggested that all the rare gases may have been outgassed from pre-earth material with the exception of small amounts of primordial gas retained in the unirradiated interiors of a few large planetesimals. The size distribution of the irradiated bodies appears to have been such that high energy (≥ 330 Mev) incident protons and secondary neutrons directly bombarded only the outer layers, comprising less than 10% of the total primitive material. Thorough mixing of the irradiated and unirradiated fractions is assumed to occur during the formation of meteorite parent bodies and the earth from planetesimals, and during this stage most of the xenon is lost: the Murray meteorite and the earth are now depleted by factors of approximately 6×10^3 and 4×10^6, respectively, relative to xenon abundances expected in primitive solar system material.

The calculated xenon anomaly pattern refers to material in which all irradiation products have been completely mixed with unirradiated primordial matter, in which about 5% of the solar xenon abundance has been retained. This pattern is therefore not unique, in the sense that variations in the mixing ratio and in the factor by which xenon is fractionated in the planetesimals can result in patterns in which the relative as well as the absolute magnitudes of the anomalies are different. It is interesting, especially in view of recent developments in the investigation of meteoritic xenon, to speculate that mixing of primitive planetesimal material may in fact have been partially incomplete and inhomogeneous, at least on a local scale. In addition, some planetesimals might have begun to lose the bulk of their xenon before the end of irradiation; other material may have been strongly depleted not only in rare gases but in volatile constituents such as iodine during all or part of the solar bombardment. If the icy moderating matrix of some of these bodies sublimated or evaporated, or were never present, reactions due to thermal neutron capture would be less important, but material would now be open to irradiation by other components of the primary solar particle flux, such as low-range, low-to-intermediate energy deuterons and α-particles. Unless all primordial material was uniformly homogenized during the subsequent development of the inner solar system, evidence for some of these effects may have survived, not only in the form of characteristic variations in the xenon general anomaly pattern, but also as variations in the distribution and relative abundances of other radiation-sensitive nuclides as well.

RECENT RESULTS

The mechanisms operating in both the Kuroda-Cameron model and the planetesimal nucleosynthesis model of Fowler et al. account fairly well for the experimentally observed anomaly pattern in total xenon samples from Richardton, Pantar, and at least three carbonaceous chondrites. We now know that this particular isotopic composition is by no means representative of all meteoritic xenon. Our recent investigations show that total gas samples from many meteorites, both stones and irons, display anomalies in the xenon spectrum which differ in important respects from the orthodox pattern. Most chondrule and pure mineral fractions separated from bulk samples of the Bruderheim and Bjurböle chondrites also contain xenon of widely variant composition. In addition, large variations in the general and special anomalies are observed in xenon fractions evolved from the *same* sample at different temperatures in almost every meteorite we have analyzed by this technique. It appears that even a single natural sample contains more than one kind of xenon, and that a total gas analysis represents only an average isotopic composition. Murray and Richardton, two meteorites whose total xenon conforms to the orthodox anomaly pattern, are no exceptions: variations in δ_M as large as several times the average value are present in different temperature fractions for all isotopes in Richardton and for the heavy isotopes in Murray.

A particularly interesting example of this effect is the anomaly data for a multi-stage temperature run on a sized fraction of chondrules from the Bjurböle meteorite, shown in Figure 9.6. The striking feature here is the *correlation* in the variations of the anomalies. Anomaly values δ_{134} and δ_{136} tend to move together; so, in the opposite sense, do δ_{124} and δ_{131}. The values δ_{126}, δ_{128}, and δ_{130}, not shown, correlate very well with δ_{131}; δ_{129} also correlates with δ_{131}, but less

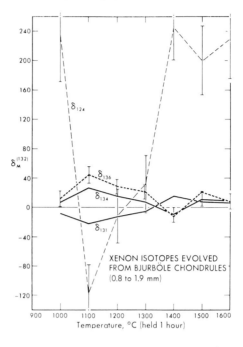

Figure 9.6 Variation of isotopic anomalies with temperature at which gas sample is evolved, for a sized fraction of chondrules, from the Bjurböle meteorite.

well.   The large variability in δ_{124} is not unusual; fluctuations of more than 2000 permil have been observed in the light xenon isotopes evolved in a run on chondrules from the Bruderheim meteorite (Merrihue, 1963).   For temperature below 1000°C the gas release was very small; large errors were associated with the data, and no useful conclusions could be drawn.

Anomaly patterns for the heavy isotopes of xenon evolved from the carbonaceous chondrite Murray are displayed in Figure 9.7 as functions of temperature.   Here again the variations in δ_{134} and δ_{136} are firmly correlated, and they are anticorrelated with the much less striking fluctuations in δ_{130}.   In this case, δ_{131} shows very little change for different temperatures.   Delta values for the light isotopes are fairly steady.   Reynolds and Turner (to be published) have found a very similar anomaly pattern in xenon from the unusual, chondrule-rich carbonaceous chondrite Renazzo.

Correlations such as these in the temperature release patterns suggest that we are dealing with xenon systems containing more than one component. Two isotopically different components, located at different mineral lattice sites within the sample, would be expected to fractionate with respect to each other in their release as a function of temperature. For such a system a plot of δ_M versus $\delta_{M'}$, where M and M' are any two isotopes, would be a straight line whose end points represent the isotopic composition of the pure components. In Figure 9.8 we have plotted δ_{130}, δ_{131}, and δ_{134} versus δ_{136} for the 1000°C–1500°C release fractions from the Bjurböle chondrules; within experimental error, all points lie on straight lines. The large, shaded points represent the average isotopic composition of xenon from the carbonaceous chondrites obtained from the orthodox anomaly pattern; the atomspheric xenon point lies at the origin. A particularly interesting feature of these δ-correlations is that all lines pass through or near the carbonaceous chondrite points and intersect in the general vicinity of the origin, including those for the light isotopes 124, 126, and 128, which are not shown. The δ_{129}–δ_{136} correlation does *not* follow this pattern. The end points of correlation lines such as these are unknown, so it is not possible to determine uniquely the isotopic composition of either component. These data suggest, however, that one

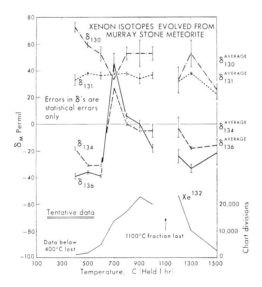

Figure 9.7 Variation of isotopic anomalies with temperature at which gas sample is evolved for the Murray carbonaceous chondrite.

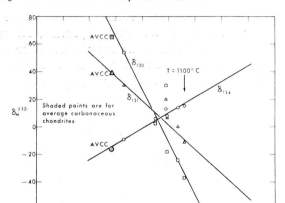

Figure 9.8 δ-correlation in release of xenon isotopes from heated Bjurböle chondrules (0.8 to 1.9 mm).

component is average carbonaceous chrondite xenon. The second component, when mixed in certain proportion with average meteoritic xenon, produces a mixture which resembles terrestrial xenon. In this interpretation the meteoritic component may be considered primordial, and atmospheric xenon of secondary origin. These results are then in essential agreement with the Kuroda-Cameron theory, provided we associate the second component appearing here with Pu^{244} fission xenon, which should be present in low abundance in meteorites as well as in the atmosphere under the assumptions of the model. The possible role of Pu^{244} in the meteorites is discussed in more detail later in this section.

The interpretation of average carbonaceous chondrite xenon as a pure component, and the primordial component, is not the only one that can be made on the basis of these data. It is perfectly possible, for example, to move *toward* the meteoritic xenon points, rather than away from them, by the addition of some second component to a primordial component lying to the right of the origin in Figure 9.8. This is precisely what happens in the planetesimal synthesis model when the component comprising the xenon irradiation products is mixed with the bulk of primitive xenon. We note, however, that terrestrial xenon cannot be a pure component in the Bjurböle chondrule system, since isotopic compositions of the mixture lie on both sides of the origin (later work has also revealed isotopic compositions, in xenon fractions from other samples, lying to the left of the carbonaceous chondrite composition). If we can generalize to the formation of atmospheric and meteoritic xenon from the very limited context of these data, we can say that the primordial xenon of the planetesimal theory did not have terrestrial abundances, and that the xenon of *both* the earth and meteorites is of secondary composition, derived from the primordial through the retention of varying amounts of the irradiation-produced component. In this interpretation it appears that this sample of Bjurböle chondrules contained primitive, partially unmixed material; it is perhaps significant that most of the gas was released only at temperatures greater than 1100°C.

A second run, with a sample of slightly smaller (0.59 to 0.86 mm) chondrules from Bjurböle, showed this supplementary xenon component to be very nearly absent; the points tended to cluster around the average carbonaceous chondrite values. A comparison of the volume release of xenon as a function of temperature for the two samples revealed that a constituent which released a large amount of gas at 1100°C in the first sample did not appear to be present in the second. Whatever the source of this supplementary xenon component may be, it does not seem to be associated with chondrules in general. A particular type of chondrule may contain highly anomalous gas, while the large fraction do not.

Figure 9.9 displays the heavy isotope δ-correlation plots for the

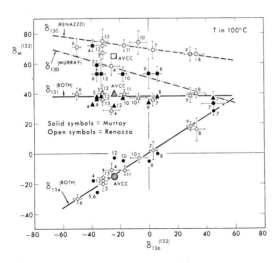

Figure 9.9 $\delta_M^{(132)}$ vs. $\delta_{136}^{(132)}$ correlation for xenon from the carbonaceous chondrites Murray and Renazzo.

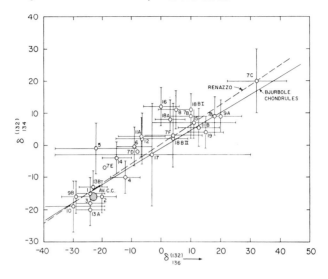

Figure 9.10 $\delta_{134}^{(132)}$ vs. $\delta_{136}^{(132)}$ correlation for total xenon evolved for a number of meteorites. The numbers refer to the meteorites listed in Table 9.3.

carbonaceous chondrites Murray and Renazzo. The correlations are convincing for all isotopes, and those for δ_{131} and δ_{134} are identical for both meteorites. The δ_{134}–δ_{136} correlation here is practically identical with that for the Bjurböle chondrules, but those for δ_{130} and δ_{131} are quiet different; we appear to be dealing with a second component of distinctly different isotopic composition. Xenon of atmospheric composition cannot be formed in this system. Assuming that the pure xenon components in both these carbonaceous chondrites have roughly the same compositions, it is evident from Figure 9.9 that each contains about the same relative amount of the second component. This suggests that this component may be associated with the gas-rich matrix material of these stones rather than with the chondrules, since Renazzo's chondrules are much more abundant and well-defined than those in Murray.

In addition to those just described, heavy isotope δ-correlation plots have been constructed for xenon release fractions from several different types of chondrules and pure matrix minerals separated from the Bruderheim meteorite (Merrihue, to be published). The δ_{134}–δ_{136} correlations are very similar to those shown in Figures 9.8 and 9.9; the δ_{130} and δ_{131} correlation lines have slopes intermediate between the extremes shown by the Bjurböle chondrule and the carbonaceous chondrite correlations.   All lines pass through or near the average meteoritic xenon points.   It is interesting to note, in view of the dissimilar results from the two analyses of Bjurböle chondrules, that Merrihue has found different types of chondrules in Bruderheim to contain xenon of distinctly different isotopic compositions.

In Figures 9.10, 9.11, and 9.12 we have plotted, against δ_{136}, the heavy xenon isotope anomalies for *total* gas samples from a fairly large number of meteorites and meteorite fractions analyzed in the Berkeley laboratory, and elsewhere, over the past few years.   Sample data are listed in Table 9.3.   The correlation lines for Bjurböle chondrules and for Renazzo are superimposed for comparison.   Note the spread in δ-values for the two analyses of Bjurböle chondrules, and for the various separated fractions from Bruderheim, especially the unsorted and pyroxene chondrules.   There is a pronounced tendency for the points to lie along the Bjurböle-Renazzo lines for δ_{134}, and between these lines, or below the Bjurböle line, for δ_{130} and δ_{131}.   The

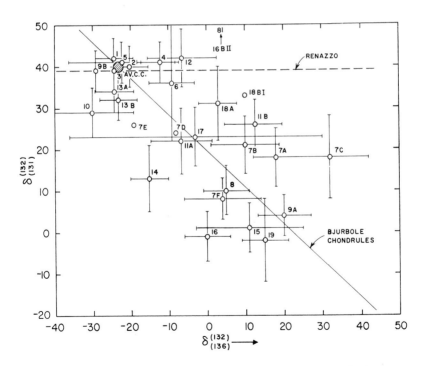

Figure 9.11 $\delta_{131}^{(132)}$ vs. $\delta_{136}^{(132)}$ correlation for total xenon evolved.

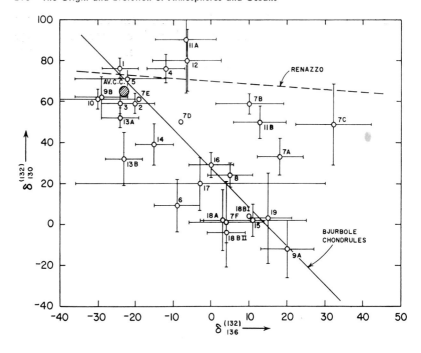

Figure 9.12 $\delta^{(132)}_{130}$ vs. $\delta^{(132)}_{136}$ correlation for total xenon evolved.

simplest interpretation of this pattern is that the isotopic compositions of meteoritic xenon in general are the result of a mixture of one component, perhaps with a composition somewhat like that of average carbonaceous chondrite xenon, with varying amounts of *two* second components. We tentatively identify one of these two components with that detected in Renazzo, the other with the second component found in Bjurböle.

While these assumptions provide a convenient working basis, they are almost certainly an oversimplification of the actual system. Average carbonaceous chondrite xenon is *not* a pure component: the analyses of Murray and Renazzo show it to be a mixture of at least two different kinds of xenon, and it is probably a mixture of all three (or more!) components. We do not know what the isotopic composition of the original xenon in the primitive solar nebula might have been; perhaps it was somewhat like carbonaceous chondrite xenon, or perhaps it was quite different, and carbonaceous chondrite xenon has derived from it through a variety of nuclear reactions and almost

TABLE 9.3   Catalogue of Meteorite Samples Analyzed at Berkeley and Other Laboratories

Number	Meteorite	Type	Fraction	Reference	Experiment
1	Murray	Carbonaceous chondrite	Total	Krummenacher et al., 1962	Melting run
2	Mighei	Carbonaceous chondrite	Total	Krummenacher et al., 1962	Melting run
3	Orgueil	Carbonaceous chondrite	Total	Krummenacher et al., 1962	Melting run
4	Renazzo	Carbonaceous chondrite	Total	Reynolds and Turner (to be published)	Integrated temperature run
5	Richardton	Veined bronzite chondrite	Total	Krummenacher et al., 1962	Melting run
6	Rose City	Black bronzite chondrite	Total	Unpublished	Melting run
7A	Bruderheim	Hypersthene chondrite	Total	Krummenacher et al., 1962	Melting run
7B	Bruderheim	Hypersthene chondrite	Total	Clarke, 1962	Melting run
7C	Bruderheim	Hypersthene chondrite	Unsorted chondrules	Merrihue, 1963	Integrated temperature run
7D	Bruderheim	Hypersthene chondrite	Pyroxene chondrules	Merrihue (to be published)	Integrated temperature run
7E	Bruderheim	Hypersthene chondrite	Olivine fragment	Merrihue (to be published)	Integrated temperature run
7F	Bruderheim	Hypersthene chondrite	Troilite	Merrihue, 1963	Integrated temperature run
8	La Lande	Hypersthene chondrite	Total	Clarke, 1962	Melting run
9A	Bjurböle	Hypersthene chondrite	Chondrules (0.8–1.9 mm)	Reynolds, 1963	Integrated temperature run
9B	Bjurböle	Hypersthene chondrite	Chondrules (0.6–0.9 mm)	Unpublished	Integrated temperature run
10	Abee	Enstatite chondrite	Total	Clarke, 1962	Melting run
11A	Indarch #3	Enstatite chondrite	Total	Krummenacher et al., 1962	Melting run
11B	Indarch #4	Enstatite chondrite	Total	Krummenacher et al., 1962	Melting run
12	St. Mark's	Enstatite chondrite	Total	Krummenacher et al., 1962	Melting run
13A	Pantar	Veined chondrite	Dark fraction	Merrihue et al., 1962	Melting run
13B	Pantar	Veined chondrite	Light fraction	Merrihue et al., 1962	Melting run
14	Kyushu	Veined white chondrite	Total	Krummenacher et al., 1962	Melting run
15	Beardsley	Grey chondrite	Total	Unpublished	Melting run
16	Potter	Grey-black chondrite	Total	Clarke, 1962	Melting run
17	Elenovka	Chondrite	Total	Krummenacher et al., 1962	Melting run
18A	Sardis	Coarse octahedrite	Metal phase	Reynolds et al., 1962	Melting run
18B I	Sardis	Coarse octahedrite	Troilite phase	Reynolds et al., 1962	Melting run
18B II	Sardis	Coarse octahedrite	Troilite phase	Reynolds et al., 1962	Melting run
19	Washington County	Nickel-rich ataxite	Total	Reynolds et al., 1962	Melting run

complete mixing processes occurring in intermediate stages of solar system evolution. A large number of isotopically different components, their separate identities now blurred or obliterated by mixing, may have contributed to the development of solar system rare gases. It seems probable that at least one of our two "minor" xenon components—that in the Bjurböle chondrules—is itself a mixture. In Figures 9.11 and 9.12, points for several meteorities, and for the earth, lie below the Bjurböle correlation line. We can imagine that a component exists whose correlation line with average meteoritic xenon passes through or to the left of the origin, such that all experimental points lie between it and the Renazzo line. The second components appearing in the Bjurböle chondrules and in the various chondrule and matrix fractions from Bruderheim may be interpreted as mixtures of this component with increasing amounts of the second component from Renazzo, which we assume for the moment is a "pure" component.

On the basis of the data just discussed, present-day solar system xenon appears to consist of at least three isotopically different components: xenon resembling that from the average carbonaceous chondrite, plus components similar to the supplementary components in Renazzo and the Bjurböle chondrules. Turner (private communication) has shown that in a three-dimensional space whose coordinate axes are δ_{130}, δ_{131}, and δ_{134}, the isotopic compositions of virtually *all* xenon samples analyzed to date lie within experimental error on the plane defined by the Renazzo correlation line and the origin. Since δ_{134} and δ_{136} are closely correlated, Figures 9.11 and 9.12 therefore essentially represent projections of points in this plane on the δ_{131}–δ_{134} and δ_{130}–δ_{134} coordinate planes. A three-dimensional correlation such as this constitutes strong experimental evidence for a three component system.

It is interesting to speculate that one of the two minor components may be fissiogenic Pu^{244} xenon. If 17 million-year I^{129} from the principal galactic synthesis were extant in the solar system at the time of formation of the earth and the meteorite parent bodies, then, as Kuroda (1960) has pointed out, we would expect 75 million-year Pu^{244} to have been present as well. If we choose, as before, $(Pu^{244}/U^{238})_0 = 0.017$ from the r-process in uniform synthesis, $\sim 6\%$ Xe^{136} yield from Pu^{244} spontaneous fission, and an average uranium concentration of 10 ppb in chondritic material, then a meteorite with an I-Xe formation interval of 50 million years should contain $\sim 4 \times 10^{-12}$ cc STP/g fissiogenic Xe^{136}; this is about 120 times as much as has accumulated over geologic time from U^{238} spontaneous fission in the same material. This component, which at mass 136 amounts to roughly 4% of the total Xe^{136} in an ordinary chondrite like Richardton, would be produced *in situ* at the uranium sites in the meteorite and might be expected to fractionate with respect to the bulk of the xenon during the outgassing of the sample.

Pu^{244} is produced *only* in *r*-process synthesis; therefore none is produced in an irradiation such as that proposed by Fowler et al., and positive identification of Pu^{244} fission xenon in meteorites would establish that formation intervals measured from the last contributing event in *galactic* nucleosynthesis were not longer than a few multiples of 75 million years. However, the bulk of I^{129} responsible for the special anomaly could still have been produced in the planetesimal irradiation; in this case the I-Xe formation intervals, now measured from the end of planetesimal irradiation, would be considerably shorter than those calculated from Pu^{244}. A close concordance between the I-Xe and Pu-Xe formation intervals would strongly imply a galactic origin for both radioactivities.

If we assume that one of the supplementary components in our three-component xenon system is fissiogenic, it is possible to determine the relative xenon fission yields from the experimental δ-correlations without further assumptions. Many of the important parameters of the system, such as the isotopic compositions of all three pure components and the relative amounts of each in a particular mixture, are in general unknown. However, δ-correlation lines such as those in Figures 9.8 and 9.9 define the family of all possible compositions for both components. Fission-produced xenon contains virtually no Xe^{130}, so for the special case of a pure fission component, $\delta_{130}^{f} = -1000$, from the definition of the δ-value. Extrapolation of the δ_{130} correlation line to this value gives δ_{136}^{f}, and from this and the two remaining correlation lines δ_{131}^{f} and δ_{134}^{f} are determined. From this isotopic composition the xenon fission yields relative to $Xe_{f}^{136} = 1$ are easily calculated. In order to make a direct comparison with known relative yields from spontaneous and neutron-induced fission of various nuclides, the second components in Renazzo, Murray, and the Bruderheim and Bjurböle chondrules are *all* assumed to be fissiogenic and their compositions determined in this way. The results are plotted in Figure 9.13, with some known fission yield curves superimposed.

On the basis of relative yields, it appears quite reasonable to attribute the second component in Renazzo and Murray to fission. The yield spectrum for the Bjurböle *f* component is definitely anomalous, displaying high fine structure peaks at Xe^{132} and probably at Xe^{131} as well. Bruderheim is evidently an intermediate case. We have pointed out, in discussing the anomaly patterns shown in Figures 9.10,

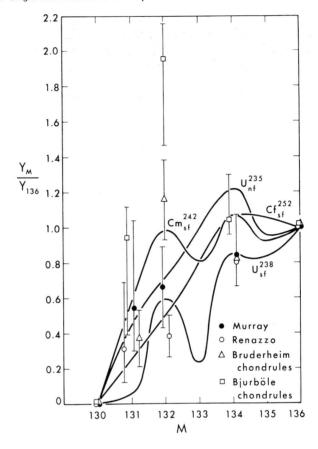

Figure 9.13 Xenon yields relative to Xe^{136} from four stone meteorites (assuming $\delta_{130} = -1000$) and from fission.

9.11, and 9.12, that the data suggest the presence of a component, as yet undetected, whose correlation with average carbonaceous chondrite xenon passes through or to the left of the origin. The second components in Bjurböle and Bruderheim may possibly represent mixtures of this component with that in the carbonaceous chondrites. It is evident from Figure 9.13 that such a component, if fissiogenic, would show an extreme yield at Xe^{132}, just as Kuroda (1960) predicts for Pu^{244} fission xenon. This is not surprising, since Kuroda assumed the existence of precisely the same component—one which produces the terrestrial heavy xenon isotope abundances when mixed with carbonaceous chondrite xenon—and attributed it to Pu^{244} fission. Of the components directly detected in meteoritic xenon, that from the Bjurböle chondrules shows a fission yield pattern not unike that required by the general Kuroda-Cameron model, except at mass 131.

We are free to make plausibility arguments on the basis of these relative fission yield calculations, but the essential question of whether any of these components are in fact fissiogenic remains open. Of considerable interest in this connection is the *amount* of the f component present in each of these meteorites. We can calculate this, provided we make an additional assumption as to the isotopic composition of the "primordial" or p component of the mixture. The total abundance of the f component is

$$[132]_f = \sum_T [132]_T \frac{(\delta_M)_T - \delta_M{}^p}{\delta_M{}^f - \delta_M{}^p}$$

summed over all temperatures. $[132]_T$ is the total amount of Xe^{132} present in a temperature fraction, $(\delta_M)_T$ the observed anomaly in mass M at that temperature, and $\delta_M{}^p$ and $\delta_M{}^f$ the isotopic compositions of the primordial and fission components of the mixture. We have already determined $\delta_M{}^f$ for the f components in the process of calculating the relative fission yields. We assume that the isotopic composition of the p component is that of average carbonaceous chondrite xenon: the amounts of the f components calculated from this equation will therefore be extreme *lower* limits, since this assumption implies that carbonaceous chondrite xenon is not itself a mixture containing the f component.

Results are tabulated in Table 9.4. The amounts of Xe^{136} expected from U^{238} spontaneous fission, U^{235} neutron fission (calculated from the planetesimal irradiation model), and Pu^{244} spontaneous fission assuming $\Delta t = 0$ are included for comparison. Error limits are large, and additional uncertainty factors of about 2 may apply to the assumptions that all these meteorites contain about 10 ppb uranium, and that the Xe^{136} yield from Pu^{244} spontaneous fission is 6%. Nevertheless it seems unlikely, especially since these amounts are lower limits, that the f component in Murray has been produced by Pu^{244} spontaneous fission. Murray appears to contain more than eight times as much fissiogenic Xe^{136} as could be produced from the Pu^{244} formed in our model of linear galactic nucleosynthesis, even if Δt were zero. We include Renazzo with Murray, since both belong to the same meteorite class and since their f component fission yield spectra are identical within experimental error. For the Bjurböle and Bruderheim chondrules the situation is marginal. Although the maximum avail-

TABLE 9.4 f Components of Several Meteorites and Comparison with Possible Models

	δ^f_{136}	δ^f_{134}	δ^f_{131}	δ^f_{130}	$[132]$ cc/gm	$[132_f]$ cc/gm	$\dfrac{[136_f]}{[136]}$ (%)	$[136_f]$ cc/gm
Renazzo	6950 ± 2600	4400 ± 1650	40 ± 500	-1000	3.4×10^{-9}	$>0.6 \times 10^{-11} \pm 50\%$	>1.5	$>1.7 \times 10^{-11} \pm 70\%$
Murray	3600 ± 1600	2300 ± 1000	40 ± 270	-1000	11.6×10^{-9}	$>3.4 \times 10^{-11} \pm 50\%$	>1.4	$>5.2 \times 10^{-11} \pm 70\%$
Bruderheim Olivine Chondrule	1600 ± 500	800 ± 250	-600 ± 190	-1000	6.0×10^{-10}	$>1.7 \times 10^{-11} \pm 60\%$	>7.4	$>1.5 \times 10^{-11} \pm 70\%$
Bjurböle Chondrules	$550 \begin{smallmatrix}+500\\-150\end{smallmatrix}$	$370 \begin{smallmatrix}+330\\-100\end{smallmatrix}$	$-390 \begin{smallmatrix}+110\\-360\end{smallmatrix}$	-1000	4.0×10^{-10}	$>2.7 \times 10^{-11} \pm 60\%$	>10.4	$>1.4 \times 10^{-11} \pm 70\%$
Fission xenon from U^{238}_{sf}; $U = 10$ ppb, $T = 4.6 \times 10^9$ y	4095	2600	-840	-1000		0.20×10^{-13}		0.33×10^{-13}
Fission xenon from U^{238}_{nf}; Irradiation model: $U = 10$ ppb, thermal neutron flux 10^7 n/cm²-sec over 10^7 y, dilution $\times 50$	3470	3740	-150	-1000		4.6×10^{-10}		6.8×10^{-10}
Fission xenon from Pu^{244}_{sf}: $U = 10$ ppb, $y^{244}_{136} = 0.06$ $\Delta t = 0$ $\Big\{$ I. Extended synthesis: $T_{eff} = 2 \times 10^{10}$ y, $\left(\dfrac{Pu^{244}}{U^{238}}\right)_0 = 0.017$	?	?	?	-1000				0.6×10^{-11}
II. "Pure" sudden synthesis: $(244/238)_0 = 1$	?	?	?	-1000				3.5×10^{-10}

able Pu^{244} can apparently produce less than half of the required amount of "fission" Xe^{136}, short but nonzero Pu-Xe formation intervals are possible because of the large errors involved. Plutonium fission xenon may be present, but if so, varying amounts of a third component must also be present, since the Xe^{132} fission yields for these two f components are significantly different. In this case the actual yield from Pu^{244} fission alone may be less than that calculated, and the possibility for a reasonable value for Δt greater.

Our analysis to this point has assumed that the supplementary xenon components detected in Bjurböle and Bruderheim are fissiogenic. This assumption allows us to specify the system quantitatively, at least to a certain degree. We find that as far as the approximate amount of the Bjurböle f component is concerned, its source might just possibly have been Pu^{244} fission; but if so the fission yields from this nuclide have an improbably high fine structure in the xenon region. It should be stressed that there is no basis for *requiring* this component to be fission-produced, aside from that implicit in the choice of isotopic composition for the primitive xenon component. Referring to Figure 9.8, if primitive xenon is chosen to lie at or to the left of the A.V.C.C. points and along the correlation lines, the second component appearing in Bjurböle xenon must be characterized by higher 134/132 and 136/132, and lower 131/132 and 130/132 abundance ratios than those in the primitive component. We tentatively attribute this supplementary component to some specific nuclear process, or combination of processes, occurring either during the early history of the solar system or *in situ* over geologic time.

A large variety of charged particle and neutron reactions, as well as particle-induced and spontaneous fission, can produce xenon isotopes in various relative abundances; Xe^{134} and Xe^{136}, however, are produced in significant quantity *only* in a full-scale r-process synthesis and by fission of r-process heavy elements. Assuming that the Xe^{134} and Xe^{136} directly synthesized in the galactic r-process were completely mixed in primitive solar system xenon, we appear to have no choice but to attribute the Bjurböle f component to fission. Now suppose that the composition of *primordial* xenon was characterized by more 134 and 136, relative to 132, than is present in average meteoritic xenon, so that its position on the correlation lines in Figure 9.8 is somewhere to the right of the 1100°C points. In this figure the supplementary xenon components produced by spallation and neutron capture events in primitive material lie far to the *left* of the A.V.C.C. points. Fowler et al. have shown that such second components, produced in the planetesimal irradiation model, can combine with "primordial" xenon of terrestrial composition to form a mixture closely resembling average carbonaceous chondrite xenon; this picture is essentially unchanged if the 1100°C fraction from Bjurböle is taken as the primordial component. There are a number of specific xenon irradiation products which might have played an important role in the production of average meteoritic xenon if conditions were appropriate; for example, Te(α, n; α, 2n; α, p) and Te(d, n; d, 2n; d, 3n; . . .) capture reactions lead to final xenon products which may have made significant contributions if the particle irradiations occurred when xenon was largely fractionated from primitive material. These mechanisms have one problem in common, however: they all produce more Xe^{126} than Xe^{124}, and both the atmosphere and the carbonaceous chondrites contain more Xe^{124}. At any rate, it certainly seems possible that one component in Bjurböle xenon may consist of a complicated combination of irradiation products, and that carbonaceous chondrite xenon may therefore be a secondary mixture.

It is interesting to consider the possible origin of the f component in the carbonaceous chondrites. On the basis of the data in Figure 9.13, it seems reasonable to assume that it is, in fact, fission-produced. Although a sudden synthesis of the elements would have produced more than enough parent Pu^{244}, we are reluctant, for reasons given earlier, to invoke this model in order to explain apparent overabundances of short-lived activities in meteoritic material. An intense and prolonged thermal neutron irradiation of a small fraction of premeteoritic matter would have resulted in the production of quite large amounts of xenon from neutron fission in U^{235}. Assuming the integrated neutron flux derived in the planetesimal irradiation model, we have calculated the amount of Xe^{136} expected from this source after irradiation of 2% of the primitive material in the solar nebula and thorough mixing with the large unirradiated fraction. Roughly an order of magnitude more Xe^{136} than is observed in the f component in Murray would be produced in such an irradiation. However, there is a fundamental difficulty involved in attributing the fission xenon in the carbonaceous chondrites to this source: the relative fission yields for the f component do not agree with those for U^{235} neutron fission. Figure 9.13 shows quite clearly that the 134/136 yield ratio for Murray and Renazzo is significantly less than that from U^{235}, and that the relative 132 yield for Renazzo is also too low.

It is interesting to note in this connection that fission yields relative to Xe^{136} from U^{235} neutron fission are functions of both the magnitude of the neutron flux and its duration, if the flux is sufficiently high. With a thermal neutron capture cross section of 2.7×10^6 barns, 9.2-hour Xe^{135} is produced in U^{235} fission in about the same abundance as Xe^{136}. For thermal neutron fluxes greater than 10^{11} n/cm^2-sec, lasting for more than about an hour, the probability that Xe^{135} $(n, \gamma)Xe^{136}$ capture reactions will occur before the Xe^{135} has a chance to decay becomes significant. Xe^{136} produced in neutron fission may be enriched to a considerable extent by this mechanism, provided the flux is high enough. It can be shown that a flux of $\sim 2 \times 10^{13}$ n/cm^2-sec irradiating U^{235} for ~ 10 hours produces xenon with the apparent fission yield ratios $134/136 = 0.86$, $132/136 = 0.46$, $131/136 = 0.31$; these values are within the error limits of the yield ratios for both Murray and Renazzo. No particular significance is claimed for these numbers, but we may consider the possibility that thermal neutron irradiations of primitive material, if they occurred at all, might have been associated with intermittent solar flare activity on a gigantic scale at some early stage in the development of the sun.

ANALYSES OF TERRESTRIAL XENON

The following presentation, except for the inclusion and discussion of some recent data and suggestions due to Clarke (1962), is taken directly from the paper *Isotopic Variations in Terrestrial Xenon* by Butler et al. (1963).

In view of the foregoing developments in the study of isotopic anomalies in xenon from meteorites, it has seemed important to look more extensively at the isotopic composition of xenon from various terrestrial sources. Of particular interest are the questions as to whether the differentiation of the earth took place before the complete decay of the I^{129} responsible for the anomalous Xe^{129} in meteorites, and whether any of the processes which may have led to the general anomalies in the isotopic composition of meteoritic xenon have left terrestrial traces.

Xenon from three terrestrial sources has recently been examined. The first was a Bavarian eclogite, a sample which could possibly contain deep-seated terrestrial gas. This sample contained about 4×10^{-11} cc STP/g, which compares with the xenon content of the earth (assumed to be outgassed) of 6×10^{-11} cc STP/g. No significant isotopic anomalies were found. The results are shown in Table 9.5;

TABLE 9.5   Isotopic Composition of Xenon from Bavarian Eclogite

$$\delta_M^{(132)} = 1000 \left[(Xe^M/Xe^{132})/(Xe^M/Xe^{132})_{atm} - 1 \right] \text{ permil}$$

M	124	126	128	129	130	131	134	136
$\delta_M^{(132)}$	246 ± 60	-45 ± 60	12 ± 19	-15 ± 14	7 ± 19	-9 ± 10	-10 ± 12	21 ± 19

little weight is given to the anomaly at mass 124 because of the extremely small size of the total sample.

The second terrestrial source consisted of three rock samples of the Old Granite of the Central Transvaal. These have been dated by the Rb-Sr method (Allsopp, 1961), which gives consistent ages of 3200 million years for the samples. These samples were included so as to see if any isotopic differences could be detected in ancient terrestrial xenon. One possible difference relative to present day terrestrial xenon might have been caused by gradual accretion in the atmosphere, over geologic time, of the anomalous solar-wind xenon postulated by Cameron (1962). Unfortunately, hydrocarbon background and memory effects in the spectrometer interfered with the analyses at masses 124, 126, and 128. The Xe^{129}-Xe^{136} analyses were satisfactory. The isotopic anomalies, referenced to Xe^{130} as a standard (since this isotope is shielded against production by fission) are displayed in Table 9.6. None of the three granites exhibit significant anomalies at Xe^{129}, but all show positive anomalies at masses 131 through 136, which are the isotopes produced in fission.

Assuming that these anomalies are indeed produced by the presence of fission gas, the excess xenon at masses 129 through 136 is computed by subtracting away a terrestrial component containing all the Xe^{130}. Excess xenon ratios relative to Xe^{136} have been tabulated in Table 9.7 (Halfway House was chosen because its analysis was substantially more precise than the others), and compared with the yield ratios of xenon produced by the spontaneous fission of U^{238}. The ratios are seen to be identical within experimental error, so all the excess xenon in the granites can be attributed to this source.

The excess Xe^{136} contents for all three granite samples were almost identical, and were equal to about 7×10^{-12} cc STP/g. It appears

TABLE 9.6   Isotopic Composition and Amount of Xenon from Old Granites, Central Transvaal

$$\delta_M{}^{(130)} = 1000 \, [(Xe^M/Xe^{130})/(Xe^M/Xe^{130})_{Atm} - 1] \text{ permil}$$

Sample	Weight, g	128	129	131	132	134	136	$[Xe^{132}]$, 10^{-10} cc STP/g
Witkoppen	3.10	<57	4.3 ± 10	13.0 ± 10	34.0 ± 9	103.3 ± 10	142.8 ± 10	1.48
Corlett Drive	4.10	<30	−5.1 ± 8	5.9 ± 8	14.0 ± 7	43.3 ± 8	62.3 ± 8	3.64
Halfway House	3.07	<85	1.3 ± 7	14.3 ± 7	46.8 ± 5	172.9 ± 7	245.5 ± 9	0.91

TABLE 9.7 Comparison of Excess Xenon Components in Halfway House, Old Granite with Xenon from Spontaneous Fission of U^{238} (the xenon samples are indistinguishable)

Sample	$(Xe^{129}/Xe^{136})_{excess}$	$(Xe^{131}/Xe^{136})_{excess}$	$(Xe^{132}/Xe^{136})_{excess}$	$(Xe^{134}/Xe^{136})_{excess}$
Halfway House	0.016 ± 0.085	0.138 ± 0.067	0.579 ± 0.061	0.830 ± 0.045
U^{238} spont. fission (Wetherill, 1953)	<0.002	0.076 ± 0.003	0.595 ± 0.010	0.832 ± 0.012
Difference	0.016 ± 0.085	0.062 ± 0.067	-0.016 ± 0.062	-0.002 ± 0.047

that with refined techniques a U–Xe method for dating old granites is feasible. The age is computed from

$$t = \tau \ln \left[(Xe_F{}^{136}/U^{238}) \cdot 1/\alpha_F \cdot 1/y_{136} + 1 \right]$$

where τ is the mean life of U^{238} (6.51×10^9 years), α_F is the fraction of decays by spontaneous fission (0.57×10^{-6}), and y_{136} is the fission yield of $Xe_F{}^{136}$ (0.06). With the $Xe_F{}^{136}$ content given above, and assuming 3.7 ppm uranium content (recommended value for standard granite G-1, Fleischer and Stevens, 1961),

$$t = 3.0^{+3.7}_{-1.8} \times 10^9 \text{ years}$$

The very large error is probably due to a overgenerous assignment of a factor of 3 uncertainty in the spectrometer sensitivity; this source of error could be reduced substantially. The agreement with the Rb–Sr age is very satisfactory.

The possibility of a new rare gas method for dating old rocks is not without importance. The frequent occurrence of argon leakage in the K–A method requires checking that method by another, such as U–Pb or Rb–Sr. The U–Xe method would probably serve as an adequate check, since xenon leakage can be expected to differ substantially from that of argon; concordance would then indicate a closed system. Since extraction and purification procedures for argon recover the xenon in the sample as well, the U–Xe method can be said to be partially built into the K–A method.

The third terrestrial source was xenon from a CO_2 gas well, (Mitchell No. 7, Harding County, New Mexico). Two wells in this field have been studied for helium and argon by Zartman, Wasserburg, and Reynolds (1961) as part of a study of helium, argon, and carbon in some 40 wells of various types. They found a very high average value of some $28{,}000$ for A^{40}/A^{36}, and the lowest ratio of $(He/A)_{radiogenic}$, 1.6, of any of the well gasses in that study. These data, and the very high purity (99.9%) of the CO_2, suggested that the gas was derived from the decomposition of carbonate rocks by intrusive basalt under conditions which expelled gases and liquids in the nearby sediments before the CO_2 accumulation. As such the xenon in the sample might be expected to reflect the isotopic composition of deep-seated terrestrial gas.

Clarke (1962) has analyzed the xenon from the Navajo C-1 helium well (approximately 6% helium) in Wildcat Field, New Mexico. There the $(He/A)_{radiogenic}$ ratio is 11.1. His data are also presented. Both analyses indicate a fission anomaly spectrum for the heavy xenon isotopes; so again Xe^{130} is chosen as the reference isotope. The results are shown in Table 9.8. For both wells there appear to be excess amounts of xenon at masses 129, 131, 132, 134, and 136, though in Navajo C-1 the 129 anomaly is barely significant. In Table 9.9 these data have been transformed to excess xenon ratios for comparison with fission xenon from spontaneous fission of U^{238}, and with fission xenon from slow neutron fission of U^{235}—in which I^{129}, and therefore Xe^{129}, is produced in significant abundance. The excess xenon from the samples closely resembles that from U^{238} fission; an appreciable contribution from neutron fission of U^{235} is ruled out by the high 134/136 ratio in U^{235} fission xenon. Accordingly, the component ascribed to U^{238} spontaneous fission has been subtracted in Table 9.9. There remains, in Mitchell No. 7 xenon, a residue at Xe^{129} and possibly at Xe^{131}; in Navajo C-1 xenon, there are significant residues at 131 and 132, and perhaps at 129.

It is possible to derive a relationship between the amount of radiogenic helium and the amount of fissiogenic Xe^{136} in rock gases. The

TABLE 9.8 Isotopic Composition of Xenon from Mitchell No. 7 CO_2 Well and from Navajo C-1 Helium Well, Referred to Xe^{130} as Reference Isotope

$$\delta_M{}^{(130)} = 1000[(Xe^M/Xe^{130})/(Xe^M/Xe^{130})_{atm} - 1] \text{ permil}$$

Mitchell No. 7

M	124	126	128	129	131	132	134	136
$\delta_M{}^{(130)}$	14.4 ± 29	-16.1 ± 22	5.5 ± 24	24.0 ± 10	12.2 ± 8	20.1 ± 6	53.5 ± 10	77.3 ± 12

Navajo C-1 (Clarke)

M	124	126	128	129	131	132	134	136
$\delta_M{}^{(130)}$	-8.5 ± 17	-4.6 ± 18	-8.5 ± 8.5	4.6 ± 3	23 ± 6	70 ± 5	186 ± 4	264 ± 5

TABLE 9.9   Comparison of Excess Component in Xenon from Mitchell No. 7 CO_2 Well and from Navajo C-1 Helium Well with Xenon from Spontaneous Fission of U^{238} and from Neutron Fission of U^{235}. (Note that there is an apparently significant residue of Xe^{129} after subtraction of U^{238} spontaneous fission xenon)

Sample	$(Xe^{129}/Xe^{136})_{excess}$	$(Xe^{131}/Xe^{136})_{excess}$	$(Xe^{132}/Xe^{136})_{excess}$	$(Xe^{134}/Xe^{136})_{excess}$
Xe from CO_2 well	0.92 ± 0.42	0.377 ± 0.26	0.788 ± 0.30	0.814 ± 0.19
U^{238} spont. fission	<0.002	0.076 ± 0.003	0.595 ± 0.010	0.832 ± 0.012
U^{235} neutron fission	0.139	0.454	0.678	1.248
Difference	0.92 ± 0.42	0.301 ± 0.26		
Xe from Navajo helium well	0.052 ± 0.035	0.208 ± 0.058	0.803 ± 0.072	0.830 ± 0.034
Difference	$\sim 0.052 \pm 0.035$	0.132 ± 0.061	0.208 ± 0.082	

gas from the Mitchell wells is known (Zartman et al., 1961) to contain 45 ppm radiogenic He^4; the source for this is ascribed to α-decay of thorium and uranium in rock with $Th/U = 3$. We calculate that this amount of He^4 should be accompanied by 1.1×10^{-13} parts $Xe_F{}^{136}$; this constitutes complete agreement within experimental error with the observed value of excess Xe^{136} for Mitchell No. 7 of about 0.9×10^{-13} parts. A similar calculation for Navajo C-1 (Clarke, 1962) shows a $He^4/Xe_F{}^{136}$ ratio too high by a factor 2 over that determined for the gas by measurement. Clarke attributes this to preferential diffusion of helium compared to xenon from the source rock. There seems to be little doubt that the excess fission xenon in both wells was derived from rock with a "normal" Th/U ratio.

In Figure 9.14, taken from Clarke (1962) with the Mitchell data added, the relative yields for the gas-well xenon and the relative yield curve for U^{238} spontaneous fission are plotted against mass number. Clarke suggests that the excesses at 131 and 132 may be due to a diffusive fractionation process in the fractional release of spontaneous fission xenon from source minerals, similar to that which he detected and analyzed in xenon from neutron-irradiated uranium oxides. We have discussed this mechanism in connection with the Kuroda-Cameron theory of the general meteoritic anomalies. Applied to the diffusion of rock gases into gas-well reservoirs, it represents an intriguing possibility. Here again it requires that the bulk of fissiogenic gas be retained in the earth.

Turning finally to the residual Xe^{129}, the following possibilities are recognized:

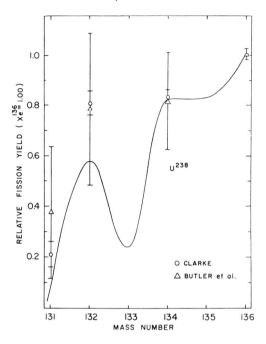

Figure 9.14　Comparison of fission yields of the fission-product component of natural gas xenon with the yields from spontaneous fission of U^{238}.

1. The residual is not real. This is possible but not likely, at least for the xenon from Mitchell No. 7, since the effect is more than twice the assigned error.

2. The Xe^{129} residual is real and is to be attributed to (n, γ) reactions on Te^{128}. The neutrons at great depths underground come primarily from spontaneous fission of U^{238} and from (α, n) reactions induced by uranium and thorium α-particles (Wetherill, 1953, 1954). Inghram and Reynolds (1950) showed that neutrons from uranium can indeed produce excess Xe^{129} in tellurium; they found an excess of both Xe^{129} and Xe^{131} in an ancient tellurium mineral which had been in association with uranium. Hayden and Inghram (1951) showed that a tellurium mineral of similar age which had not been in association with uranium did not contain comparable excess amounts of these isotopes. However, assuming that the uranium resides in rock of granitic composition for which Th/U = 3, it is possible to show that to produce the observed excess Xe^{129} by fast neutron (n, γ) reactions on tellurium would require a tellurium content

greater than 450 ppm. This far exceeds any conceivable concentration of tellurium in granite or diabase, where it might be expected to lie in the range 2 to 20 ppm. With regard to the possibility of slow neutron capture in Te^{128}, it can be shown that even if *all* neutrons produced as fast neutrons are thermalized before absorption, it is highly improbable that this mechanism could have been responsible for more than 0.4% of the Xe^{129} residue. It appears that neutron reactions on tellurium are out of the question as mechanisms for producing this amount of excess Xe^{129}.

3. A highly speculative possibility, but one which might be mentioned in view of Clarke's suggestion concerning the anomalous yields exhibited by the fission xenon components in Navajo C-1 and Mitchell No. 7, is that the Xe^{129} residual is related to the residuals at masses 131 and 132, and all three are due to fractionation effects in the release of U^{238} spontaneous fission xenon from the source rock. I^{129} is produced in U^{238} fission, though in very small and unknown relative abundance: Wetherill (1953) gives $(Xe^{129}/Xe^{136}) < 0.002$ for U^{238} spontaneous fission xenon. If Clarke's mechanism for Xe^{131} and Xe^{132} augmentation in well gases, based on preferential diffusion and decay of xenon precursors, does in fact operate for spontaneous fission in natural minerals, and can be applied for precursor half-lives as long as 17 million years, then a very large enrichment of Xe^{129} is apparently predicted in the first release fraction of fission gas. Forthcoming experiments with old uranium minerals may provide some information in this connection.

4. A remaining possibility is that the excess Xe^{129} was produced by the decay of I^{129} very early in the history of the earth. This would mean that the outgassing of the earth's interior is incomplete and that the decay products of such short-lived elements as I^{129} have not been homogenized. This suggests that Xe^{129} and possibly other such daughter isotopes are presently being added to the atmosphere and the upper crust. It follows that thorough convective mixing and outgassing did not occur during the early stages in the differentiation of the earth.

It is instructive to attempt to calculate a formation interval for the earth assuming the excess Xe^{129} to be from I^{129} decay. If the system has been closed with respect to uranium, iodine, and daughter xenon for 4.6×10^9 years, then from the data above and assuming the atomic ratio $U/I = 10$ (based on meteoritic values by Goles and Anders, 1962):

$$\frac{Xe^{129*}}{I^{127}} = 3.1 \times 10^{-9} = \left(\frac{I^{129}}{I^{127}}\right)_0 e^{-\Delta t/25}$$

If time 0 is assumed to refer to the end of galactic nucleosynthesis, then from our model of uniform synthesis $(I^{129}/I^{127})_0 = 0.00125$ as before, and the I-Xe formation interval of the earth is 320 million years. This formation interval cannot be taken very seriously in an absolute sense if we stop to consider the role which Pu^{244} would play in this scheme. Present at the end of nucleosynthesis with an abundance about $\frac{1}{60}$ of U^{238}, it would generate about twenty times as much spontaneous fission xenon in this system as generated by U^{238}. Since there is strong evidence from the isotopic composition of the fission component that it was produced by spontaneous fission of U^{238}, it is not possible to adopt both this simple closed model and the hypothesis of galactic synthesis for I^{129}. If the I^{129} were produced by some process which did not produce Pu^{244} along with it, for example, some "local" irradiation synthesis (Fowler et al., 1962), and if its production in meteorites was the same relative to I^{127} as in the terrestrial material, the difference in formation intervals calculated for meteorites and the earth would be significant. Latest Berkeley results for the formation intervals of stone meteorites, set out in Table 9.1 (Jeffery, Merrihue, and Reynolds, to be published), give values in the range 34 to 52 million years. This suggests that the earth postdates the meteorites by about 275 million years. Even this conclusion cannot be given much weight at present because of the extreme nature of the assumptions made in setting up the closed system model, but the general character of the computation is instructive.

REFERENCES

Allsopp, H. L., 1961. Rb-Sr age measurements on total rock and separated-mineral fractions from the Old Granite of the Central Transvaal, *Jour. Geophys. Res.*, **66**, 1499.

Brown, H., 1947. An experimental method for the estimation of the age of the elements, *Phys. Rev.*, **72**, 348.

Burbidge, E. M., G. R. Burbidge, W. A. Fowler, and F. Hoyle, 1957. Synthesis of the elements in stars, *Rev. Mod. Physics*, **29**, 547.

Butler, W. A., P. M. Jeffery, J. H. Reynolds, and G. J. Wasserburg, 1963. Isotopic variations in terrestrial xenon, *Jour. Geophys. Res.*, **68**, 3283.

Cameron, A. G. W., 1958. Nuclear astrophysics, *Ann. Rev. Nucl. Sci.*, **8**, 299.

———————— 1962. The formation of the sun and planets, *Icarus*, **1**, 13.

Clarke, W. B., Studies of isotope effects in fission-product rare gases, Doctoral thesis, McMaster University, September, 1962.

Clayton, D. D., Cosmoradiogenic chronologies of nucleosynthesis, preprint.

Eberhardt, P. and J. Geiss, 1960. Comment on the age of the elements, *Z. Naturforsch.*, **15a**, 547.

Fish, R. A. and G. G. Goles, 1962. Ambient xenon: a key to the history of meteorites, *Nature (London)*, **196**, 27.

Fleischer, M. and R. E. Stevens, 1961. Summary of new data on rock samples G-1 and W-1, *Geochim. et Cosmochim. Acta*, **26**, 525.

Fowler, W. A., J. L. Greenstein, and F. Hoyle, 1962. Nucleosynthesis during the early history of the solar system, *Geophys. Jour. Royal Astron. Soc.*, **6**, 148.

Goles, G. G. and E. Anders, 1962. Abundances of iodine, tellurium, and uranium in meteorites, I, *Geochim. et Cosmochim. Acta*, **26**, 723.

Goles, G. G., R. A. Fish, and E. Anders, 1960. The record in the meteorites, I: The former environment of stone meteorites as deduced from K^{40}-Ar^{40} ages, *Geochim. et Cosmochim. Acta*, **19**, 177.

Hayden, R. J. and M. G. Inghram, 1953. Further results on the double beta decay of Te^{130}, in *Mass Spectroscopy in Physics Research*, Proceedings of the NBS Semicentennial Symposium on Mass Spectroscopy in Physics Research, September, 1951, issued as *Natl. Bur. Std., U.S. Circ.*, **522**.

Hyde, E. K., 1962. A revised version of a review of nuclear fission, I: Fission phenomena at low energy, *University of California Radiation Laboratory Report 9036-Rev.*

Inghram, M. G. and J. H. Reynolds, 1950. Double beta decay of Te^{130}, *Phys. Rev.*, **78**, 822.

Jeffery, P. M. and J. H. Reynolds, 1961. Origin of excess Xe^{129} in stone meteorites, *Jour. Geophys. Res.*, **66**, 3582.

Krummenacher, D., C. M. Merrihue, R. O. Pepin, and J. H. Reynolds, 1962. Meteoritic krypton and barium versus the general isotopic anomalies in meteoritic xenon, *Geochim. et Cosmochim. Acta*, **26**, 231.

Kuroda, P. K., 1960. Nuclear fission in the early history of the earth, *Nature (London)*, **187**, 36.

Merrihue, C. M., 1963. Excess xenon 129 in chondrules from the Bruderheim meteorite, *Jour. Geophys. Res.*, **68**, 325.

———— R. O. Pepin, and J. H. Reynolds, 1962. Rare gases in the chondrite Pantar, *Jour. Geophys. Res.*, **67**, 2017.

Patterson, C. C., 1956. Age of meteorites and the earth, *Geochim. et Cosmochim. Acta*, **10**, 230.

Reynolds, J. H., 1960. Determination of the age of the elements, *Phys. Rev. Letters*, **4**, 8.

———— 1963. Xenology, *Jour. Geophys. Res.*, **68**, 2939.

———— C. M. Merrihue, and R. O. Pepin, 1962. Extinct radioactivity and primordial rare gases in iron meteorites (abstract), *Bull. Am. Phys. Soc.*, **7**, 35.

Wetherill, G. W., 1953. Spontaneous fission yields from uranium and thorium, *Phys. Rev.*, **92**, 907.

———— 1954. Variations in the isotopic abundances of neon and argon extracted from radioactive minerals, *Phys. Rev.*, **96**, 679.

Zartman, R. E., G. J. Wasserburg, and J. H. Reynolds, 1961. Helium, argon, and carbon in some natural gases, *Jour. Geophys. Res.*, **66**, 277.

DISCUSSION

Dr. Wetherill: I would tend to disagree with your statement that no major outgassing took place. It is possible to make up models, with formation intervals of 250 to 350 million years, including the Pu^{244} and having quite large amounts of outgassing—at least 90%—and still be reconciled with your discovery.

Dr. Pepin: However, the models should agree with the observations made here that the fission component found in the well-gas xenon comes from spontaneous fission of U^{238}. The possibility of extensive fission xenon from Pu^{244} being present is unlikely.

Dr. Abelson: Have any anomalies been observed in krypton isotopic abundances?

Dr. Pepin: We have not, as yet, found any significant krypton anomalies in carbonaceous chondrites, but what appear to be rather large anomalies for Kr^{80} and Kr^{82} have been found in separated fractions such as the Bruderheim chondrules and some of the Bjurböle chondrules. We do not believe these anomalies are due to fission, because they are large and positive. Although krypton and xenon are found in about the same quantity in meteorites, the fission yield for krypton is less than that for xenon. Also, Kr^{80} and Kr^{82} are shielded in fission production, so we would expect negative anomalies for these isotopes in a fissiogenic component when referenced to Kr^{84}. These are positive. They appear as if they might be due to spallation reactions.

Voice: If this Xe^{129} anomaly is real, one is then interested in the mechanics of how it got into the escaping gas. It just happens that in the same general region, there are basaltic rock types of very deep-seated origin. They may in fact be involved in the mechanics of releasing the helium in these wells. There are also kimberlite pipes in this area, in which one could get samples that were brought up, but were not heated to high temperatures. In other words, samples are available that might shed some light on the problem.

10

Interpretation of Xenon
Measurements

A. G. W. Cameron

The problem of the xenon isotopes has already been discussed by Pepin; we would like here to try to make further interpretations of these measurements. As has been mentioned, there is in general much more xenon per gram of meteorite in the objects that have been studied than there is atmospheric xenon per gram of the earth. Consequently, the natural assumption that we tend to make is that it is the xenon in the meteorites that is more primitive than the xenon in the atmosphere, and we wish then to look at the xenon in the atmosphere to see to what extent the abundance differences can be interpreted as being due to various events in the early history of the earth.

In Figure 10.1 we see the abundance pattern of xenon in the carbonaceous chondrites. The Murray abundance pattern has been taken as a standard; at the top of the figure are shown the differences between Murray and two other carbonaceous chrondrites. As can be seen, the essential differences, if any, are lost within the probable errors of measurement, with the possible exception of mass number 129, which results from the decay of the extinct radioactivity I^{129}. On this basis the carbonaceous chondrite composition does make a good standard against which we can measure all of the deviations. It requires very refined techniques to bring out the apparent fact that the carbonaceous chondrite composition has a component which is due to fission decay.

Ordinary chondrites contain less gas per gram than do the carbon-

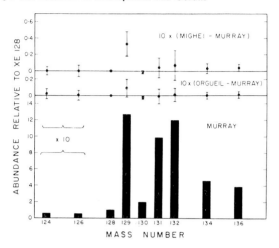

Figure 10.1   Abundances of xenon isotopes in carbonaceous chondrites. At the bottom is the abundance pattern in the Murray meteorite, which is adopted as a standard, and at the top are shown the abundance differences between Murray and two other carbonaceous chondrites, magnified by a factor of ten.

aceous chondrites. In these we start to see the overabundance of Xe^{129} (Fig. 10.2), which gives rise to the various kinds of formation intervals that are proposed for different meteorites.

For the atmosphere we see a drastically different abundance pattern (Fig. 10.3). The isotopic abundances of mass 131 to 136 are those that can be formed by the decay of I^{129} and fission of Pu^{244}. Pepin has discussed this general process (Chapter 9). We would like, however, to concentrate on the other abundances, which may not look very discrepant. But if we examine what these errors really are by blowing up the scale, we then get what is shown in Figure 10.4.

Here are shown the abundance differences of the shielded isotopes that cannot be formed in any manner from the decay of extinct radioactivities. It is clear that the discrepancies here seem well outside the experimental errors of the measurement. However, these differences are precisely in the direction in which we would expect to find them, if there were neutron capture in a medium in which the xenon had not been fractionated relative to its neighboring elements. In that case the Xe^{124} and Xe^{126}, which from the point of view of nucleosynthesis are shielded isotopes—they are not made in nature by any neutron capture process—could, if anything, only be depleted. Actually, because they contain even numbers of both neutrons and protons, we expect the cross sections for neutron capture in these isotopes to be rather small compared to those for the isotopes with odd mass numbers. As can be seen from the abundance pattern, there is a very great amount of Xe^{129}—much larger than the natural amounts of Xe^{128} and Xe^{130}. Consequently, neutron capture in the Xe^{129} would tend to produce more Xe^{130} than would be removed by neutron capture. We then expect that Xe^{130} would be enriched. Similarly, neutron capture in I^{127}, which would have an abundance comparable to that of Xe^{131}, should lead to an enrichment of Xe^{128}. Hence, we get the impression that the natural way of examining these abundances would be to adopt 124 and 126 as points of normalization; unfortunately this cannot be done because the errors of measurement there are too large. However, it is clear that if we think that the levels of 124 and 126 have been unchanged, then relative to these levels we see an enrichment of 128 and 130; on this basis, Xe^{128} has been enriched by 15 ± 2%.

Where, then, could we possibly find neutron capture taking place in such a way that could produce a difference between the composition of xenon in meteorites and in the earth's atmosphere? It

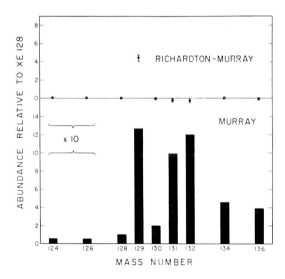

Figure 10.2 Comparison of xenon isotopic abundances in the Richardton ordinary chondrite and the Murray carbonaceous chondrite.

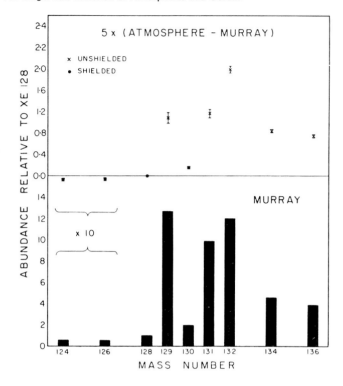

Figure 10.3   Comparison of xenon isotopic abundances in the atmosphere and in the Murray carbonaceous chondrite. The abundance patterns are normalized at mass number 128. Isotopes which can be formed by the beta decay of fission fragments are denoted by crosses; the shielded isotopes are denoted by full circles.

seems unlikely that this occurred in the earth's atmosphere itself, for if we consider the neutrons produced by cosmic ray bombardment, we find that to produce just the overabundance of the Xe^{130} would require that the average cosmic ray flux throughout the past 4.5 billion years should be five orders of magnitude greater than it is observed to be at the present; this hardly seems to be a possibility. In addition, this would not lead to the enrichment of Xe^{128}.

On the other hand, if we were to look at the sun early in its history, we would find that if it contained about the same ratio of deuterium to hydrogen as in terrestrial water then there would be a mechanism for producing neutrons during the deuterium-burning thermonuclear reactions. It should be noted that the question as to how much deuterium the primitive sun should have is certainly a very contro-versial one. Fowler, Greenstein, and Hoyle (1962) believe that the deuterium was produced by mechanisms of particle bombardment of the planetesimals that were going to form the planets in the early history of the solar system, and consequently they would not expect the following processes to occur.

It is my belief that the deuterium we have in nature is formed as a natural consequence of Type II supernova explosions, and conse-quently at the same time the solar system was formed, the terrestrial deuterium-to-hydrogen ratio was probably typical of the interstellar medium. When the sun contracts out of the interstellar medium and starts to burn deuterium, the main reaction will simply be proton capture, $D^2(p, \gamma)He^3$. Significantly competing with this, because there is a fair amount of deuterium—1.5 parts in a thousand by

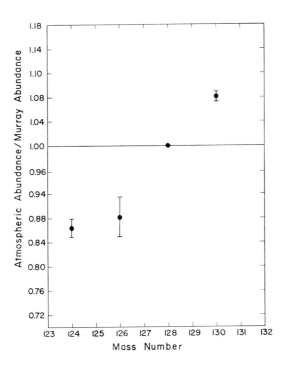

Figure 10.4 An expansion of part of Figure 10.3 showing the abundance differences between the at-mosphere and the Murray carbonaceous chondrite of the shielded isotopes of xenon. The point of normalization is at mass number 128.

number, if the terrestrial ratio is the applicable one—then we would expect, in approximately equal amounts, the reactions $D^2(d, n)He^3$ and $D^2(d, p)H^3$. The number of neutrons produced would depend on the relative thermonuclear reaction rates. It appears that on the order of 0.06 neutrons are produced per deuteron, integrating over the changing ratio of deuterium to hydrogen as the deuterium gets burned up. The reaction temperature is about 1.2×10^6 °K.

The next problem is to explain how the deuterium gets destroyed throughout the solar interior. Figure 10.5 shows the results of some calculations done by Ezer and Cameron (1962) for the early evolution of the sun. We were examining some effects that were predicted by Hayashi (1961), who pointed out that the sun should have been at one time a really hot red giant, and that its temperature could not have been much less than about 3000°K. Above

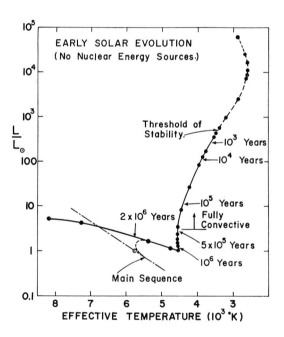

Figure 10.5   The early evolution of the sun according to calculations of Ezer and Cameron (1962). These solar models have been constructed with the assumption that the contraction is homologous at each point and that only gravitational energy release is effective. The models are fully convective above the indicated line, but unreal above the threshold of stability.

the threshold of stability, the models are unstable against collapse, and thus are purely of academic interest, since they cannot exist in nature. The models below this point outline how, if the sun is suddenly formed, it must follow the path shown on the Hertzsprung-Russell diagram, finally going over on to the main sequence. For the present purposes, however, there are only two aspects that are of interest: first of all, above the point shown on the rising branch, all models are completely convective throughout. Second, the central temperature exceeds 1.2×10^6 °K on this branch. Hence, on the descent along this branch the sun will burn up whatever deuterium it has, and the effects of the neutron capture will then become evident all the way out to the surface of the sun. Hence, we can dispense with the question as to how thermonuclear reactions at the center of the sun can affect material at the surface (which will presumably be the matter that is ejected in the solar wind).

Another problem that arises is to determine the relative abundance of xenon relative to its neighbors. We must also be concerned with the relative abundance of krypton, because we have to consider whether or not there will be any effects due to neutron capture in the krypton itself. These have been looked for and not found.

Perhaps the most significant early adjustment of the abundances of the elements was that carried out by Suess and Urey (1956), who used meteorite data to put together the abundances of all the nonvolatile elements, and used a criterion of smoothness of the abundances of odd mass numbers as a means of interpolating other elements.

This has sparked two important developments. First of all, it allowed a classification of the mechanisms that gave rise to nucleosynthesis. Second, it spurred a great deal of activity in the further measurement of abundances in meteorites, so that the experimental basis for these abundances is much better established. Figure 10.6 shows a readjustment recently carried out by Cameron (1963a) based almost entirely on meteorite abundances, and with a very minimum amount of interpolation. For example, almost all of the abundance data from the iron peak down through germanium come from carbonaceous chondrites (with the exception of gallium, which is interpolated). The arsenic and selenium are determined from abundances in ordinary chondrites, and strontium from abundances in both ordinary chondrites and carbonaceous chondrites. Krypton can be fitted in very nicely in this trend. There does not seem to be too much leeway in the amount of readjustment that one can do here.

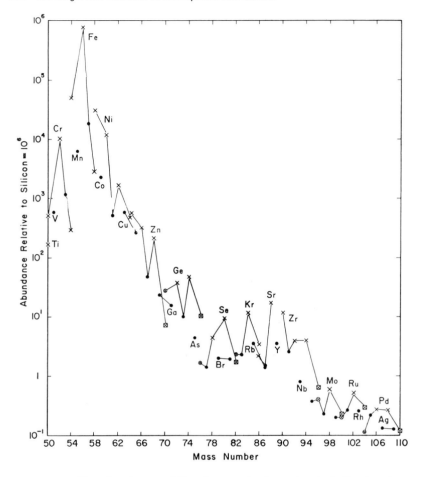

Figure 10.6   The abundances of the elements in the region including krypton according to a recent compilation by Cameron (1963a). Only isotopes which can be formed by neutron capture in nucleosynthesis are plotted. Closed circles denote odd mass number isotopes; crosses denote even mass number isotopes. Isotopes formable only by neutron capture on a fast time scale are enclosed in squares; those formable only by neutron capture on a slow time scale are enclosed in circles.

Figure 10.7 shows the region containing xenon. Plotted here are only those isotopes of the individual elements that can be formed by neutron capture in one way or another. The iodine and tellurium abundances are derived from the data of Goles and Anders (1962) on carbonaceous chondrites. Barium and cesium are derived from meteorite abundance data. So once again we feel that xenon can be interpolated into the abundances of its neighbors with very little uncertainty.

There are a number of calculations that have to be made in order to determine the xenon production in the sun, and there are several sources of error involved. First of all, we do not yet have the proper nuclear data for Xe^{129} which will allow us to determine the neutron capture cross section averaged over a Maxwell distribution of neutron energies in the vicinity of 130 ev (corresponding to a temperature of 1.2×10^6 °K).

However, the situation is different for I^{127}. In this case, we can calculate the cross section, because the individual resonances of I^{127} are known, and their neutron widths are known quite accurately up to energies of the order of 400 to 500 volts. The main unknowns are the individual spins, and this introduces a probable error of about 10% in the calculation of the I^{127} cross section. A further difficulty is that the abundance of I^{127} relative to xenon is uncertain by perhaps 30%. The value chosen for the deuterium

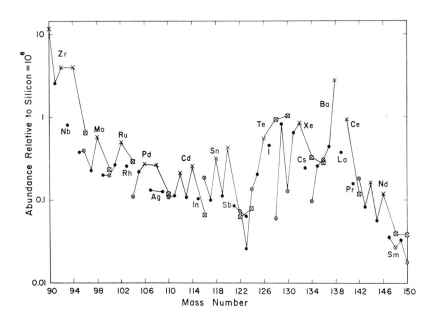

Figure 10.7 The abundances of the elements in the region including xenon according to a recent compilation by Cameron (1963a). The symbols are the same as those described for Figure 10.6.

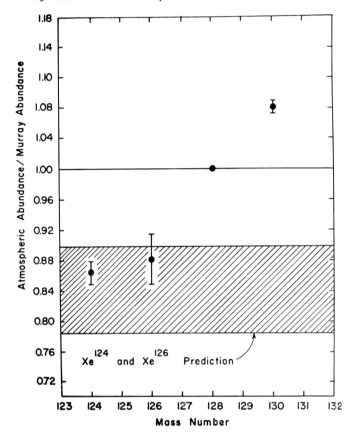

Figure 10.8   The atmospheric abundance anomalies of Figure 10.4 for the shielded xenon isotopes showing the predicted depletion of Xe[124] and Xe[126].

hydrogen ratio is significant; if the abundance of deuterium relative to hydrogen is increased, the amount of neutron capture by I[127] is somewhat reduced, because as deuterium burning progresses, He[3] is produced, and He[3] has a high cross section for the absorption of neutrons. If we assume the uncertainty in deuterium abundance to govern the error, then the error in the amount of xenon formed is about 10%.

The proton capture rate has an uncertainty which is quoted as about 17%, from recent measurements by Griffiths et al. (1963) of the proton capture cross section and its extrapolation to low energies. It is not entirely certain that this error may not in fact be even larger. We have not looked in detail at the errors associated with the d–d reactions, and we use an error of 24% as determined by Salpeter (1955). The uncertainty associated with the temperature of deuterium-burning is estimated as 30%.

These errors are summarized in Table 10.1. The total probable error in the calculation that we get from compounding these is thus about 54%.

Figure 10.8 shows again the atmospheric abundance anomalies. Superimposed on this is the region (taking into account the 54% probable error) in which the values of Xe^{124} and Xe^{126} are predicted to lie by the calculation, assuming that all of the xenon in the earth's atmosphere which has not resulted from the radioactive decay of I^{129} and the fission of the Pu^{244} had once been in the sun. The agreement is entirely satisfactory within the limits of error. It is better than was reported previously (Cameron, 1963b) principally because recent solar evolution calculations indicate that a higher temperature should be used for the deuterium-burning stage. If this basic mechanism for the change in the abundances of the light xenon isotopes is correct, then the majority of the nonradiogenic and nonfissionogenic xenon in the earth's atmosphere must have once been in the sun.

How, then, do we get xenon from the sun into the earth's atmosphere? If we take the effective radius of the magnetosphere as about 10 earth radii and assume that the solar wind has essentially the solar composition, then the amount of xenon in the quiet solar wind incident on a disc of ten earth radii over 4.5 billion years fails to account for the amount of xenon in the earth's atmosphere by approximately one order of magnitude. If we increase the average

TABLE 10.1 Probable Errors in the Calculation of the Amount of Neutron Capture in I^{127} That May Be Expected to Occur during the Deuterium-Burning Phase of Early Solar Evolution

I^{127} Cross section	10%
I^{127} Abundance	30%
Deuterium/hydrogen ratio	10%
$D^2(p, \gamma)He^3$ rate	17%
$D^2(d, p, \text{ or } n)He^3$ or H^3 rate	24%
Solar temperature	30%
Total probable error	54%

value of the earth's magnetic field by a factor of two, as has been suggested by MacDonald (see Chapter 7), this will help. If we take into account the fact that gusts in the solar wind at times of greater solar activity result in plasma densities much greater than the quiet solar wind, this may also help. So again, there is still hope for this mechanism.

Let us look at how the solar wind interacts with the magnetosphere. We think of the magnetosphere as having a tear-drop shape, with the solar wind flowing around it, and we expect that this flow is set up in such a way that the bulk of the solar wind is not captured. Thus we require a very great fractionation such that the heavy elements (e.g., xenon) are captured, while the lighter elements, which make up the bulk of the solar wind, are not. As further evidence of this, we observe that the ratio of neon to xenon in the sun is considerably greater than in the earth's atmosphere. Thus we need a mechanism which captures xenon with great efficiency, but rejects neon, helium, etc.

A possible mechanism might relate to the fact that the material in the ordinary solar wind comes from the corona, where it may be stripped of up to 13 or 14 electrons without difficulty. Hence most of the light isotopes would be fairly completely stripped. Thus helium and neon would have mass-to-charge ratios of about 2; argon and iron would have ratios of about 4. Xenon, on the other hand, would have a ratio of approximately 10, and krypton, perhaps 6 or 7. Therefore, a capture mechanism strongly dependent on the mass-to-charge ratio, possibly having to do with the fact that ions with large ratios have large Larmor radii in the earth's field, might do the trick. The situation is clearly very complicated and needs investigation.

Another aspect of the problem is to explain why we do not see similar effects in krypton. We can calculate what isotope effects to expect, since the bromine neutron resonances are known accurately enough. The cross sections are much less than in the case of iodine and xenon. Consequently, the effects should be small, but should nevertheless be perhaps twice or three times the errors quoted in the measurements made. To account for this, we must go back to the Suess and Urey abundances. When they set up their original abundances, they took as one of their fundamental data the ratio of krypton to xenon in the earth's atmosphere. In making the new compilation of element abundances shown earlier, I have had to abandon this assumption and lower the krypton-to-xenon ratio by about a factor of two.

Thus, not only do we require the bulk of the xenon in the earth's atmosphere to have come in from outside, but also we need a large fractionation of the krypton and xenon that have been outgassed from the earth, to the extent that xenon should be retained in the earth much more than krypton.

There are many uncertainties in the determination of these data. The theory is not completely satisfactory in any sense; on the other hand, the isotope differences in the xenon composition exist and represent a great challenge.

REFERENCES

Cameron, A. G. W., 1963a. Notes on nuclear astrophysics (a course given at Yale University).
——————— 1963b. The origin of atmospheric xenon, *Icarus*, **1**, 314.
Ezer, D. and A. G. W. Cameron, 1962. The early evolution of the sun, *Icarus*, **1**, 422.
Fowler, W. A., J. L. Greenstein, and F. Hoyle, 1962. Nucleosynthesis during the early history of the solar system, *Geophys. Jour. Royal Astron. Soc.*, **6**, 148.
Goles, G. G. and E. Anders, 1962. Abundances of iodine, tellurium, and uranium in meteorites (I), *Geochim. et Cosmochim. Acta*, **26**, 723.
Griffiths, G. M., M. Lal, and C. D. Scarfe, 1963. The reaction $D(p, \gamma)He^3$ below 50 kev, *Canadian Jour. Phys.*, **41**, 724.
Hayashi, C., 1961. Stellar evolution in early phases of gravitational contraction, *Publ. Astron. Soc. Japan*, **13**, 450.
Salpeter, E. E., 1955. Nuclear reactions in stars. II: protons on light nuclei, *Phys. Rev.*, **97**, 1237.
Suess, H. E. and H. C. Urey, 1956. Abundances of the elements, *Rev. Mod. Phys.*, **28**, 53.

DISCUSSION

Dr. Holland: It seems to me that one way of settling this problem would be to look at some gases that have come out of the interior and thus could not have been diluted by the solar wind. I wonder if Dr. Wasserburg has any data on the isotopic composition of xenon in his well gases.

Dr. Wasserburg: In almost all of the terrestrial samples that have been looked at, the xenon is isotopically the same as in air, as accurately as we can measure.

Dr. Cameron: Let me remind you that the critical isotopes—124, 126, 128, and 130—are very difficult to measure with the required accuracy. Also, just doing one of these doesn't help; we must see to what extent there is fractionation among these four isotopes.

Dr. MacDonald: If the solar wind does have the solar abundance, this implies a great deal, for if the solar wind were an exospheric phenomenon, then we would not expect to find any heavy elements. But if you require heavy elements in the solar wind, then it has to be a hydrodynamic phenomenon.

Dr. Cameron: I would say that the Mariner II data seemed consistent with the hydrodynamic picture, if we interpret the charge spectrum as being due to the hydrogen and helium. However, this is just the first glimpse.

Dr. Gold: The obvious thing to do, it seems to me, is to fly a mass spectrograph in the solar wind. This is a difficult task, and it is a very large undertaking. It is not a quick or cheap experiment. But on the other hand, if the solar wind does represent a hydrodynamic flow, mass spectrography of the solar wind would then give us the entire solar surface composition in fine detail. That, of course, would represent a fantastic improvement of our knowledge.

NOTE.   Shortly afterward, Dr. Gold prepared and read the following resolution.

"Mass spectroscopy of the gas in interplanetary space, both during chromospheric outbursts and at quiet times, would provide detailed information as to the nuclear composition of the solar surface. Such information would be of great consequence to the discussion of nuclear evidence concerning the origin of the bodies of the solar system, and would provide a basis for comparison of the nuclear abundances observed in meteorites and on the earth.

"The present meeting would like to suggest that the possibility of such an experiment be carefully investigated by the Space Science Board of the National Academy of Sciences, and by NASA."

It was agreed by those present at the meeting that such an experiment would in fact be very desirable if possible to carry out, and the resolution was accepted.

11

Outgassing Processes on
the Moon and Venus

Thomas Gold

I would like to mention some points that have occurred to me with respect to the question of outgassing of planetary bodies. They are just a stray collection and possibly not novel, but it may still be appropriate to mention them here.

Let us first consider the following problem: what would be the situation if there were a body similar to the earth exhaling the same materials from its interior, but some of the circumstances on its surface were quite different? Venus seems to be a body very similar to the earth; such considerations may therefore shed some light on the problem. On the earth (if we accept Rubey's estimates; see Chapter 1), it appears that of the volatiles that have come to the top, water is, of course, the dominant one. About 300 atm of water have come up and condensed on or near the surface. Carbon has been supplied, probably mainly in the form of CO_2 or possibly in significant measure in the form of CH_4. The quantities of these substances, if estimated in terms of CO_2, would have amounted to about 20 atm. One atmosphere of N_2 and small amounts of argon and other gases seem to complete the story, apart from chlorine and other chemically reactive constituents which would readily combine with the surface rocks. The free oxygen in the earth's atmosphere is, of course, only a consequence of vegetation, and the quantity is a small part of that which could have been liberated by the dissociation of CO_2. Thus the first point to make is that the present-day earth's atmosphere is really only a small by-product of the gases that have come out of the ground.

Carbon dioxide is no longer present, for reasons that are very specific to processes on our planet. Carbon dioxide is dissolved in sea water, and the carbon is used partly through the intervention of organisms to make a deposit of limestone. If the circumstances were very different—for example, if we had an earth with a higher surface temperature and with no biology, or with no continents rising above the sea—it is not clear how much carbon would have been deposited and how much would have remained in the air. Possibly hydrocarbons would form and make a floating deposit on top of the water.

The present rate of outgassing of CO_2 is probably not very different from the mean rate over the existence of the earth, judging from the fact that the rate of deposition of fixed carbon into the ground in geologically recent times is not dramatically different from the mean rate. Also, the present content of carbon in the atmosphere is so small that it could not be thought of as a reservoir for the fixing processes and it would seem strange to suppose that just in our epoch we have come to the end of the supply of carbon. Thus the outgassing of CO_2 or other carbon-containing gasses is still in full swing. Possibly the same is true of water and nitrogen.

Let us now consider an earth with a much higher surface temperature. As the temperature approached the boiling point of water for that atmospheric pressure, large amounts of water vapor would start to go into the atmosphere and the atmospheric pressure would therefore rise. This poses a rather interesting problem.

Suppose that in the case of the earth the surface temperature had risen gradually for reasons of atmospheric changes and had reached the boiling point of water. Then as water is evaporated into the atmosphere, the greenhouse effect would almost certainly increase, as there would be a large increase in the thermal protection without a correspondingly large increase in the optical opacity. The temperature would therefore rise more, and therefore more water would be evaporated. Can this lead to a runaway process? Could it be that as each increment of water is added, the additional greenhouse effect raises the temperature by more than the boiling point has been raised by the extra pressure? Of course, if no equilibrium were obtained, the oceans would be converted into steam. It is highly possible, dependent on the detailed optical and infrared properties of such an atmosphere, that the process would halt itself at some particular ratio of steam to water.

The discussion of the surface temperature and of the processes that occur there have not much to do with the question of the escape of gases from the top of the atmosphere. The earth's surface temperature could be much higher and much more water could be in the atmosphere without having a great effect on the levels from which escape into space would take place. The outer atmosphere, and with it the cold trap which restricts the upward diffusion of water vapor, would be determined by much the same circumstances no matter how much water was available below. The mere existence of a lot of water vapor on a planet does not necessarily mean that a lot will have been lost.

The comparison of Earth and Venus is such that the rates of loss of water vapor from the atmosphere are not likely to have been different by several orders of magnitude. The earth cannot be thought of as having lost more than a few atmospheres of water vapor in all of geological time, and Venus could then not easily be thought of as having lost 300 atm of water. It would be a great problem to account for a waterless Venus. The fact that it is hot on the surface is irrelevant, for this will only have caused more atmosphere and less ocean. It would be necessary to suppose that the cold trap is very much less intense there than here.

The temperatures that have been measured on the colder parts of Venus are in the general range of 485–550°K. These temperatures correspond to a range of pressures at the boiling point of 20 to 60 atm. We can make an argument which would show that it is the temperature at the cold side of the planet that would control the atmospheric pressure. The water may well have an overlay of a substance of smaller density and higher boiling point, such as any one of various hydrocarbons, and a large temperature differential may then exist between the bottom and the top of this layer. We have to remember that on the earth it is mainly biological processes and oxidation which keep the surface of the ocean clean. A steam atmosphere would in such a case have to be in equilibrium with water in the coldest region, for if the atmospheric pressure were excessive for that condition, water would readily condense there. This would mean a pressure much less than the equilibrium value for the hottest part of the surface. On the hot side, water would boil up, no doubt through cracks in the overlying layer, at a rate at which it would remove, by means of the heat of evaporation, all the heat conducted downward through that layer.

I do not know whether such a situation could correspond to Venus. The essential evidence, which seems at the present time to be against such an interpretation, is the absence of spectroscopic evidence for water vapor above the clouds and the high temperature even at the shortest radio wavelengths observed. These short radio wavelengths would not be expected to penetrate a dense steam atmosphere. If Venus is really waterless, we would have to suppose that it had a very different composition or a very different career from that of the earth.

Let us now look at another outgassing problem. Let us consider the escape of gases from a much smaller body than Venus or the earth—a body like the moon, for example. We are interested in this not only because of concern with the moon itself, but also because we would like to know what course the atmospheric evolution would take during the period of growth of a body like the earth, provided it grows by accretion of solid pieces.

What occurs on the moon when gases escape from the interior? The thermal rates of escape of various gases have often been calculated and turn out to be fairly short for most gases. It is not until we come to molecular weights on the order of 50 that gases could be held against thermal evaporation. These calculations are quite misleading because the actual rate of escape would be enormously faster than the thermal evaporation would have made it, as a result of interaction with the solar wind.

On a small body with no magnetic field or a field less than 10^{-3} gauss, the solar wind would penetrate right to the surface, bringing with it its own magnetic fields with strengths of a few gammas. These fields become augmented by the compression of the gas as it strikes the surface to the order of the stagnation pressure of the flow, which often seems to be 10^{-3} gauss. In this situation an atmospheric molecule in the exosphere will be removed instantly the moment it becomes ionized. The ionized molecule is now imbedded in a wind containing a magnetic field in which the radius of gyration for the relative velocity between molecule and wind is quite small. For a proton this velocity often corresponds to a kilovolt energy, and at that energy a proton's radius of gyration in a field of 20γ would be about 200 km. Thus at the moment such a particle is ionized, it commences the gyrating motion around a center of curvature which is traveling along with the velocity of the wind. This velocity is usually of the order of a few hundred kilometers per second.

Any gases that come up from the interior of the moon would be retained there only for periods that are of the order of the ionization times, and the longest ionization times occurring in the presence of sunlight are probably less than one month. For most gases it would be a great deal shorter. Judging from the evidence from comets, ionization times are in fact considerably shorter than photoionization would have made them, for reasons that are not fully understood.

In any case, it is clear that this mechanism completely dominates over thermal evaporation and that the moon and other small bodies like it cannot be expected to retain even the heaviest gases that come up from their interiors. The only atmosphere that can be present is the temporary one that is built up from the equilibrium between the fast incoming solar wind which hits the surface and the much slower removal of this gas from the surface. This can lead to a temporary atmosphere whose density is greater than the solar wind density by the factor by which the solar wind is faster than thermal speeds for the moon's surface temperature. In practice, this factor can be as large as 500, and at a solar wind density of 10 particles/cm^3 we might have a temporary atmosphere of 5000 particles/cm^3. This atmosphere would, however, be predominantly neutral, with recombination as well as cooling having taken place on the moon's surface.

Let us now consider one other point about the moon, namely the question of water there. What would happen if, as on the earth, a certain amount of steam were forced up from the interior? Water is so much the dominent volatile constituent for earth-like material that it is hard to think that none of it would have been made available there. The moon must have had some radioactive heating in its interior, although apparently it was not enough to melt it; but it almost certainly was enough to drive off substantial amounts of water.

Steam percolating upwards through the body of the moon could not reach the surface, as it would in the case of the earth. The moon's surface material, apart from a very thin diurnally-varying layer, is at a temperature of about 240°K—well below the freezing point of water. Any water coming upward in little cracks and fissures would thus tend to freeze and block its own route of escape. The moon would contain, at some level beneath the surface, a layer of permafrost in which all the pores of the rock are filled with ice, preventing steam from rising. All water coming up through pores below this layer would then accumulate, and at the depth at which the temperature begins to exceed the melting point of ice the pores would be filled with liquid water.

We suppose here that the situation in the interior is somewhat similar to the case of the earth, namely that the water coming up first has to create a layer of fully hydrated silicates before any of it can come to the surface. The difference is only that then the water will still not contrive to come up, but instead it will be caught in the rock at a comparatively small depth where the temperature is somewhere below the freezing point.

We have actually done experiments of seeping water vapor and other gases through various depths of porous materials and from this have calculated what quantities of water would be lost to the vacuum outside from a given depth on the moon. The answer seems to be that at depths of more than about 150 meters in the ground, ice could be maintained virtually indefinitely. Only a few grams per square centimeter would be lost in the whole of geologic time. The protection of the ice by the overlying layer is required in order to prevent too rapid an evaporation to the exterior. On the other hand, the overlying layer does not need to be very thick and is certainly quite shallow compared with the heights of surface features of the moon. We would have to think of the permafrost lining the hills and valleys and following the major contours of the ground rather than being deep underneath these structures.

If the situation is that the porosity of the ground is filled with a permafrost layer at a depth of the order of 100 meters, with liquid water in turn underneath that at the depth at which the temperature exceeds the melting point of ice, what will happen at the time of formation of a crater? Let us suppose the crater is deep enough to cut into the zone of liquid water. Then the water will immediately shoot out and boil off. Some internal drainage will now take place before all the newly opened ground has been cooled and frozen, and an internal system of rivers will develop running toward the place where the water can escape freely.

We must think of these internal rivers as running upside down, since the hydrostatic pressure gradient will be pressing them upward against the permafrost layer, and the running water will tend to wear some kind of pattern by melting the ice. If a large amount of such flow has occurred it might wear away enough ice and enough soil to cause the overlying layers eventually to sink in after the supply of water has run out, and in this way to show on the surface some replica of the shape of the internal river bed. We would then expect to see river-like patterns of depressions in the surface going toward craters.

In fact, it is a common feature to see rills converging on craters in flat ground, sometimes in patterns of more or less straight lines that are suggestive of internal stresses, but sometimes also in patterns that look more like meandering rivers and that could not be thought of as resulting from stress. Sometimes these patterns even include shapes that are reminiscent of deltas, and it is certainly very common for the rills to increase in width and depth as they approach the final crater.

Perhaps what we are seeing here is evidence for the outgassing of water which has occurred principally through craters temporarily breaking down the permafrost barrier, with the subsequent collapse of the surface over the drained-out river beds.

DISCUSSION

Dr. Whipple: I wonder whether Dr. Whitaker would like to comment on this question of the rubble that falls back into the crater? That would leave a nice layer. I can picture water seeping into the rubble, then freezing.

Dr. Whitaker: I don't think there will be any fall-back in the ordinary sense of the word in any craters. All the material that escapes is thrown out ballistically. There is breccia that forms inside of the crater. I could well imagine that this would soak up a lot of water. I am really concerned, however, about this process of actual flow. I think Dr. Gold ought to talk about this with a ground-water hydrologist.

Dr. Gold: I have looked into this. We don't seem to have any sub-permafrost internal rivers. There are only a few areas on the earth where there is deep permafrost in the ground. I am wondering if we have any cases where there is water that is trying to come up through permafrost and is not able to, and therefore doing this upside-down river flowing. This has not been discovered on the earth, but it may exist.

Dr. Whipple: Perhaps we can ask the Russians to do an experiment in Siberia—to do one of those nice large explosions—and see what happens. If it will go right into the permafrost, there will be no argument about it.

Voice: With regard to the loss of water vapor from Venus, isn't this controlled by the exosphere temperature?

Dr. Jastrow: The bottleneck is the cold trap. There is a minimum temperature corresponding to the saturation vapor pressure, below which water vapor is limited from diffusing into the upper atmosphere where it can be photodissociated by the ultraviolet. We know that the temperature is low enough, below $235°K$, so that the water vapor is shielded from the ultraviolet.

Dr. Kellogg: This is true,, but if we consider Dr. Hess' ideas about the early history of Venus, it may have had a very hot or molten surface, in which case the level of the cold trap may have been so high that it was in the region where ultraviolet radiation could reach.

Dr. Gold: Let me not argue more than I want to. All I want to say is that the question of how much water vapor escapes from the top is critically dependent on the cold trap. It is not a straightforward matter to suppose that if the ground is heated up, water is going to be boiled off the planet.

Dr. Jastrow: What may have happened in the early history was that dissociation did occur, the hydrogen escaped, and an oxygen atmosphere built up, which shielded the remaining water vapor from the ultraviolet.

Dr. Gold: Yes. The only point I wish to make, however, is that an earth-like body, if made hotter, has some trouble in losing 300 atmospheres' worth of water from its surface into space.

Dr. Goody: With regard to this boosting effect—where the increased water vapor raises the temperature, causing more boiling—I would like to point out that the basic mechanism for the atmosphere to run away in this manner is with us, yet it does not run away. There must be some inherent stability in this particular case.

Dr. Gold: I agree. But the amount of water vapor that is drawn up now per degree rise in temperature is a great deal less than what it would be near the boiling point.

12

Observations of Water
Vapor on Mars and Venus

A. Dollfus

Recently we made new observations on the amounts of water vapor in the atmospheres of Mars and Venus. The purpose of this paper is to discuss the method used and the results obtained.

A few years ago, we designed a special 20-inch telescope for the purpose of measuring water vapor in planetary atmospheres. The measurement of an absorption band of H_2O was performed photometrically without using a spectrograph, but with the use of a birefringent monochromatic filter, as shown in Figure 12.1. The upper line represents the absorption band we wish to measure. Line 1 represents the transmission of the birefringent filter used to measure the absorption. The filter can be quickly tuned to give a transmission as shown by line 2. In this position, we obtain the intensity of the background. By changing the transmission 20 times per second, we obtain modulation, and make the intensity comparisons photoelectrically. The signal-to-noise ratio for Mars was about 3 to 1.

The choice of the most appropriate absorption band was somewhat difficult to make. A faint band will not be saturated in the earth's atmosphere, but the sensitivity will be low. On the other hand, for a strong band the sensitivity is high, but we must be high up in the atmosphere for it to be unsaturated. The choice narrowed down to the 1.15-μ band or the 1.4-μ band in the near infrared. We chose the 1.4-μ band because the band is more intense, may be desaturated in some particular conditions, and corresponds to the maximum sensitivity of the photocells.

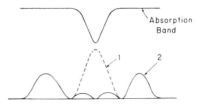

Figure 12.1   Transmission characteristics of birefringent filter. Lines 1
and 2 represent the transmission of
the filter in each of its two positions.

The 1.4-μ band is so intense that in order to observe it unsaturated,
we must make our measurements high up in the atmosphere. This
can be done by balloon flights. We can also make the observations
on high mountains in winter, provided the temperature of the air is
very cold. We tried both of these techniques.

For the balloon flight, we used a stratospheric gondola. The observer operates the telescope from the inside of a sealed cabin. The
telescope is driven manually, and the gondola can be turned by
means of gas jets. The gondola was lifted by 104 large sounding
balloons, clustered along a vertical cable; to descend, we used radio
switches which activated the bursting of several balloons. We were
thus able to attain a height of 14 km, above the tropopause. Our
high mountain observations were made at a height of 3.5 km, at the
Jungfrau Scientific Station (Figs. 12.2–12.6).

We obtained our data by making photometric comparisons of the
observations on planets with those on the sun or moon. In the
stratosphere, the water vapor content is very low, so that we could
use the moon only as a control. On the other hand, for the mountain
observations, one has to compensate more carefully for the water in
the earth's atmosphere. In January 1963, Mars was high in the sky,
close to the zenith, so we were not looking through much atmosphere.
On the nights of clear sky we followed the amount of water vapor
above the station by studying the moon or some stars; before sunset and after sunrise we looked at the sun (reflected on some dark
beads to reduce the intensity). When the amount of water was such
that the 1.4-μ band was not saturated, we took readings of Mars.
We then interpolated our terrestrial water vapor data, and subtracted from the Mars reading to give the difference. Finally, our
mountain results were better than the balloon results.

We had five nights in which we took measurements on Mars, and in each case, the amount of water vapor measured was greater than that expected for the earth's atmosphere alone. On the best night, the amount in the earth's atmosphere was 4.2×10^{-2} g/cm², with an error of $\pm 1.1 \times 10^{-2}$. On Mars, the value deduced was 2.6×10^{-2} g/cm². This value has to be corrected for the fact that the light passes twice through the atmosphere, and for the cosine effect at the edge of the disc. The result is that the water vapor value is reduced by very close to a factor of 4. This makes the value 0.65×10^{-2} g/cm². We also have to correct for pressure and temperature. The telescope was calibrated at normal atmospheric pressure on the earth. The

Figure 12.2   The 20-inch telescope is shown, as set up for the balloon flight.

Figure 12.3   The gondola, with the telescope on top, is being prepared for the ascent.

pressure at the surface of Mars is low—we assumed a value of 85 mb—so the calibration must be corrected to that pressure. We used spectra taken in the laboratory at various pressures to make this correction and obtained a final value of 1.5×10^{-2} g/cm^2 of water vapor on Mars.

This result is the first estimate of the amount of water on Mars, but it is not the first proof of the existence of water vapor on Mars. We had already shown that the polarization properties of the polar caps can be reproduced in the laboratory by deposits of water frost. On the basis of the known properties of the polar caps, we estimated what should be a reasonable amount of water vapor on Mars. Our estimate was 2.0×10^{-2} g/cm^2, which is in reasonable agreement with the value observed.

Now, let us turn to the case of Venus. Venus is more difficult to observe than Mars for two reasons. First of all, Venus is close to the horizon; we will therefore have a long path in the earth's atmosphere and more difficulty in obtaining an unsaturated band. In addition, Venus has CO_2 bands, which interfere with the water vapor band. Thus the technique used so far would give the total amount of H_2O plus a contribution of CO_2. We were obliged to design the birefringent filter so it would be able to distinguish between CO_2 and H_2O. Figure 12.7 shows a laboratory absorption spectrum, due to Kuiper, of CO_2 with a small quantity of H_2O added. We chose a transmission band so as to completely absorb the intense CO_2 bands. Therefore, in the normal position of the filter, the signal comes from the H_2O only. In the second position, there is a small signal due to a few weak bands of CO_2. The very intense band at 1.44-μ has no effect. The small signal is not negligible, so we must compute its effect and correct for it in the background reading.

Figure 12.4 The gondola and telescope in flight; 104 small balloons were used to provide the lift.

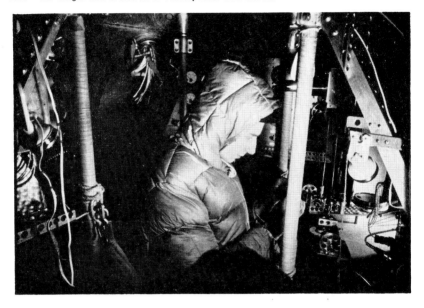

Figure 12.5   A view inside the gondola, showing the operator at the controls.

In making the observations, we very fortunately were able to take advantage of the occultation of Venus by the moon on January 21, 1963. During two days of observations, the distances between the moon and Venus were 7 degrees on the first night, and 6 degrees on the second night. Also, the heights of the moon and Venus above the horizon were about the same, so we could easily use the moon for background readings. Furthermore, we needed very appropriate dry weather conditions. In fact, the conditions were unexpectedly good. The amount of water vapor above the station was about 1×10^{-2} g/cm², about a factor of 5 smaller than expected. Our balloon observations were unsatisfactory because of a half-hour delay in launching, but we had much better luck with our ground observations.

The direct measurements obtained on the two nights are shown in Figure 12.8. They show clearly that the signal for Venus is greater than for the moon, indicating the existence of water vapor on Venus. In Figure 12.9, the differences between the Venus and moon readings are plotted; the values are the signals due to CO_2 and H_2O on Venus, and each point represents a different line of sight. To the right, at

A, the water vapor line is completely saturated, so the reading is due to CO_2 alone. The curve is extrapolated to the left at B, where we have the reading due to CO_2 plus H_2O. The difference between the two readings is 2.8×10^{-2} g/cm² of H_2O. Applying the factor of 4 path correction gives us a value of 0.7×10^{-2} g/cm². Now we must make the correction for pressure. We do not know exactly what the pressure is at the level of the Venus clouds, but we do know that it is less than one earth atmosphere. Thus the amount of water vapor is probably about 1×10^{-2} g/cm², with a probable error of a factor of 2.

Figure 12.6 The telescope, as set up for observation at the Jungfrau Scientific Station.

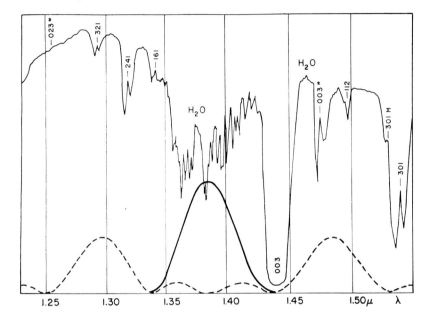

Figure 12.7   Transmission lines of the birefringent filter.
——————— Normal Position
– – – – – – Second Position

To check whether this result was reasonable, we made a rough calculation. We assumed that the temperature of the clouds on Venus was about —40°C. Assuming that the clouds are due to water, we expect that the first kilometer or so is saturated, and above that the concentration decreases with height. Integrating all along for reasonable values of water vapor content and temperature, we arrive at a value of 1.15×10^{-2} g/cm². So on the basis of our rough estimate, the measured value seems reasonable.

We should also point out that during our stratospheric flight, a measurement was made of the amount of water vapor above the gondola, at an altitude of 13 km. At this height, the amount was also of the order of 1×10^{-2} g/cm². So if the earth was completely covered over with clouds at 13-km height, and an observer looked at the earth from space with similar equipment, he would detect the same amount of water vapor that we have detected on Venus. Thus, in spite of the assurance that there is a large amount of water vapor on the earth, it is seen that if we observe the earth and Venus in the same way, the amount of water vapor found would be exactly the same.

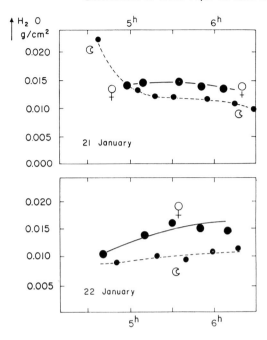

Figure 12.8 Comparison of the signals observed for the moon and Venus, reduced to the same paths in the earth's atmosphere (uncorrected for CO_2 absorption).

We would also like to mention that during the past year we organized an international program for the photographing of Venus in the ultraviolet. As you know, ultraviolet pictures of Venus show markings which seem to be due to clouds, because they move very quickly. If we were to take pictures every night in a single observatory, we would have a sequence of one picture to every 24 hours. But in 24 hours, the configurations change so completely that it is impossible to follow their evolution. However, by cooperating with several observatories at different longitudes around the globe, we were able to obtain sequences of pictures taken every three or four hours over several days. Cooperating observatories have collected about 700 pictures, and we are in the process of studying them. We have already processed two sequences in which we can trace the evolution of these clouds. From these first results, we have observed that the period of rotation of these clouds is longer than 40 days. We

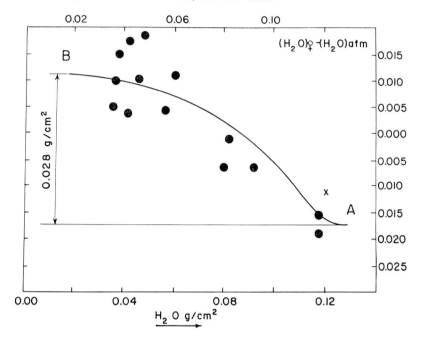

Figure 12.9 Correction for the effect of CO_2 in the determination of the amount of H_2O on Venus.

hope, before too long, to have completed our study so we can present all the information.

DISCUSSION

Voice: What kind of fluctuations did you get in your measurements of the water vapor of the earth's atmosphere?

Dr. Dollfus: We found that the water vapor was not uniformly distributed, but was patterned in the sky, so we had to be very careful to follow the variations, and took a great many readings before we drew up our curve of variation with time and position.

Dr. Arking: Assuming that the Venus clouds are ice crystals, wouldn't they make some sort of contribution to the background reading?

Dr. Dollfus: If you have a reflection at the surface of this ice layer, the band would be displaced to a longer wavelength, and the effect would be to give a small negative signal. In that case, we would have to increase the amount of water vapor above. So we performed some laboratory experiments on artificial frost to determine what the correction factor would be. We found that the correction depends on the size of the grains; for large grains, there are more internal reflections giving bands, and thus the correction would be larger. From polarimetric measurements, we would expect the grains to be small—perhaps 2- to 3-μ in size—and so the correction factor is small: about 1.2.

Dr. Holland: Did you get any measurements on CO_2 as well?

Dr. Dollfus: No. This is better done by conventional spectroscopy. The telescope is, at present, specialized for H_2O measurements, and the accuracy of CO_2 measurements would not be very high.

Dr. Sagan: I would like to point out that there have been ground-based measurements using the Doppler effect made when the velocities relative to Earth of Venus and Mars were large. Spinrad and Richardson have set an upper limit for Mars of 3.5×10^{-3} g/cm². This is a factor of 10 lower than your result. There is a similar discrepancy in the case of Venus.

Dr. Dollfus: I am aware of these results. But if one obtains a positive result, one gives a value. If one obtains a negative result, one gives a threshold. It is attractive to give for the upper limit a very low value.

Dr. Field: Would one expect seasonal variations of the water vapor content on Mars, and might this be the cause of the discrepancy?

Dr. Dollfus: Yes. We know, by conventional telescopic observations, that there is variation in the water vapor content, but we don't know about the amounts. The polar cap begins to evaporate at the beginning of spring, and the water vapor moves toward the equator; then in autumn, it begins to be deposited as frost on the other pole. So water vapor moves continuously from pole to pole. At the time of our measurements, it was the end of spring for the northern hemisphere of Mars.

Dr. Gold: If it is true that there is water vapor above the clouds on Venus, and that the clouds are ice, then it seems to me that it is difficult to think of Venus as having lost a large amount of water. If it started out with 300 atmospheres of water, and the method of evaporation has been so effective as to have gotten rid of nearly

300 atmospheres, why should it have left behind such a small amount? Therefore, a moist atmosphere without oceans on the bottom seems to me to be a most unlikely circumstance.

Dr. Kellogg: But something like an exponential boil-off would leave something behind at all stages.

Voice: You assumed that the reflection of light takes place on the upper surface of the clouds. Yet, Spinrad made some CO_2 measurements at about 0.78-μ in the CO_2 band, and his results indicate that the reflected light must come from a much deeper level.

Dr. Dollfus: I know of this result, and I was very surprised at it. I would like to see some confirmation of his results.

Dr. Kellogg: These results are not necessarily inconsistent. One can imagine a model of Venus in which there is a thin cloud layer, and if somehow there is a break in it, then both observations could be explained. The difficulty is in imagining that a thin cloud layer exists.

13

The Atmosphere of Mercury

G. Field

It has often been stated in the literature that Mercury has no atmosphere; this paper would turn out to be the simplest one in the conference if that were to be the case. We would like, however, to present what evidence we have that there is an atmosphere, and we will try to give a tentative interpretation of this evidence.

In Table 13.1 we have summarized some of the pertinent data on Mercury. Mercury is particularly interesting because it is similar in many respects to the moon. Its radius is about 30% greater than that of the moon (although Mercury has about 4.2 times more mass). Mercury, like the moon, has synchronous rotation with respect to its parent body. The albedo and polarization effects on both bodies are quite similar.

TABLE 13.1 Data on Mercury

Mean distance from sun	0.387	A.U.
Period	88	days
Eccentricity	0.206	
Radius	2420	km
Mass (earth units)	0.054	
Mean density	5.4	g/cm^3
Escape velocity	4.2	km/sec
Temperature (subsolar point)	615°K	

The reason that people have always thought that the atmosphere would be very tenuous, if it existed at all, results from the fact that the escape velocity is small and the surface temperature is very high. In fact, we find that the surface temperature approaches the critical temperature for the exospheric escape of light gases. Since the light gases will escape at 600 to 700°K, and it is unlikely that the exosphere temperature for Mercury is much less than that, it does not appear that a Mercury atmosphere would contain any of the common atoms, such as carbon, nitrogen, oxygen, and/or their molecules.

Nevertheless, we are confronted with two pieces of information about the atmosphere. The first of these is illustrated in Figure 13.1. Here are shown the results of some very difficult measurements made by Dollfus over the surface of Mercury (Dollfus, 1961). He was looking for differential polarization effects, and he studied these differential effects as a function of the phase angle and also as a function of the wavelength of the light. He used two filters, one in green and one in red, and looked for differences between the center and limbs of the planet. To begin with, there is a large polarization

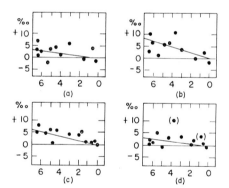

Figure 13.1   Differential polarization, ΔP, by the atmosphere of Mercury (in units of 0.1%), based on observations of the center of the disc and the cusps, in both red and green light. The abscissa represents a function of the phase angle $[10 \sin^2 V/(1 - \cos^2 V)]$ which is expected to be linearly related to the polarization. The diagonal solid lines represent the theoretical results expected from Rayleigh scattering. (a) $\Delta P = P_{green} - P_{red}$ (center of disc). (b) $\Delta P = P_{green} - P_{red}$ (near cusps). (c) $\Delta P = P_{cusp} - P_{center}$ (green). (d) $\Delta P = P_{cusp} - P_{center}$ (red).

effect which is simply due to the scattering properties of the surface of Mercury. This effect has been compared to that of the moon, and found to be quite similar. But in the case of the moon, it is found that the polarization does not depend on the inclination of the surface to the sunlight. Since in every other way the polarization for Mercury is very similar to that of the moon, it is therefore suggested that any effect deviating from that may be explained by an atmosphere.

In fact, it can be seen in graphs (c) and (d) that there is a differential polarization between the center and the limb, and graphs (a) and (b) show that the effect is greater for green than for red. These effects are what would be expected from Rayleigh scattering. Thus we have an indication that there is a differential polarization effect over the surface of Mercury which varies with the phase angle and with the wavelength in such a way as would be expected from Rayleigh scattering in an atmosphere.

The second piece of evidence is shown in Figure 13.2. This concerns some radio observations made in 1960 by a group at the University of Michigan (Howard et al., 1962). They measured the brightness temperature in the 3-cm wavelength band for Mercury, making measurements at different phase angles. The curves shown on the graph are those that would be expected if the infrared measurements were a good clue to the temperature distribution on the surface of Mercury. It has always been assumed that the temperature on the dark side of Mercury is extremely low. Yet there is a systematic tendency for the measurements to lie above the theoretical curve assuming a dark-side temperature of $0°K$. One possible interpretation of this result is that the dark side is not entirely cold, but has a temperature which is significantly different from zero— perhaps as much as half that on the bright side. It can be seen that the data are in better agreement with a theoretical curve assuming a much higher dark-side temperature. This in turn seems to suggest that there is some mechanism for heat transport from the bright to the dark side. The radioactive heat contribution from the interior is undoubtedly inadequate to raise the temperature to anything like $300°K$ (Walker, 1961). So again we are led to the possibility of an atmosphere on Mercury.

As we have mentioned, in postulating an atmosphere for Mercury, we must look for gases that are considerably more massive than carbon, nitrogen, oxygen, etc. Let us consider the possibility of an atmosphere of A^{40} (which is radiogenic). Of course, we might also think of including the more massive noble gases xenon and krypton,

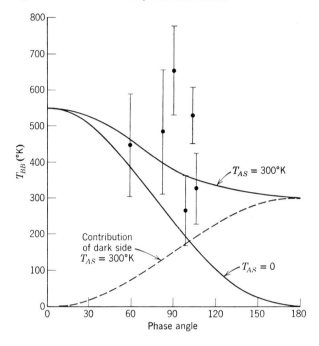

Figure 13.2 Computed apparent blackbody temperatures of Mercury at centimeter wavelengths. Lower solid curve applies if dark side is cold. Upper solid curve includes contribution of dark side at 300° K.

but the amounts to be expected are far too small to explain any of the effects we have observed.

Let us begin by calculating the amount of radiogenic argon available on Mercury by making a simple comparison with the earth. We assume that since the densities of the earth and Mercury are comparable, they are made of roughly the same material. In particular, if we take a model of Mercury in which we obtain the observed density of 5.4 by taking a core of density 8 and a mantle of density 3.4, we find that the mass of the mantle in Mercury is about 60% of the total mass, which is roughly the same proportion as in the earth. If we then assume that the mantle is made of roughly the same material as the mantle of the earth, we can then compute the amount of argon which would have entered the atmosphere of Mercury over geologic time, assuming no loss and assuming that the degassing is effectively the same as on the earth. Let us call this amount of argon N_0; it is calculated to be 6.3×10^{22} A^{40} atoms/cm².

Let us for the moment suppose that such an argon atmosphere has escaped from the mantle and is available. We can compute the scattering power of this atmosphere; since the scattering power of argon is 93% that of air, this atmosphere would be equivalent in scattering power to 5.9×10^{22} air molecules/cm^2, or 0.0027 atm. Dollfus interpreted his results in terms of Rayleigh scattering by an atmosphere, and found that a value of 0.003 atm would account for the results. It therefore seems that we ought to pursue this idea a little further and investigate whether or not argon is a reasonable constituent.

It is clear that there are a number of things we have to take into account here. First of all, there are three main influences which would tend to change the argon abundance in the atmosphere of Mercury:

(a) *Degassing of the interior:* this would, of course, tend to increase the atmospheric abundance.

(b) *The solar wind:* this could possibly have either a positive or negative effect. However, it seems more likely that the solar wind will sweep away a portion of the atmosphere which is ionized.

(c) *Evaporative loss:* this is the most usual type of loss, occurring at the critical level in the exosphere.

It is possible to write expressions for these mechanisms as functions of time; we can thus obtain a differential equation which will indicate how the atmosphere would behave as a function of time.

We can write an approximate expression for the input due to mechanism (a) as follows:

$$\frac{dN_a(t)}{dt} = \lambda N_0 \frac{e^{-\lambda t}}{1 - e^{-\lambda T}} \tag{1}$$

where $N_a(t)$ is the amount of argon/cm^2 in the atmosphere at time t due to mechanism (a); λ is the decay constant for K^{40}; and T is the age of the planet, which we can take to be 4.5 billion years. The average value of $dN_a(t)/dt$ is given by N_0/T; numerically, $\overline{dN_a(t)/dt} = 4.8 \times 10^5$ argon atoms/cm^2-sec. The rate of input at the present time, or $dN_a(T)/dt$, would be 1.1×10^5 argon atoms/cm^2-sec.

Now let us consider mechanism (b). If we consider a simple picture of this mechanism, in which it is assumed that the solar wind penetrates to a level in the atmosphere where the impact pressure can be balanced by the atmospheric pressure (assuming no planetary magnetic field), and all the atoms above this point have a certain probability of being ionized, we obtain the expression

$$\frac{dN_b(t)}{dt} = \frac{-P_{sw}q\sigma}{4\,mg} \tag{2}$$

where P_{sw} is the pressure of the solar wind; q is the solar ionizing flux in quanta/cm²-sec at Mercury; σ is the cross section for ionization; m is the mass of the atom concerned; and g is the acceleration of gravity on Mercury. We can now put in reasonable estimates for the factors involved to get a numerical result. A solar wind of particle density 30/cm³ and velocity 300 km/sec was used. These values were selected from some pre-Mariner satellite data and doubtless are imprecise. However, one observation by Mariner perhaps should not be taken as representative of the last 4.5 billion years. Let us set $dN_b(t)/dt = -K$, and call K the rate of loss due to the solar wind. We obtain a value of $K = 2.5 \times 10^5$ argon atoms/cm²-sec.

For (c), we have the expression

$$\frac{dN_c(t)}{dt} = -\frac{N(t)}{\tau} \tag{3}$$

where

$$\tau = 0.7T_c^{\frac{3}{2}}10^{\frac{18200}{T_c}} \tag{4}$$

τ is the characteristic escape time for the exosphere, and T_c represents here the temperature at the critical level in the exosphere.

We can now add up the three terms and solve the resulting differential equation. Assuming that at $t = 0$, $N = 0$, we obtain

$$\frac{N}{N_0} = \frac{\lambda t}{1 - \lambda t}\left(\frac{e^{-\lambda t} - e^{-t/\tau}}{1 - e^{-\lambda T}}\right) - \frac{KT}{N_0}\left(\frac{1 - e^{-t/\tau}}{T/\tau}\right) \tag{5}$$

Here, the first term represents the effect of constant replenishment of the argon from radiogenic sources and its depletion by loss from the exosphere; the second term represents the effect due to the solar wind. We now take some representative values of the critical temperature T_c, set $t = T$, and compare the two terms. The results are listed in Table 13.2.

It is clear from this table that for $T_c > 1500°K$ the atmosphere cannot exist at all. For low values of T_c, τ becomes very large (since the probability of escape must become small), and the first term

TABLE 13.2 Contributions to Atmosphere
(Equation 5)

$T_c(°K)$	1st Term	2nd Term	N/N_0
1200	1	0.5	0.5
1300	0.98	0.49	0.49
1400	0.79	0.42	0.37
1500	0.20	0.19	0.01
1600	0.025	0.042	−0.017

approaches 1. At the same time, the second term, due to the solar wind, approaches $\frac{KT}{N_0} \approx 0.5$. Thus the solar wind may play a large part in the depletion of the atmosphere at low temperatures. As the temperature increases, N/N_0 goes very rapidly to 0. The minimum temperature required for the retention of a substantial atmosphere is about 1400°. If we neglected the solar wind term, the required temperature would be about 1450°. Thus the solar wind causes only about a 50° change in the required critical temperature. However, it was shown previously that in order to agree with Dollfus' observations, a value of $N/N_0 \approx 1$ was required. This would seem to indicate that our original estimate of N_0 was inadequate, and that degassing may be a more efficient process on Mercury. In any case, it is apparent that a temperature somewhat lower than 1400°K is required for retention of an atmosphere.

It appears that it is going to be very difficult to explain how the temperature of the exosphere of Mercury could be at this level. For if we look for cooling mechanisms to act against the solar flux, we are troubled by the fact that argon is an extremely poor radiator; also conduction would probably be inadequate to keep the temperature at such a low value.

One possible mechanism is that as atoms in the ionosphere are ionized, the electrons will experience inelastic collisions, and will radiate some of their energy away as bremsstrahlung before they are recaptured. This would tend to depress the temperature somewhat. A rough computation suggests that the temperature would be determined by the equation

$$T = 2000(\overline{\Delta E})^{0.8}$$

where $\overline{\Delta E}$ is the ejected electron energy in electron volts. The estimated value of ΔE is about 10 to 20 ev, so this mechanism will not be much of a help. However, a detailed calculation has not been done.

Thus our investigation tends to show that unless we can find a mechanism for cooling the exosphere, such an atmosphere is unlikely, and we must find some other interpretation for the observations.

We come back now to the radio observations which seem to indicate that the dark side of Mercury is not extremely cold. The question arises as to whether convection around from the bright side can in fact heat the dark side to the required temperature in an argon atmosphere. Here we can use some calculations recently given by Mintz (1962) for the case in which a planet is being heated on one side alone. He finds a relationship for the velocity of material over the terminator required to bring the temperature at the antisolar point to a given value. In order to obtain a temperature of about 300°K, a velocity of about 500 m/sec is required. This is nearly Mach 1—an obviously unlikely situation. 56°K is of interest because it happens to be the sublimation temperature of argon at the pressures of interest. Thus, if the temperature of the antisolar point in fact were lower than 56°K, the proposed atmosphere would be in danger of freezing out. It can be calculated that a rather reasonable velocity of 60 cm/sec would be required to keep the antisolar point at 56°K or above. So the best guess would put the temperature between 56 and 300°K; this would not be inconsistent with the radio results.

Finally, we could suggest some further tests of this idea. Of course, the most obvious test would be to look in the ultraviolet for spectroscopic evidence of argon; there is a resonance line at 1048 Å. However, this would not be an easy experiment because of the faintness of the light reflected from Mercury at these wavelengths. It would also be of great interest to have other workers check the polarization data. We could also hope for future attempts to determine the temperature of the dark side by refined radio measurements.

REFERENCES

Dollfus, A., 1961. Polarization studies of planets, in G. P. Kuiper and B. M. Middlehurst, editors, *Planets and Satellites,* University of Chicago Press.
Howard, W. E., III, A. H. Barrett, and F. T. Haddock, 1962. Measurement of microwave radiation from the planet Mercury, *Astrophys. Jour.,* **136**, 995.
Walker, J. C. G., 1961. The thermal budget of the planet Mercury, *Astrophys. Jour.,* **133**, 274.
Mintz, V., 1962. The energy budget and atmospheric circulation on a synchronously rotating planet, *Icarus,* **1**, 172.

DISCUSSION

Dr. Thaddeus: What happens if you apply this analysis to the moon? What kind of an argon atmosphere would you get there?

Dr. Field: To maintain a lunar atmosphere would require an extremely low exospheric temperature—about a third of the value for Mercury—simply because the escape velocity is so low.

Dr. Cameron: One suggestion which comes to mind is that since the surface temperatures are high, some heavy, nonnoble gases such as chlorine might go up into the atmosphere as impurities.   Since these are much more efficient radiators than argon, they might help in bringing down the temperature.

Voice: Wouldn't atomic sulfur have sufficient fine structure in the ground state to radiate at these temperatures?

Dr. Field: That is an interesting suggestion.   Indeed, sulfur has a level at 400 cm^{-1} which would radiate effectively.   On the other hand, atomic sulfur would escape more easily than argon.

Voice: It seems to be that a very critical point in this discussion is the accuracy of the 0.003 atmosphere pressure that is measured.   I would like to ask Dr. Dollfus what the accuracy of this measurement is.

Dr. Dollfus: The accuracy of the pressure is not very clear.   But the important point is that the polarization measurements show that they can be explained by the existence of an atmosphere.

Dr. Gold: Can't these polarization measurements be accounted for by a surface with no atmosphere?   There are plenty of surfaces that have a polarization property which is a function of the angle, if that is all that is involved.   The moon is peculiar in that all its optical properties are independent of the phase angle.

Dr. Dollfus: Yes, but the polarization properties of the moon and Mercury are so similar in every other respect, that it is quite reasonable to assume that the material is the same.   In addition, the departure is not only in the phase angle, but in the wavelength.   Otherwise we would have to assume for Mercury a material having the same properties as the moon, but departing from it exactly like an atmosphere.

Dr. MacDonald: In the solar wind interaction, there is sharing of energy between the plasma and the ionized particles in the atmosphere. Therefore, I think your solar wind calculation would have been more realistic if you had balanced the dynamic pressure against the ion pressure, rather than against the total pressure.

Dr. Field: That may be so. This depends, I believe, on the collision rates involved.

Voice: Using the radio measurements to get temperature is quite an exotic procedure. It might be a lot easier to get the temperature with an infrared bolometer.

Dr. Field: Of course, both methods may be used. But the infrared radiation depends on T^4, so that if the dark-side temperature is only a third of the bright-side temperature, then the emission is lower by two orders of magnitude. This would make such a measurement difficult to obtain. On the other hand, radio emission depends on T and is therefore relatively greater from cool surfaces.

Mr. Walker: Wouldn't circulation in the atmosphere tend to ease the escape problem? If the gases were continually flowing around to the dark side, it would tend to cool the exosphere on the bright side.

Dr. Field: Yes, but I don't think it will change things very much. There still would be considerable escape on the bright side.

14

The Atmosphere of Venus

*Carl Sagan**

The problem of the atmosphere of Venus has been riddled with difficulties from the very beginning. The most elementary observations show Venus as being devoid of visible features and having a very high albedo. The first conclusion reached was that the surface was covered by water clouds. Early spectroscopic searches for water vapor gave negative results, however; the view then arose (in the early 1920's) that the clouds were made of fine dust particles and that the surface was a desert.

In subsequent unsuccessful searches for water vapor, Adams and Dunham (1932) found CO_2 in large amounts. This discovery posed the question of explaining simultaneously the high abundance of carbon dioxide and the low abundance of water. Urey (1952) proposed that the long sequence of reactions which proceed from CO_2 outgassing to carbonate deposition could be summarized by equilibrium reactions of the type

$$CaSiO_3 + CO_2 \overset{H_2O}{\rightleftharpoons} CaCO_3 + SiO_2$$

It can be shown that the resulting equilibrium partial pressure of CO_2 at the Venus temperature would be several orders of magnitude lower than the expected CO_2 partial pressure on Venus. This led Urey to believe that there is approximately such an equilibrium on

* Alfred P. Sloan Research Fellow, 1963–1965.

the earth, but not on Venus; in the absence of liquid water, the reaction does not take place, and the abundance of outgassed CO_2 increases with time. However, to show how malleable the subject is, Menzel and Whipple (1955) suggested that we could achieve the same result if, instead of there being no liquid water, there was enough liquid water to cover the whole planet with an ocean. Access of CO_2 to the silicates would be impeded, and the CO_2 abundance would again increase.

An alternative explanation was proposed by Hoyle (1955). Early in its history, he said, a planet has a certain complement of water and a certain complement of hydrocarbons. Suppose the planet has more water than hydrocarbons. Then, through water photodissociation, the hydrogen escapes and the oxygen remains behind to oxidize the hydrocarbons to CO_2. If, on the other hand, there is an excess of hydrocarbons, presumably all the water is used in the oxidation of the hydrocarbons. The result will be no water, large amounts of CO_2, and partially oxidized hydrocarbons on the surface. This gives a model of Venus having oil on the surface and a smog cloud layer.

It is clearly time to discuss some further observations. As we have mentioned, the only gas which has been identified unequivocally is CO_2. There have been unsucessful searches for a number of organic molecules, as well as CH_4 and NH_3. There is disputed identification at the present time of O_2, CO, and of ice. The O_2 observations were made by Prokofiev in the vicinity of 7500 Å; the CO observations, at 2.35 μ, by Sinton; and the ice identification, also by Sinton, in the near infrared. Several observers have been unable to find O_2; Kuiper has been unable to find CO or ice, and the argument is still in progress. Nevertheless, some CO and O_2 would be expected from the photodissociation of CO_2 in the upper atmosphere.

The inability to detect such substances as CH_4, C_2H_2, C_2H_4, etc., is relevant to the idea that the clouds are composed of hydrocarbons and that hydrocarbons may also be found on the surface. But it should be pointed out that there are low vapor-pressure organic compounds, which, when photodissociated at the level of the clouds, would not give large amounts of the aforementioned substances. So the fact that these substances have not been successfully identified does not entirely exclude the possible existence of some hydrocarbons in the lower atmosphere.

The CO_2 observations at 7820 Å by Spinrad (1962) have opened a new door in studies of the Venus atmosphere. Using plates made 30 years earlier by Adams and Dunham, Spinrad has obtained, assuming a certain model of the mode of scattering of the light of this wavelength out of the atmosphere, temperatures from the distribution of the rotational components in the band and pressures from the contours of the lines. He finds that there is a sizable variability; on some days there are much higher temperatures and pressures than on other days. He also finds that there is a good correlation between high temperatures and high pressures. One interpretation of this effect is that the transmissivity of the upper atmosphere of Venus at this wavelength is variable, and that on some days we see, on the average, to much deeper levels than on others.

The highest pressure-temperature point that Spinrad observed was 5.5 atm and 440°K. This is quite deep in the atmosphere. He has obtained a whole range of temperature-pressure points; the lowest point is 1.1 atm at about 210°K. There is a question as to what the weighting function is, since we are looking at many depths at once. Accordingly, there is some uncertainty as to whether the pressures and the temperatures apply to the same atmospheric depth. But there is no doubt that we are seeing to much higher temperatures and pressures than are observed using the 8-to-13 μ window, for which the measured temperature is about 235°K.

There is also a serious question about the composition of the clouds. The first datum used to approach this question seriously was the polarization curve of the light reflected from Venus, first obtained by Lyot in the late 1920's. Here the fractional polarization of the reflected light was plotted against the phase angle (Sun-Venus-Earth). Lyot found that he could reproduce the general shape of the polarization curve by using small droplets of bromonaphthalene in water. The differential index of refraction of bromonaphthalene in water is the same as that of water in air. (It is difficult to make small enough droplets of water in air for an experimental measurement; they evaporate away.) Lyot concluded that substances of a few microns diameter and an index of refraction equal to that of water would explain the polarization curve. However, the details of the observed and laboratory curves do not in all respects match. In addition, there is the point that if the droplets are going to evaporate in the laboratory, they will also evaporate on Venus.

A number of other attempts have been made to explain the polarization curves. Van de Hulst (1952) has suggested that transparent salts of diameter ~10 μ might explain the measurements. It appears, however, that the observations do not permit a more rigorous statement than that there is some distribution of transparent particles in the upper atmosphere of Venus in the micron-diameter range. A compositional specification of high reliability has yet to be obtained, and we do not now know the cause of the most obvious feature of Venus—its cloud layer.

At the time that there seemed to be no water *vapor* on Venus, there was, of course, the question of how the clouds could contain water. So let us go back to the water vapor problem. There have been a long series of spectroscopic attempts to observe water on Venus. Spinrad has used the particular spectrum which showed the highest pressure-temperature point in CO_2 and obtained a negative result for water. He gives an H_2O volume mixing ratio of less than 10^{-5}. If the pressure at the 235°K level is ~ 1 atm, the water vapor concentration is then $< 10^{-2}$ g/cm² at the 235°K level. This may be barely consistent with the positive value of 10^{-2} g/cm² reported by Dollfus. There is also an observation by Strong, using a stratospheric balloon. He gives a figure for the water abundance on Venus of 2×10^{-3} g/cm², with a probable error of the same order as the observation. Despite the uncertainties in this result, it should be at least an upper limit. Here, then, is a positive observation which is a factor of 5 less than the value reported by Dollfus and is smaller than the negative result of Spinrad. Finally, there is an observation by Gibson and Corbett that yields a brightness temperature of about 520°K at 1.35 cm, which is a resonance line of water. Their result shows that the atmosphere does not contain more than 1% water for simple adiabatic models of the atmospheric structure. The water vapor problem, therefore, is also not resolved at the present moment.

We should mention another tentative result which appears to come out of Adams and Dunham's data. Kaplan (1961) has looked at a plot of line intensity vs. rotational quantum number in the 7820 Å band and finds two intensity peaks, as if there were a superposition of two Boltzmann distributions. One peak is at a temperature of about 325°K, and the other at about 700°K. This seems to indicate that there is another cloud layer at 325°K and that the surface temperature approaches 700°K. Kaplan points out that these clouds would not be water clouds, since the pressure required for their stability would be too high. He suggests that they are clouds of hydrocarbons.

This result is highly preliminary, and if the interpretation of Spinrad's data in terms of temperatures and pressures at the same level is somewhat questionable, then Kaplan's interpretation is also subject to similar uncertainties.

We now come to the microwave observations. There is now a considerable body of data, both as a function of wavelength and as a function of phase angle. We now have, for the first time, temperatures as a function of position on the disc, as a result of the microwave observations made by Mariner II. Figure 14.1 shows the variation of brightness temperature with wavelength near inferior conjunction. The flatness in the microwave spectrum from 1.4 to beyond 21 cm provides quite a strong argument for thermal emission (not necessarily from the surface), as opposed to synchroton or cyclotron radiation.

There are two possible interpretations of the curve. One possibility is that we are seeing the surface at centimeter wavelengths, and that at millimeter wavelengths, where the temperature has fallen off, there is some unspecified atmospheric absorber; we are thus looking at contributions jointly from the surface and from the atmosphere. The other possibility is that there is an opaque emitting layer, at $T \geq 580°K$ quite high in the atmosphere, which becomes transparent at millimeter wavelengths, allowing us to see the cooler ground underneath. These two views have quite different consequences for surface temperatures and ionospheric electron densities. However, the weight of the evidence now seems to lean toward the first interpretation and surface emission.

The phase effect has been followed by observing the change of temperature away from inferior conjunction and trigonometrically extrapolating to small phase angles, and more recently by Drake, who actually performed observations quite close to superior conjunction. Radar reflectivities have been measured at three wavelengths: 12.5, 43, and 68 cm. From these, a reflectivity of 0.1 ± 0.03 has been obtained. Using this result along with the phase effect data and assuming Kirchhoff's law, we obtain an average surface temperature at 10-cm wavelength of 640°K for the dark side and 750°K for the bright side. It should be noted that the Mariner II results of Barath, Barrett, Lilley, and Jones gave equal temperatures

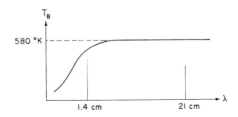

Figure 14.1 Brightness temperature vs. wavelength for Venus (near inferior conjunction).

on the bright and dark side. However, the observations were made in a region where there is microwave absorption, and when we account for the differences in path length, the results are not inconsistent with a small phase effect.

If we knew whether the maximum in the temperature occurs before or after inferior conjunction, we would have some idea whether Venus has direct or retrograde rotation. There is, as in several aspects of this problem, a difference in the results of the Soviet Union and the United States. Passive microwave observations at the Lebedev Physical Institute seem to show intensity minima before inferior conjunction—therefore, direct rotation—but similar observations at the Naval Research Laboratory and the National Radio Astronomy Observatory give minima after inferior conjunction and retrograde rotation. The interpretation of the radar results in the Soviet Union indicates direct rotation with a period less than 11 days; interpretation of radar results in the United States indicates retrograde rotation with a period of the order of 250 days. In obtaining these results, it was assumed that the axis of rotation is not close to the orbital plane; there is some data, both in the ultraviolet and in the infrared, to substantiate this assumption.

Retrograde rotation means, of course, that the resolved rotation vector has a component antiparallel to the revolution vector. Standing on the surface of Venus, we would see two days and two nights a year. This is clearly different from synchronous rotation and represents a unique circumstance in the solar system, even considering the anomalous rotation of Uranus.

We have already mentioned the radar reflectivity determination. One way of interpreting this information is to put it in terms of an equivalent dielectric constant, realizing that this assumes a smooth, uniform, and plane parallel surface, which is, of course, not exactly the case on Venus. The resulting dielectric constant is between 3 and 7. For comparison, a smooth ocean of pure liquid water has $\epsilon \approx 80$, whereas a smooth pool of common liquid hydrocarbons would have $\epsilon \approx 2$. These observations exclude the view that Venus is covered with a plane parallel surface of pure liquid water and no waves. But this is already evident considering the high surface temperature.

For models of the structure below the clouds, a very simple procedure has been used. We take some pressure and temperature point at the clouds on the bright side, take the temperature at the surface on the bright side, assume an adiabatic lapse rate, include the variation of γ and C_p with pressure and temperature, and thus obtain the surface pressure. The input which is most poorly known in this procedure is the cloud-top pressure. If we take a value of the cloud-top pressure on the bright side of 0.6 atm at the 230°K level, the pressure at the surface (presumably the same on both the bright and the dark sides) is of the order of 30 atm.

The figure of 0.6 atm comes from three different lines of evidence: the lowest pressure obtained by Spinrad at 7820 Å, which was coupled to a temperature within 20° of the presumed cloud-top temperature; interpretation of the observations at 1.6 μ; and Dollfus' polarimetric data, which originally gave a figure of 90 mb, but gave a value around 0.6 atm when corrected for multiple scattering.

There is also another pressure determination, made by Menzel and de Vaucouleurs (1960) from the occultation of Regulus, which gives a pressure at some occultation level. We know the distance of the occultation level to the cloud level extremely poorly for the accuracy desired; from published values, we can derive the pressure at the clouds on the dark side. This pressure is at least an order of magnitude below the bright-side pressure, thus raising the possibility that the cloud-top pressures are different on the dark and bright sides. This has puzzling meteorological consequences; but it is not worthwhile to pursue it further, because of the difficulty in integrating down from the occultation level to the cloud tops.

The volume mixing ratio of CO_2 in the vicinity of the visible clouds is about 5%, within a factor of 2. The presumption is, as in the case of Mars, that the remainder of the atmosphere is molecular nitrogen. The figure of 5% CO_2 can be determined as follows: we can calculate at a given wavelength how much CO_2 is required to give the observed absorption seen on Venus. From this is obtained an equivalent path of CO_2. We also calculate a total pressure, from line broadening, for example; combining these two pieces of information, under the assumption that the rest of the atmosphere is nitrogen, then gives a volume mixing ratio of CO_2. Assuming that the mixing ratio is constant, the value of 5% is obtained.

Now let us look at some models for heating the surface. Several have been proposed. In the greenhouse model, some visible light penetrates the clouds and heats the surface. But the atmosphere and cloud layer have much greater opacity in the infrared than at visible frequencies, so the infrared radiation has difficulty in getting out. The equilibrium temperature attained is then higher than if there were no atmosphere. Until quite recently, the effect of the clouds has not been included. It would appear from the results of Ohring, for a greenhouse model which specifically includes the effect of clouds, that temperatures can be rather neatly maintained within the observed range without, surprisingly enough, invoking any other absorber besides CO_2. But the clouds must be rather different from terrestrial water clouds, with a high ratio of infrared to visible opacity.

Another model that has been promulgated is the aeolosphere model of Öpik, in which winds driven by sunlight carry tremendous amounts of dust down to the surface, which is then heated by friction. This model specifically predicts no phase effect. Observations contradict this; but we can get around the contradiction by putting in some other mechanism which works on the bright side but not on the dark side. Such a mechanism has been proposed by Tolbert and Straiton, who invoke spark discharges in aerosols. In this way, we can reproduce the falloff in brightness temperature at millimeter wavelengths and perhaps also explain the centimeter phase effect.

The issue is still in doubt; an explanation of how the surface stays as hot as it does is one of the key unsolved problems in understanding the Venus environment.

We obtain the impression that Venus is rather an unappetizing bundle conceptually, but we must live with it and try to put the pieces together. There is as yet no view which integrates all of the observational material.

REFERENCES

Adams, W. S. and T. Dunham, 1932. *Publs. Astron. Soc. Pacific,* **44**, 243.

Hoyle, F., 1955. Frontiers of astronomy, Harper and Row, New York.

Kaplan, L. D., 1961. A new interpretation of the structure and CO_2 content of the Venus atmosphere, *Planet and Space Sci.,* **8**, 23.

Kellogg, W. W. and C. Sagan, 1961. *The Atmospheres of Mars and Venus,* National Academy of Sciences-National Research Council Publication 944, Washington, D.C.

Menzel, D. H. and G. de Vaucouleurs, 1960. Results from the occultation of Regulus by Venus, July 7, 1959, *Nature,* **188**, 28.

Menzel, D. H. and F. L. Whipple, 1955. The case for H_2O clouds on Venus, *Publs. Astron. Soc. Pacific,* **67**, 161.

Sagan, C., 1961. The planet Venus, *Science,* **133**, 849.

Sagan, C. and W. W. Kellogg, 1963. *Ann. Rev. Astron. Astrophys.,* **1**, 235.

Spinrad, H., 1962. Spectroscopic temperature and pressure measurements in the Venus atmosphere, *Publs. Astron. Soc. Pacific,* **74**, 187.

Urey, H. C., 1952. *The Planets; Their Origin and Development,* Yale University Press, New Haven.

Van de Hulst, H. C., 1952. Scattering in the atmospheres of the earth and planets, in G. P. Kuiper, editor, *The Atmospheres of the Earth and Planets.* University of Chicago Press.

DISCUSSION

Dr. Holland: In discussing the Urey equilibrium, we should realize that there are other equilibria to be considered. For example, the reaction

$$CaCO_3 + H_2O \rightleftarrows Ca(OH)_2 + CO_2$$

would also produce small amounts of CO_2, adding to the partial pressure on Venus. Without considering the aeolosphere model, what sort of wind velocities would one expect on Venus?

Dr. Sagan: This depends entirely on the mode of circulation, which in turn depends on the period of rotation. There is a computation by Mintz in which synchronous rotation is assumed. He determines what wind velocities would be needed to transfer enough energy from the bright side to the dark side so that the dark side will radiate at $235°K$; a velocity of 0.3 mph is obtained.

Voice: I think one of the problems with Mintz's calculation is that he assumes a uniform velocity gradient downward from the top of the convection surface. This model certainly doesn't apply to the earth's atmosphere, where maximum velocities are found right down to the surface. If, on the other hand, we apply a nonlinear velocity with elevation, we can get quite high velocities down close to the surface. But at the same time, I don't believe that Mintz considers the heats of condensation of materials. Conceivably the bulk of the heat could be carried as the heat of condensation of water vapor, and the wind velocity may be very low indeed.

Dr. Dollfus: I had mentioned previously our studies on the rotation of the Venus clouds. Our preliminary results indicate wind velocities about the same as on the earth—less than 100 km/hr.

Dr. Jastrow: If the surface of Venus is covered by clouds containing even a small amount of liquid or solid water, I do not understand how it is possible for these clouds to be transparent at 7820 Å, and yet be opaque at 8 to 13 μ. It doesn't take much water to make the cloud opaque in the infrared.

Dr. Sagan: Either the clouds are made of some substance which is transparent in the near infrared and opaque in the far infrared—and it may not be water—or else there are occasional breaks in the clouds.

Dr. Jastrow: This is what I thought Spinrad seemed to imply, yet the Mariner II results show no detectable breaks in the clouds.

Dr. Sagan: The limit of topographical resolution in the Mariner II infrared experiment was quite large. In addition, Spinrad does not know whether he was looking at the whole planet or a section of it, since Adams and Dunham didn't say how the slit was oriented. Presumably the slit was put somewhere across the whole planet. In that case, there would have to be a pretty large break, or a lot of little ones lying along the slit, in order to see to deeper levels. This result is a little difficult to understand on the basis of breaks in the clouds. Differential transparency is a more promising possibility. It would be useful to investigate the infrared opacities of a variety of possible cloud constituents.

Dr. Goody: Since this question has arisen about Spinrad's results, I would like to give my personal opinion that the analyses are extremely well done. I do not see how we can get away from the combinations of line widths and intensities and the interpretation in terms of a pressure and a Boltzmann temperature. But to make all this into a pressure-temperature diagram is quite another story.

Dr. Field: Isn't it possible to have a considerable amount of water on Venus and yet not violate any observations made so far?

Dr. Sagan: Several atmospheres of water would be inconsistent with the 1.35-cm measurements. If we assume a CO_2-water atmosphere with a 30-atmosphere pressure, for large amounts of water we would expect an absorption dip in the brightness-temperature curve (Fig. 14.1) at 1.35 cm. This is not observed.

Dr. Field: But suppose we were to assume a subadiabatic lapse rate, very near to isothermal, in fact, and arrived at a very large pressure, say 300 or even 1000 atmospheres? Couldn't this be made to agree with the observations?

Dr. Sagan: That may barely be possible. I think there would be a problem in explaining the radar reflectivities and the microwave spectrum. The microwave opacity of CO_2 due to pressure-induced dipole transitions would probably exclude such huge pressures. Incidentally, if Venus were to have in its atmosphere the 3×10^5 gm/cm^2 of water of the terrestrial oceans, and still preserve the water vapor mixing ratio of its upper atmosphere, the total mass of the Venus atmosphere would be $>3 \times 10^5/10^{-5} = 3 \times 10^{10}$ gm/cm^2, or $>3 \times 10^7$ atm. This seems rather too large, and I think we are safe in concluding that the surface and atmosphere of Venus are relatively depleted in water, compared with the earth.

15

The Atmosphere of Mars

Richard M. Goody

There are many pieces of information about Mars, but only a few of these are relevant to the composition of the atmosphere. We will discuss the information, whenever possible, from the point of view of reliability, since the bulk of this information depends on spectrographic measurements, and we maintain that the difficulty of obtaining reliable quantitative results from such data is often underestimated.

Figure 15.1 is a temperature-height diagram due to Chamberlain (1962), which illustrates that according to the best of computations, the exosphere temperatures of the two planets, Mars and the earth, are about the same. This has the consequence that the planetary escape factor is simply inversely proportional to gravity, and since gravity is three times lower on Mars than it is on the earth, the time constant for evaporation will be three times shorter on Mars. Thus we would expect Mars to have somewhat less atmosphere than the earth, and in particular we certainly do not expect it to have any of the light constituents which are absent on the earth in any case—hydrogen, helium, etc. In fact, it is questionable whether this temperature is low enough to retain atomic oxygen for periods comparable to the age of the planetary system. We would, however, expect it to maintain molecular species, such as molecular nitrogen.

With this in mind, we would like to look over what we consider to be the solid observational facts, and we shall work our way down from the most solid facts available to the least solid. We begin with

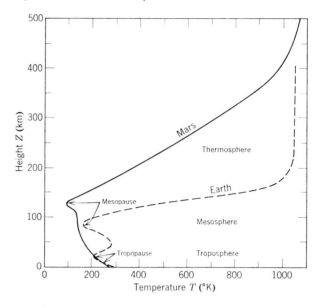

Figure 15.1 The temperature of the Martian atmosphere (after Chamberlain, 1962).

the first and fundamental measurement; namely, the total mass of the Martian atmosphere. On the basis of polarimetric measurements, the prediction is that there is between one-fourth and one-fifth of the earth's atmosphere above the surface of Mars. The reliability of these measurements is questionable. If we run down the list of comments that de Vaucouleurs (1954) makes about previous pieces of work, including one of his own, we have the following series: rejected, rejected, doubtful, doubtful, indirect, doubtful, illusory, approximate, illusory, preliminary, approximate. These are very difficult measurements to make; it is almost impossible for anybody but the experimenter to make a good estimate of the accuracy, since it is almost impossible to explain in print the detailed judgments that one makes along the way. Our feeling with regard to Dollfus' value of 85 mb (see Chapter 12) for the surface pressure is that it is probably correct to within a factor of 2.[1]

[1] Added in Proof: Recent work by Kaplan, Münch, and Spinrad (1964) based on the strength of two CO_2 bands (one pressure-dependent and the other not) gives 25 ± 15 mb for the ground level pressure. This estimated error of a factor of 2 may be conservative.

However, our most positive piece of information relates to the CO_2 abundance. This is determined from a comparison between spectra of Mars and of the moon made by Kuiper (1952), as shown in Figure 15.2. The identification is based on two very weak bands, which are due to transitions from the ground state to the 221 and to the 141 bands of CO_2. It is fortunate that they are both ground-state bands; thus they are not very temperature dependent. It is also fortunate that the lines are about 1.56 cm^{-1} apart; the Doppler shift was on that occasion 0.27 cm^{-1}; and finally the line widths were of the order of 0.03 cm^{-1}. This wide spacing enables us to analyze with some precision the absorption area of this band. Many other corrections must also be taken into this kind of analysis, but the significant thing

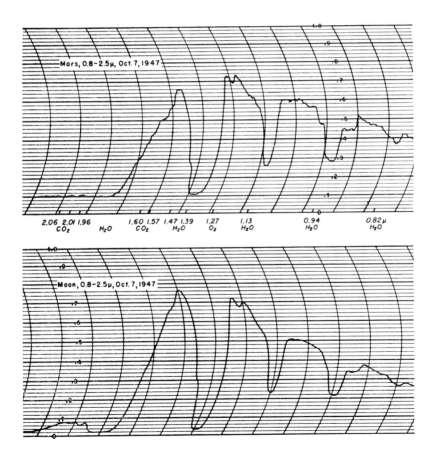

Figure 15.2   The CO_2 bands at 1.60 and 1.57 μ in the Martian spectrum (after Kuiper, 1952).

is that with these kinds of molecular vibration-rotation bands, provided that the measurement is a good one, it is usually possible to make a very clean analysis.

Kuiper obtained a curve of growth of these bands for various zenith angles, which he compared with the curve for the earth's atmosphere alone. He came to the conclusion that the Mars bands were three times as strong as in the earth's atmosphere.

This is a very daring statement to make, because the result depends entirely on how we interpolate the background. It is extremely difficult to interpolate background on molecular spectra any better than 1 or 2%, and these bands were not much deeper than that.

However, if we accept the statement that these bands are three times stronger than in the earth's atmosphere, from that point on we can make a completely clean interpretation, and we obtain a mixing ratio of $160/P_0^2$ (expressed in terms of volume proportion), where P_0 is the ground level pressure on Mars. Taking Dollfus' figure of 85 mb for the ground level pressure gives a volume proportion of 2%. This is the figure commonly used upon which even design problems of re-entry into Mars are being based. It is hoped that the engineering is not very sensitive to this figure.[2]

We next look at the spectrographic method for oxygen or water vapor. Here we get high-resolution Coudé spectra for the advancing planet, for the receding planet, and for the sun. We then hope that the planetary lines are sufficiently shifted so that they can be distinguished from the terrestrial lines. Here we know the data, Doppler shifts, and line widths quite precisely. In Figure 15.3 we see a drawing by Spinrad and Richardson (1963) of a possible combination of the telluric and hypothetical Mars line, assuming an intensity ratio of 30 to 1. The Doppler shift of the Mars line gives the bump shown on the wing of the combined Mars-Earth line. For comparison, a recorded spectrum is shown. The problem is to decide what the magnitude is of the bump on the recorded line. Spinrad and Richardson's analysis of this data gives an amount which corresponds to one-third of that reported by Dollfus, who gives a value of 2×10^{-2} g/cm². If we were to have the amount reported by Dollfus, then the bump in the curve would be three times as large as shown in the figure.[3]

---

[2] Added in Proof: Kaplan, Münch, and Spinrad (1964) have recently made a direct determination of 55 ± 20 m-atm from the strengths of lines near 8700 Å. This is about twice the total amount quoted here.

[3] Added in Proof: Kaplan, Münch, and Spinrad (1964) now claim a positive identification of water vapor on Mars, amounting to $1.4 \pm 0.7 \times 10^{-3}$ g/cm². The discrepancy with Dollfus' measurement appears to be irreconcilable.

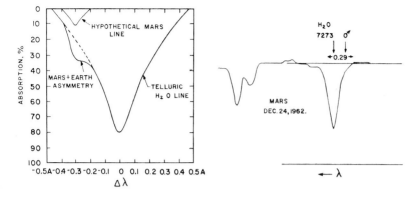

Figure 15.3 Left: Synthetic H_2O spectrum. The Martian line had $\frac{1}{30}$ the intensity of the terrestrial line. Right: Observed H_2O spectrum. (After Spinrad, and Richardson, 1963.)

It is difficult to see how to reconcile these two results. On the one hand, Dollfus' observations seem to be quite definite. Yet, it is hard to imagine how the Mars line can be trebled in size and yet not be observed on the spectrum.

At the bottom of the scale of reliability of results, there are a series of upper limits to certain gases—SO_2, N_2O, CH_4, NH_3, etc. These are rather crude limits and are not particularly of value because they are so high.

This, then, is all the solid information that there is on the atmosphere of Mars. On this basis, it has been said that we know so much about Mars that there is no need to send any investigating probes there. It is sincerely hoped that this is not a serious view.

There are, on the other hand, a number of inferences that have been made which are of some value. One of these is the well-known inference with respect to the Martian polar caps. The caps are generally held to be ice for a variety of reasons. Mainly, it is very difficult to think of any other possibility; also, the polarimetric curves compare reasonably well with those of ice. But there is one fairly serious difficulty. According to publications quoted by de Vaucouleurs (1954), there have been some fairly accurate measurements which give an albedo of 0.3 for the mist which during the winter months seems to cover over the cap. If the caps are in fact ice caps, it is difficult to escape from the conclusion that this is an ice mist. If it is an ice mist, it is a peculiar one, because we cannot get an obscuring ice mist on the earth, which has an albedo much less than 0.8. There may well be a way around this dilemma, but we want to point out that there is a fly in the ointment of what is generally accepted to be an accurate description of one of the Martian features.

A second inference is that if we know the amount of oxygen in the atmosphere, we can obtain upper limits to the abundances of the various allotropes of oxygen by making photochemical computations. Such computations are not very accurate, but they do give a good indication of the situation.

The ozone computation gives for Mars a distribution with most of the ozone close to the surface, as opposed to the layer we find up in the earth's atmosphere. The value commonly quoted for O_3 is 0.05 cm at STP; that is, less than 15% of the terrestrial value. The first thing that any ozone in contact with the surface will do is to oxidize any oxidizable material, but presumably once the surface is oxidized, any further ozone striking the surface will simply break up into oxygen again and recycle. Ozone is the most important allotrope of oxygen from the observational point of view. The techniques for observing ozone have been well developed; in fact, the Hartley band of ozone is so strong that the earth's atmosphere has a transmission of about 10^{-30} in the center of the band. Thus, if we want to get information on Martian oxygen allotropes, it might be wise in early flights to Mars to make measurements on ozone rather than oxygen.

Figure 15.4 shows the results of a calculation due to Chamberlain (1962) on the atomic oxygen distribution in the Martian atmosphere. A slight oxygen layer is expected at about 150 km, and there will be trivial amounts of O_2 and O_3 here through recombination.

If there is CO_2 present, then high in the atmosphere it will dissociate to CO and oxygen. Thus we expect CO in the atmosphere, but the amount should be so small as to be unmeasurable from the earth using conventional methods.

The final, and perhaps the most accepted, inference about Mars is that the atmosphere is predominantly nitrogen. The main reasons for saying this seem to be that nitrogen is moderately cosmic abundant, that it is unreactive, it is undetectable anyway, and finally—and this seems to be the main reason—we are mainly interested in the thermodynamics of the atmosphere, and it doesn't really matter from the point of view of thermodynamics what the constituents are, as long as they are neutral. But there is no observational evidence for nitrogen.

To conclude, we will mention some of the surface features of Mars that could have some relevance with regard to atmospheric processes, insofar as there is some kind of interchange between the surface and atmosphere.

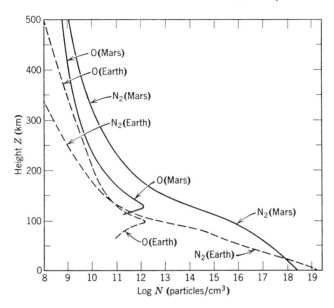

First of all, we have no difficulty in explaining the existence of clouds on the basis of reasonable amounts of water. It does not seem that we can use the existence or topography of these clouds to obtain much information about the composition of the atmosphere.

However, the fact that the clouds are there and moving indicates that there is atmospheric motion. This means that at certain heights in the atmosphere there is turbulent mixing of gases; this in turn affects the exospheric escape rates.

We also observe light and dark areas on the surface of Mars, with the light areas covering two-thirds of the planet. There have been two sets of pertinent measurements: the polarimetric measurements made by Lyot (1929) brought him to conclude that the light areas might be due to some kind of volcanic ash; Kuiper (1952) concluded as a result of his infrared measurements that it might be some sort of felsite. We know that the temperature varies greatly from day to night; therefore, the surface is quite likely to be of a low-conductivity, porous material. There are no large seas on Mars, so when we put all this information together, the consensus of opinion is that we are dealing with some kind of desert surface.

Finally, the dark areas, covering one-third of the planet, may have some relevance to atmospheric studies. We observe in them secular changes—large dark areas have been seen to develop over periods of years. Also, there appears to be a seasonal change in the form of a wave of darkness going from one hemisphere to the other, moving at a speed of about 0.5 m/sec. This may very well have something to do with water vapor and the existence of primitive vegetation.

REFERENCES

Chamberlain, J. W., 1962. Upper atmospheres of the planets, *Astrophys. Jour.*, 136, 582.

Kaplan, L. D., G. Münch, and H. Spinrad, 1964. An analysis of the spectrum of Mars, *Astrophys. Jour.*, 139, 1.

Kuiper, G. P., 1952. Planetary atmospheres and their origin, in G. P. Kuiper, editor, *The Atmospheres of the Earth and Planets,* University of Chicago Press.

Lyot, B., 1929. Recherches sur la polarisation de la lumiere des planetes et de quelques substances terrestes, *Annales de l'Observatoire de Meudon,* 8, 1.

Spinrad, H. and E. H. Richardson, 1963. High dispersion spectra of the outer planets, II: A new limit for the water vapor content of the Martian atmosphere, *Icarus,* 2, 49.

de Vaucouleurs, G., 1954. *Physics of the Planet Mars,* Faber and Faber, Ltd., London.

DISCUSSION

Dr. Field: With regard to the problem of reconciling the results of Spinrad and Dollfus, could this not be due to seasonal variations? We know that when the water is changing from pole to pole, the atmosphere is filled, and at other times there is very little water vapor. Dollfus' measurement was made at the beginning of Martian summer, when the atmospheric water vapor content would be at a maximum.

Dr. Goody: Spinrad gives his date of measurement as December 24, 1962, and Dollfus' measurement was made the following January. So we would not expect much variation. Seasonal variation is certainly one aspect of the situation, but I think the discrepancy is deeper than that.

Dr. Dollfus: Doppler shift measurements lead to difficulties because we are looking for some departure from the symmetry of the line, and this is very sensitive to the astigmatism of the instrument. The observations of Mars advancing and receding were taken three or four months apart, and we do not know whether the astigmatism of a large spectrograph will remain constant over this period of time.

Another point is that we are comparing the intensity of the shifted line to the intensity of the telluric line. It is very surprising to see how rapidly the water vapor content of the earth's atmosphere can change—by a factor of 2 or 3 within a half hour. All of this can produce an error of a factor of from 3 to 5.

I would also like to state that I agree completely with your placing a factor of 2 accuracy on the 85-mb pressure. These measurements are extremely difficult to make, and we must make assumptions as to the composition, the amount of dust in the atmosphere, etc. Thus the accuracy will not be very high.

As for the polar-cap measurements, these are difficult to do because the cap is so close to the edge of the disc. At any rate, we found an albedo of about 0.7 at the beginning of spring. With summer, the polar cap grew smaller, and the albedo decreased also. By the end of summer the albedo is around 0.3. This is due to dust deposits. By the end of the summer the caps are very dirty, and the color is not absolutely white.

We attempted to experimentally reproduce the structure of the polar cap, using liquid nitrogen and water. By duplicating the pressure and radiation conditions expected on Mars, we were able to reproduce a frost deposit having the same polarization as observed on Mars. Also the albedo of this deposit was about the same as we see for the polar cap. So it seems to me quite reasonable that the polar cap is really this kind of frost.

I would also like to mention that the polarization measurements of the Martian clouds showed that the white clouds probably consist of ice crystals. If we reproduce in the laboratory a cloud of ice crystals, the polarization of this cloud is very similar to that of Martian clouds. The only problem is the existence of the yellow clouds, which have a quite different curve of polarization.

Voice: Would the presence of CO in the atmosphere reduce the amount of ozone, and thereby give a misleading anticipation of oxygen?

Dr. Goody: The CO should be found mainly around 135 km. Ozone is going to be a low-level phenomenon on Mars, so they will not mix very much.

Mr. Walker: In view of the presence of a wind and quite large temperature variations, wouldn't you expect some erosion of the

Martian surface? This would undercut your argument about the ozone ceasing to be used up by oxidation at the surface.

Dr. Dollfus: I would also like to make some comments on the surface features of Mars. A more recent interpretation of Lyot's polarimetric measurements is that the curve is more consistent with that of limonite. In fact, we tested about 400 samples; only limonite reproduced exactly the polarization of the light areas on Mars.

Dr. Sagan: Did you test the polarization of rhyolite, which is how Kuiper interpreted his infrared measurements?

Dr. Dollfus: Yes. This material is not absorbing enough. The polarimetric properties are not consistent; also, the infrared measurements are not very specific—several materials can give the same infrared curves if they are mixed appropriately.

With respect to the dark areas, we have observed seasonal variations in contrast and color. The polarization curve of the dark areas is not much different from that of the light areas, but there is a change in this polarization taking place from the beginning of spring to the end of summer. It is as if during this variation something was changing in the microscopic structure of the surface. It is difficult to explain these changes in terms of mineral effects. This is certainly a piece of evidence that we can invoke in favor of life on the surface of Mars.

16

Are the Interiors of Jupiter and Saturn Hot?

P. J. E. Peebles

Traditionally, Jupiter has been considered to be a cold planet with a relatively shallow atmosphere. Attempts have been made to relate the observed semipermanent features, such as the red spot in Jupiter's atmosphere, to permanent features on a fixed surface. However, there are reasons to believe that this picture is wrong, and that Jupiter has in fact a hot interior.

It is quite reasonable to suppose that the abundance of heavy elements (atomic number greater than two) in Jupiter is at least as great as the solar abundance, roughly 2% by mass (Aller, 1961), and that the radioactive part roughly corresponds to the estimated cosmic abundance. In this case, it is well known that unless there were some heat-transfer process more efficient than heat conduction, the heat flux generated by radioactive decay would be sufficient to drive convection in the upper layers of the planet. Following any reasonable adiabatic gradient, it would be concluded, then, that the interior of Jupiter is in fact very hot, ruling out the idea that Jupiter has a fixed surface below the cloud layer.

It is interesting that the evidence to be drawn from model planet calculations (DeMarcus, 1958) points very strongly to this same conclusion; namely, that both Jupiter and Saturn have hot interiors with very deep atmospheres. The known gravitational multipole moments J and K of Jupiter and of Saturn, arising from planetary rotation (Brouwer and Clemence, 1961), provide information on the general structure of the planetary atmosphere, for it is readily apparent that the short-range, spherically unsymmetric part of the gravitational field (and hence the size of the gravitational moments) depends on how much mass is in the outer layers of the planet.

Further tentative conclusions about the planetary atmospheres may be drawn from the general picture of the evolution of the major planets. It is supposed here that the planets formed from material of solar composition by the contraction of a diffuse protoplanetary blob. During the early stages of contraction, dust would have moved readily to the center of the system, but from the known laws of gaseous diffusion we would not expect to find gravitational separation of the volatile components—hydrogen, helium, argon, methane, ammonia, etc. In any case, a deep convecting atmosphere would certainly be well mixed. If any appreciable losses of matter from the surface of this protoplanet had been due to bulk motion of matter only, the abundances relative to hydrogen of the volatile elements would have remained equal to the solar abundances, while the heavy element abundance in the planet would have increased. If there had been appreciable loss by evaporation, there is some possibility that the abundances of the other volatile elements relative to hydrogen might have increased also (Dicke, private communication).

Following these remarks it is assumed that Jupiter and Saturn both consist of a high-density core surrounded by a uniform mixture of hydrogen and helium. Without appreciable error, the nitrogen and other volatile elements above this core may be replaced here with an equal mass of helium. The fractional hydrogen abundance is chosen to obtain the observed value of J, and the mass of the core is chosen to fit the observed mass with the radius of the planet. The moments J and K according to this model have been obtained (by means of the IBM 7090 computer at the Princeton University Computing Center) from equations that have been described elsewhere (Peebles, 1963). Very roughly, the moment J for the model for Saturn has been computed to 2% accuracy, K to 15% accuracy.

Fairly reliable estimates of the equations of state of hydrogen and helium are obtained by interpolating from the ideal gas law, valid at sufficiently low pressures, to the calculated properties of the ground states (DeMarcus, 1958, Table 3.3), known to apply in the limit of very high pressures. This interpolation is guided by the known characteristic densities at which there are significant departures from the ideal gas law, and (from the Debye model) by an estimate of the perturbation to the compressibility of the ground state due to the energy in lattice waves. Further details of this problem are considered by Peebles (1963). Typical curves for the

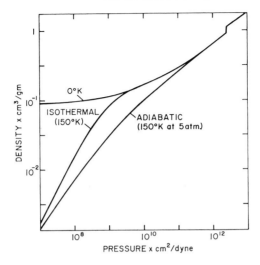

Figure 16.1   The compressibility of hydrogen.

isothermal and adiabatic compression of hydrogen are shown in Figure 16.1. The hydrogen, helium, and heavy elements in the planet may be taken to mix like immiscible fluids; notice that hydrogen is generally the least dense and at the same time the most abundant component, so that it is the properties of hydrogen which play the dominant role in determining the properties of the mixture.

Various model planets are listed in Table 16.1. If the planet were taken to be completely cold, the density of hydrogen in the upper layers would be so high according to the assumed equation of state that the calculated value of J for Saturn would be too big, even assuming pure hydrogen in the upper layers, while the indicated abundance of hydrogen in Jupiter would greatly exceed the cosmic and solar hydrogen abundances (Aller, 1961). This is an unsatisfactory result, because we have no reason to look for appreciable enrichment of hydrogen in the layers near the surface. These difficulties are avoided to some extent by assuming that the density of molecular hydrogen, according to the adopted equation of state, exceeds the correct density (DeMarcus, 1958), perhaps by 25% at pressures of the order of 10^6 atm. With this assumption, the completely cold model (the second model in Table 16.1) for Saturn can be fitted to the observed value of J; but then the calculated value of K is appreciably larger than the observed value, indicating that there is still too much mass in the surface layers. With the

TABLE 16.1 Model Planets Adjusted to Agree With the Observed Planetary Mass, Radius, and Moment J

Model	K	Jupiter Core Mass[a]	X[b]	K	Saturn Core Mass[a]	X[b]
Observed	0.0025 ±0.0014	—	—	0.0039 ±0.0003	—	—
Isothermal, 0°K	0.0029	0.07	0.91	—	—	—
Isothermal, 0°K, Molecular hydrogen density reduced 25% at high pressures	0.0027	0.03	0.82	0.0063	0.25	0.91
Isothermal, 150°K	0.0028	0.05	0.89	—	—	—
Adiabatic, 150°K at 3 atm	0.0026	0.02	0.81	0.0051	0.18	0.81

[a] The core mass is expressed in units of total planetary mass.
[b] This is the hydrogen abundance, by mass, in the material surrounding the core.

temperature throughout the planet equal to 150°K—roughly the temperatures observed at the cloud layers of Jupiter and Saturn—the same difficulties are encountered: with the original equation of state (third model in the table) the observed value of J for Saturn cannot be obtained, and agreement with both J and K for Saturn could not be secured by any reasonable modification of the equation of state.

Adopting an adiabatic model and the original equation of state, the atmosphere is so deep that to obtain the observed value of J, the material in the upper layers must contain a reasonable amount of helium, and even with this helium the density of the material fairly near the surface is quite low, so that the calculated value of K for Saturn is reasonably consistent with the observed value. The pressure of 3 atm at the cloud layer in the adiabatic model shown in the table has been chosen so that the composition of the material above the core in Jupiter is the same as in Saturn. This is consistent with the assumption that in both planets this material represents the volatile elements of solar composition. This pressure is well within the fairly wide range of estimates of the pressure at Jupiter's cloud layer (Peebles, 1963). The abundance of hydrogen in the material above the core is roughly 81% by mass, in fair agreement with the available information on the solar composition

(Gaustad, 1963), but appreciably larger than the cosmic hydrogen abundance. It should be noted, however, that the material in the solar system was isolated from interstellar matter roughly 5 billion years ago. If the abundance of helium in interstellar matter were increasing more or less linearly with time, and if the galaxy were roughly 10 billion years old, such a discrepancy would be expected.

REFERENCES

Aller, L. H., 1961. The abundance of the elements, Interscience, New York.

Brouwer, D. and G. Clemence, 1961. Orbits and masses of planets and satellites, in G. P. Kuiper and B. M. Middlehurst, editors, *Planets and Satellites*, University of Chicago Press.

DeMarcus, W. C., 1958. The constitution of Jupiter and Saturn, *Astrophys. Jour.*, **63**, 2.

Gaustad, J. R., 1964. The solar helium abundance, *Astrophys. Jour.*, **139**, 406.

Peebles, P. J. E., 1964. The Structure and composition of Jupiter and Saturn, *Astrophys. Jour.*, **140**, 328.

17

The Atmosphere of Jupiter

R. Wildt

It is appropriate to call attention to the results of recent work by Spinrad which shed new light on the atmospheric behavior and composition of Jupiter.

Last year Spinrad (1962) startled the astronomical fraternity with an overdue discovery. He found in the Mt. Wilson files some old spectra of Jupiter, taken as early as 1934, on which the absorption lines of NH_3 indicated a differential rotation in Jupiter's atmosphere between the NH_3 gas and the cloud material. The effect is striking. When a slide of the spectrogram was projected on the screen one could see with the naked eye the difference in inclination between the NH_3 lines and the Fraunhofer lines of sunlight reflected from the cloud layer.

Spinrad also discovered Jupiter spectra at Victoria, taken in 1954, on which the inclination indicated a differential rotation of 4 km/sec, with the NH_3 rotating slower than the clouds. This phenomenon has come to be known as the Spinrad effect. However, several new spectra taken during the last year showed that no effect was present at that time. So here is a striking phenomenon greatly variable in time.

Spinrad's (1963) second contribution to our knowledge of Jupiter is a determination of the equivalent widths of a few quadrupole lines of the hydrogen molecule in the near infrared; using this information and the known *f*-values, he determined the total amount of molecular hydrogen above the cloud layers of Jupiter. The result is 27 km-atm H_2; this corresponds to about 0.6 atm partial pressure.

Moreover, by analyzing the line widths and assuming a Lorentz shape, an absolute limit to the total pressure responsible for line broadening was set; this upper bound is 1.4 atm.

Spinrad and Trafton (1963) have proposed what they call a "working composition" for Jupiter's atmosphere on the basis of this total pressure and the mean molecular weight. This was obtained from the lapse rate in the high atmosphere, as deduced from occultation observations. They suggest the following composition:

NH_3 and CH_4	0.2 km-atm	
H_2	27	"
He	16	"
Ne	0.7	"

Since absolute spectroscopic values for the amount of CH_4 above the clouds are available from Kuiper's early work, we can also compute the ratio H/C (by numbers of atoms). This is equal to 360 for Jupiter. He also states values for Uranus (H/C = 70) and Saturn (H/C = 230) without giving detailed information about what was assumed for the atmospheric models. These numbers differ strikingly from the solar value of about 2000.

Finally, two unidentified lines were observed, and several molecules have been checked and ruled out as possible sources, although no quantitative limits are given. The eliminated molecules are NO_2, CH_2, NH_2, HNO, HDO, HCN, O_2, acetylene, formaldehyde, and water vapor.

REFERENCES

Spinrad, H., 1962. The anomalous inclination of the Jovian ammonia lines, *Astrophys. Jour.*, **136**, 311.

Spinrad, H. and L. M. Trafton, 1963. High dispersion spectra of the outer planets, I: Jupiter in the visual and red, *Icarus*, **2**, 19.

DISCUSSION

Dr. Field: The hydrogen abundance determination disagrees by a factor of 5 with a theoretical value obtained by Kiess, Corliss, Kiess, and Zabrisky. I think it is very unlikely that the quadrupole transition probability is off by such a large factor. Recent laboratory observations of the H_2 quadrupole spectrum suggest that in fact the lines are extremely narrow and that saturation effects may be very important.

Voice: In regard to these values, I believe Spinrad gives references to the *f*-values. One is the old determination, made in about 1935, which Zabrisky used, and one is a more recent study of the *f*-values themselves. Apparently the discrepancy is due to the fact that Zabrisky used old *f*-values.

Dr. Wildt: I would suggest that we should not be too disturbed about the discrepancy between the He/H ratio of 0.6 proposed here, and Dr. Peebles' value of 0.075. After all, this is a tentative composition designed to match the density gradient determined from the occultation observation. Without being unfair to the observers, I think there is considerable latitude in estimating the molecular weight from the occultation data.

Dr. Wasserburg: Is there any possibility that we might confirm, by some direct optical means, the presence of some of these gases?

Dr. Wildt: Unfortunately, helium is most likely to be the most important constituent, and there is very little we can hope for in the way of observing lines.

Index